Behind the Sound Cart
A Veteran's Guide to Sound on the Set

Patrushkha Mierzwa

Ulano Sound Services, Inc.

Your thoughtfulness, clear thinking, and writing style are wonderful, and you bring up so many of the things that are so close to my heart, a celebration of our craft and our creative contribution.

—Jeff Wexler, Oscar-nominated sound mixer for *The Last Samurai, Independence Day*. Bafta Winner, *Almost Famous*.

All I can say is I am amazed at the great detail and well-rounded approach you have taken. The mindset section blew me away.

—Joe Aredas, Jr., Hollywood Sound union Local 695 Asst. Business Agent

Your writing has this lovely, personal, honest style to it that I just haven't seen in other industry-based literature. It is refreshing. And there is a SERIOUS amount of knowledge packed in there; it's impressive.

The book is such a gift. You are a powerhouse of knowledge, insight, and entertaining stories.

It has been a privilege to read your manuscript.

—Monica Bannon, Recent film school graduate, Screenskills Program participant, United Kingdom

Distilling 40 years of experience and knowledge into such an easy-to-read, easy-to-follow, and easy-to-understand format is simply astonishing. I also really appreciate the bits where you try to separate how it may be done in L.A. versus how it may be done elsewhere, and under what various contracts...and perhaps more importantly, how some things are just universal.

I said it before, but I'll say it again. This is the book we ALL wish we'd had when we started in this business.

—Aaron "Cujo" Cooley, Head of the Audio Dept., Tyler Perry Studios

I love the forms. Love the pictures. Love the book. Thank you for shining an eloquent light on our craft. An unparalleled insight to the dynamics of perfecting cinematic sound.

—**Eva Rismanforoush, Much-sought-after UST, IATSE Local 695 Director,**
Bombshell*, *Marriage Story*, *The Lion King*, *Yesterday

The book is easy and fun to read, I ate it (as we say here in Brazil when a book is so good). The chapters connect to each other, and you go from the beginning of the subject until the end of it. I never read something so complete about the non-technical things in the film industry (and the technical, too). The way you explain how to act, how to relate with the crew, how to deal with and solve problems that are not about sound itself, all of these are things you don't learn at film school, and it takes years or a lifetime to learn (when you have ability enough to understand, and some people never do). That's why it's so important to all the sound crew members and to everyone involved in filmmaking! (I think all Producers should read this.) It is so explanatory about the duties of a UST that it gives an overview of the work of the entire sound team. It is perfect, accurate, and taught me a lot about how to train and always seek the best of my team in the future! It's really impressive how many movies and works you've done. This a good example of how women can have an extensive career and a personal life. This book is so important, and considering the lack of specialized literature you should have a Portuguese and Spanish version, too.

—**Carolina Barranco, Documentary sound mixer, Brazil**

Behind the Sound Cart

A Veteran's Guide to Sound on the Set

Published by Ulano Sound Services, Inc.
Los Angeles, California

Library of Congress Control Number: 2020926031

ISBN: 978-1-7362900-0-2 (print)
       978-1-7362900-1-9 (ebook)

This book is dedicated to the global sound community,
who were immediately supportive of my desire to write this book.
I am humbled to have their unwavering faith and trust
in representing our creative contribution to the world.

This book is dedicated to utility sound technicians,
so they will finally have a foundation of knowledge necessary
to reinforce their careers.

Contents

CHAPTER 5

Communication

Communication — 27

CHAPTER 6

Pre-Production

Pre-Production — 37

CHAPTER 7

Company Tasks

Company Tasks — 63

CHAPTER 8

Equipment

Equipment — 71

CHAPTER 9

Show Prep for Sound

Show Prep for Sound — 95

Foreword

Patrushkha Mierzwa has managed to pour decades of knowledge, wisdom, and experience into this highly efficient career guide. If your path is to enter the world of production sound, and more specifically in the craft of *utility sound technician*, or UST, you will not find a more direct distillation of the steps necessary to succeed in this esoteric specialty.

It is particularly timely to consider becoming a utility sound technician as a career choice. The post-Covid-19 world only further impacts the complexity of approaches needed in the fast-moving world of filmmaking. The demand for highly trained, competent individuals with the specialized skillset that Ms. Mierzwa details in these pages will only grow.

Her style of writing is empirical, forthright, and clear. It's obvious that she draws easily from her direct professional experiences and succeeds in sharing this intelligently. Application of technology and technique are here in force but not in language excluding the uninitiated or dumbed down for the more experienced reader.

I have been very fortunate to know and collaborate with the author in a professional context for 40 years, and I have benefited enormously from her filmmaking instincts, set savvy, and solution-based philosophy. Her approach to sound became an essential part of my team's success in the dynamic world of film and television production. I have no doubt that her application of those same principals in this book can become a key factor in both moving your career forward and informing the industry, as a reference, of the true work of the utility sound technician.

—Mark Ulano, CAS, AMPS
IATSE 695 president, past CAS president, AMPAS
Credits include *Titanic*, *Once Upon a Time...in Hollywood*,
Inglourious Basterds, *Ad Astra*, *The Hateful Eight*, *Kill Bill* 1&2, *Iron Man* 1&2,
and *Austin Powers: International Man of Mystery*.

Acknowledgments

I'd like to acknowledge:
Mark Ulano, my mentor who became my business partner, cheerleader, and companion of my favorite adventures and life experiences.

Kathy, the 10th muse, a never-ending fountain of ideas and inspiration, my spiritual and biological sister and lifelong art critic, and the best collaborator I've ever known.

Carole Papson, my high-school drama teacher, who risked her professional career to support me practically and emotionally.

Mr. B, who never doubted me or my artistic ability

Monica Bannon, Jeff Wexler, Simon Clark, Eva Rismanforoush, Carolina Barranco, Jennifer Winslow, and Aaron Cujo Cooley, who took time from their busy work schedules to review and comment on my rough draft. Thank you.

All the grips, electricians, and camera guys I worked with in the beginning of my career. It was an anomaly to see a woman booming 40 years ago, and I thank you most sincerely for your respect and support as I forged a new path for myself and women.

The creative arts community, in whom I've found my true family, giving me an opportunity to contribute to the world and explore my humanity.

Bill Clark and BOSS Film Productions for the use of production materials.

The contributors to Facebook trade groups, for sharing their photos and creative solutions—you are inspiring!

The network of film schools around the world: By promoting this book and other practical crafts books, you've stopped the insidious magma of uninformed behavior that exploits crews and now fosters an appreciation for the crafts and artisans who bring to life the vision of the director.

Introduction

My Life in Sound

I was once asked by a Mixer to sweep the gravel of a set called "Western Town" for a walk-and-talk dolly shot between two cowboys because it made too much noise under their boots. Another time, a Mixer asked me to walk up 78 stairs to the top of a stage at night to find a cricket that was chirping—and then spray the cricket with hairspray so his legs would stick together, and he would no longer be able to chirp. And I once lay in a curb gutter to mic a shot of an actor inside a car with an open door, only to have the director of photography step on my hand with his hard wooden clogs. A nasty-tempered cinematographer once had a hissy fit while shooting a horror movie and just missed hitting me with a baling hook he threw in my direction.

me

When I was booming a scene of an actress milking a cow, the cow peed on camera—and on *me*!

Sex scenes are the least sexy bit of business to capture because there's *a lot* of tension, nerves, alcohol, and whatever.

And I wouldn't trade those experiences for anything because I love making movies. This book illustrates the job of the *utility sound technician* (UST), a career almost invisible, minimally considered, yet extremely interesting and exciting—and paying a high five figures per year.

Welcome to My World

I started working in TV and films in 1980, first as a costumer, something that I began in theatre, then as one of the first women boom operators, and later as a UST. I've costumed, produced, and worked on more than 80 films in the US and around the world.

My first paid job sent me to Kauai, Hawaii, to work at beautiful waterfalls and in lush gardens.

I've had the unique opportunity to work in an anechoic sound chamber, use a military flight simulator, and in a desert location I once had a stealth bomber whoosh right over my head!

I've walked the red carpets at the Cannes Film Festival and the Oscars several times.

I've flown to London for multiple BAFTA awards, where nominated crew-members were provided with the same hair and makeup services as the actors!

Why I Wrote This Book

"*I never learned any of this.*" This is what an intern said to me, just having graduated from a four-year film program, and shadowing me for 3 days.

My Approach

In this book, I take you from the first work call to the final wrap, explaining the order of the work and the details that experience can provide, so you don't make mistakes that can sabotage your career before it's even started.

Who This Book Is For

This book is for film students, film school graduates, people considering sound as a career in movies and television, working professionals who are curious about how to get better at their jobs and understand the other crafts departments, and people who want an inside look at the practical business of moviemaking.

What You Will Learn

More than the tasks and importance of preparation, you'll learn about the social dynamics of a set and why you can know everything there is to know about film but not be able to sustain a career.

What I hope for you is that you'll develop the thinking processes that will keep you ahead of the workflow, and that you'll come to the chaos with an inner calm.

Production Notes

In the United States, the IATSE (International Alliance of Theatrical Stage Employees, Moving Picture Technicians, Artists, and Allied Crafts) union has multiple contracts that specify the rules regarding specific work practices in the region of your job. The employer is required to inform you under what contract you are working. If you find conflicting information between this book and IATSE regulations, follow the IATSE contract or contact your Local.

In the UK, the boom operator is referred to as the 1st assistant sound (1st AS) and the utility sound technician as 2nd assistant sound (2nd AS), and UK grips do not handle attenuating lamps as they do in the US.

Because the word *mixer* defines both a piece of equipment and the commonly used term for the person who blends the tracks on the set, for clarity's sake I am capitalizing "Mixer" when referring to the person doing the job.

We often speak about departments by their names, and especially on set when we need someone from that department to address a concern, as in, "Ask Sets to remove that coat rack." Or simply, "Electric! There's a kickout somewhere." Or "Ask Costumes to be here for the rehearsal." If I'm referring to the department, I capitalize it.

Your Coach

Patrushkha (the author)
with Robert Altman

From the article "The Making of an Expert" (*Harvard Business Review*, 2007):

> *The journey to truly superior performance is neither for the faint of heart nor for the impatient. The development of genuine expertise requires struggle, sacrifice, and honest, often painful self-assessment. There are no shortcuts. It will take you at least a decade to achieve expertise, and you will need to invest that time wisely, by engaging in "deliberate" practice—practice that focuses on tasks beyond your current level of competence and comfort. You will need a well-informed coach not only to guide you through deliberate practice but also to help you learn how to coach yourself.*

I hope to be that coach for you. The stories I'm sharing and attitude I suggest are to give you an insight into how the top movies are made and how A-list talent expects to be treated. The minute interactions you have all day long tell people what your experience level is and are an indication of your potential level of proficiency. If you're not moving ahead in your career, look within; see how others see you and gain an amazing insight. I wish only the best for you on your journey.

—Patrushkha

CHAPTER 1

What's a UST?

As film production becomes more competitive, is trending toward ensemble casting, and companies wish to shorten production schedules by using multiple cameras, the *utility sound technician* (2nd assistant sound in the UK) has become, more than ever, an indispensable member of the Sound Department. Thinking of the Sound Department as a two-person department for narrative work is outdated, especially considering the new safety protocols in a Covid-19 world. The complexity of sound work today necessitates that we shed that old image, even in lower-budget projects, and I suggest that a more effective assessment of the number of sound people needed should relate to the actual work that needs to be done. That can be accomplished by asking the production sound Mixer to review a work-in-progress budget.

Patrushkha with
Brad Pitt and
Quentin Tarantino

The Composition of the Sound Department

A standard complement for a feature film sound crew is a production sound Mixer (PSM), a boom operator (or boom op), and a utility sound technician (UST). Depending on the work, there may also be an intern, a Y-16A trainee, a playback operator, and/or video assist operators and video playback operators. During the Covid-19 period, it's common to have an additional person for sanitizing and managing sound equipment used by other departments.

The *production sound Mixer* (PSM) is the contractual head of the department and makes recommendations to the employer as to which sound members to hire, determines the main approach to the sound work, and is responsible for recording the dialogue and sound elements present during the shooting phase of the project.

The *boom operator* is the on-set sound representative and is responsible for the selection, placement, and operation of microphones (in collaboration with the Mixer) and the capturing of the dialogue and sound elements present during the shooting phase of the project.

The *utility sound technician* (UST) is the support person for the Sound Department—able to step into any of the aforementioned positions when needed, as well as setting up, maintaining, and even repairing the equipment, placing wireless microphones on the actors, maintaining supply inventory, maintaining all paperwork and timecards, acting as a liaison with all the other departments for information and collaboration, and managing additional equipment and personnel as the project dictates. On many film and television projects, the UST is the ambassador of the Sound Department to the other crafts, the director, the producers, and the company. The UST is often the main connection to the actors.

A *trainee* can provide an important set of extra hands that is welcome under the collective bargaining agreement. The trainee is compensated as a full employee, accruing benefits and status in a valued entry position. A trainee will usually learn how the department works together, how a set operates, begin to learn about anticipation, and get the kind of film knowledge only direct experience can teach. For the experienced crew, the value of a trainee is the additional help in moving equipment from set to set and running to the Sound truck for last-minute items needed as well as providing opportunity for mentorship and nurturing new talent.

For students, there is often the possibility of an internship. Unlike the trainee, an *intern* is present specifically as a student. The producing companies have detailed rules and requirements regarding interns. Generally, they include current enrollment in a recognized institution of learning from which they will receive academic credit for their participation, documentation of insurance coverage from their school, and they may not be asked to stay longer than 8 hours per day during their internship. They also are specifically *not* designated as employees and when participating on a union project are prohibited from performing bargaining unit work and must not displace a qualified worker normally assigned to the day-to-day tasks of the Sound Department. Salary and a film credit are sometimes available.

In general, being in the Sound Department requires a broad understanding and awareness of all the elements that go into production. Typically, the Costume people don't know the names of lamps, and the grips don't know about the script supervisor's book. But the Sound Department must know about lighting to be able to discuss ways in which light can be attenuated to remove microphone shadows or otherwise modified. We need to know how the script supervisor assigns numbers to scenes as much as how to communicate with the costume people over issues that involve the placement of radio microphones on the actors. Grips may cut the light, add a cucoloris to soften or hide boom shadows, or provide us with apple boxes and ladders when we need height.

(In the UK, electricians under a "gaffer spark" handle all things lighting related, and grips oversee anything that you can mount a camera on. Thus, the grip would be the one handing out apple boxes and ladders, but the electricians/sparks would position flags for lamps.)

We need to know camera lenses and be able to imagine accurately what the operator is framing so we can adjust our movements as the camera dollies, zooms, pans, and tilts. We need to tune into the director and into the specifics of the actors' performances, so we know the blocking and when the timing or the dialogue is changing. We need to work with the Props and Art Department people to solve noisemaking problems or create opportunities for planting microphones in the set. Even the Locations Department will hear from us while we work out issues involving unwanted sounds from a building or location near the shoot. I believe that when we do our job well, the Sound Department becomes far more involved with and knows far more about filmmaking than most of the departments know about sound.

A Short History of the UST Position

Beginning in the late 1920s and early 1930s, the technology and technique of recording sync sound for film was racing along. From a starting point of almost no basic tools for postproduction sound to the advanced sound of *Citizen Kane*, filmed in 1939, the studios gave a clear mandate for capturing performance and telling the story with sound. Though the tools were very primitive, the collective pool of creative minds achieved amazing results.

This was labor intensive, very mechanical, and the gear was *heavy*. After a brief period of competition between double-system wax discs and optical recording on 35mm film, optical sound became the universal technology for almost 40 years. Because of the necessary bulkiness of the sound recording equipment and cabling, the composition of the sound crew was four people and included a production Mixer, a recordist, a boom operator, and a cable man, plus a sound grip as a fifth to handle the movement of the wheeled platforms that the boom operators worked from.

The term *recordist*, often misapplied to the production sound Mixer these days, was the individual who started and stopped the recording machines and loaded and unloaded the film magazines—the recording medium of the day. The recordist usually worked from the centralized machine rooms installed beneath the sound stages of the studio lots or in mobile sound trucks for the relatively rare location work, while the production Mixer directed the creative work of the on-set sound crew.

The tools began to shrink immediately following World War II. The development of dramatic improvements in magnetic recording by the Germans for use in radio transmissions fast-tracked the use of this technology for motion picture production. This brought a new creative freedom to both production and postproduction sound methods. It also impacted the composition of the Production Sound crew. The advances of practical magnetic recording, originally on magnetically coated 35mm film, evolved to ¼" tape recorders on set with smaller mixers, microphones, and cables, and ended the need for the recordist in films, although the position continues in the television world, especially with four-camera sit-coms requiring more complex setups.

The advent of the Nagra (a portable field recorder) by Stefan Kudelski in the late 1950s created pressure to reduce the sound crew personnel. Howard Fabric, the attorney representing the employers in labor negotiations at the studios, negotiated with IATSE Local 695's business agent, Tom Carman, attempting to reduce the number of sound crewmembers.

The use of callboards (a system whereby someone at the union office routes work calls directly to preferred members) was illegal but was still in use by some crafts, including sound. That forced production Mixers to begin competing for jobs by succumbing to employer pressure to work with a two-person crew. But the work was too much for two people; they couldn't keep up and were frequently fired unfairly. To compensate for the unrealistic workload, some employers began utilizing an untrained third person, such as a craft service person or a production assistant (PA). Subsequently, studios began supplying lesser-sized sound crews to productions, which violated the IATSE contract. This soon resulted in a chaotic race to the bottom and lead to intense negotiations to resolve the conflict.

As part of that process, the equipment and personnel needed for the work in question was set up and demonstrated to a Labor Relations committee for 20th Century Fox Studios. After the demonstration and a lengthy 10-hour discussion, the Labor Representative from Fox agreed there was a need for another person and wrote Paragraph 106, "The Composition of the Sound Crew," creating the new contractual position. This position was mutually envisioned as someone who would assist the Mixer and boom operator as well as set up the (very cumbersome) video assist monitors. Until this time, the term *cableman* was informally used since one main component of the job was to manage the hundreds of feet of cable that production sound work entailed. By the time these negotiations began, the job had already evolved into a much more diverse responsibility, somewhat similar to the Grip or Electric Department's best boy. It is unfortunate that today many production personnel truly do not know the history and do not understand the function of this essential position. The UST's job is often misinterpreted as a simple production assistant for sound or a trainee position, when in fact, the skillset required is as weighty, if not more so than the other members of the Sound Department.

The producers coined the term *utility sound technician*, or UST. They didn't want the term assistant used because they considered that *de minimus* (too trivial or minor to merit consideration), and the label did not describe a skill.

Remember, the studio executives were instrumental in the inclusion of Paragraph 106, guaranteeing the existence of a three-person sound crew in the IATSE Basic contract.

The utility sound technician classification is intended to be beneficial to all parties: the crew benefits from needed help, and the employer benefits by bolstering efficient workflows. By utilizing a UST, a production can save many minutes a day. That saved time adds up over the course of a show, so the case can easily be made for proving that a UST definitely saves them both time *and* money.

In the United Kingdom, the sound crew consists of a production sound Mixer, the 1st assistant sound (1st AS), and the 2nd assistant sound (2nd AS). These recent designations came about as an effort to have the positions seen in a more professional light and are modeled after the camera assistant's positions 1st AC and 2nd AC. I'm told it has been successful in attributing more respect and compensation to those individuals. Many of the procedures and protocols for film work in the UK and US are similar, so for the sake of readability, I use the designation UST throughout this book.

Why Consider Being a UST?

Utility sound technicians are similar to the best boy in the Grip and Electric departments; it's a position of responsibility in which you'll interact with every department—from production assistants to producers—and are privy to watch and learn from directors. The pay rate is above the best boy's rate and reflects the specialized knowledge and responsibility of the position. Freelancing, the most common method of acquiring work, ensures that your time is somewhat flexible. Women are in demand, and there are immediate needs for USTs.

The Duties of a UST

The entertainment industry is exciting in that your job title doesn't necessarily define you, and that's true for any of the positions in which you find yourself in this business. You get to choose where you belong and how you relate to the work (more on that later).

The sound utility technician can mistakenly be seen as an entry-level position (but one that requires knowledge and training) yet one that can be a gratifying career in itself but also allow you to develop as a filmmaker. Being a UST keeps you moving on a set and throughout the production company. Your duties will be divided among those that take place on set, in your department, and as a member of the production company.

On-Set Duties

▸ Preparing the carts for the day's work

▸ Getting stock, batteries, expendables, and additional equipment ready

▸ Placing the equipment carts

▸ Powering the equipment

▸ Securing the bell & light system on stages

▸ Setting up microphones

▸ Handling music playback

▸ Managing personal monitor receivers

▸ Assisting the Mixer

▸ Setting up speakers and amplification systems

▸ Setting the antennae mast(s)

▸ Coordinating frequencies for radio microphones

▸ Coordinating with assistant directors (ADs) for shots and wiring actors

▸ Jamming sync boxes and slates and providing those to the Camera Department

▸ Distributing megaphones and miscellaneous equipment to multiple departments

▸ Running cables

▸ Planting microphones

▸ Identifying and mitigating noises

▸ Protecting gear from the elements by setting up rain tents, sun covers, etc.

▸ Coordinating movement of gear and sound crew to multiple locations

▸ Scouting the next location

▸ Setting up in advance of the company

▸ Wrapping the previous set

▸ Wrapping the gear at the end of the day

▸ Setting up gear for car driving/tow shots

▸ Mounting microphones in cars

▸ Representing the Sound Department when the Mixer and boom op cannot do so

▸ Confirming scene and take numbers with script and 2nd ACs

▸ Supplying batteries to the company

▸ Boom operating

▸ Filling in for the Mixer when needed

▸ Keeping the carts and equipment clean and organized

▸ Getting food/drink orders for your department when they cannot leave the set

▸ Following numerous Covid-19 protocols

Department Duties

▸ Managing distribution of paperwork

▸ Tracking expendables, including their inventory and ordering

▸ Cleaning and maintaining the equipment truck

▸ Supervising pre-production and/or on-production repairs

▸ Maintaining timecards and departmental paperwork

▸ Handling administrative records/calls to production

▸ Coordinating additional people and/or gear as needed

▸ Cleaning and repairing gear and cables

▸ Managing items coordinated between two or more departments

Production Duties

▸ Reporting equipment loss and damage

▸ Tracking repair or replacement of gear

▸ Renting of specialty equipment

▸ Acting as the main liaison to the Transportation Department, equipment suppliers, and repair shops

▸ Fulfilling the production's battery needs

▸ Procuring and managing expendables

▸ Managing departmental relationships with the other craft departments

▸ Being the main liaison to the Accounting Department, Production offices, and Editorial suite

▸ Representing the Sound Department when the Mixer and boom op cannot do so

NOTES

CHAPTER 2

Is Your Personality a Good Match for Film?

How do you know whether your personality is a match for working in the film industry? Consider the following attributes that make for a good UST.

Beneficial Qualities

▸ Be professional. Your behavior reflects on the entire department.

▸ Be self-motivating. No one has time to tell you what to do. But if you're not sure, do ask; it's preferred to just guessing!

▸ Be flexible. Movies are made "in the moment."

▸ Be engaged. Be interested in making each shot the best you can.

▸ Be organized. Sound Departments have hundreds of items, most of them small and black.

▸ Be a quick study. Take notes so you don't have to repeat questions.

▸ Be anticipatory. If you're only reacting, you're already behind.

▸ Be sociable. No one wants to spend 14 hours a day with a grouch.

▸ Be a bit thick-skinned. There is a human rainbow of personalities.

▸ Be a multi-tasker. Doing only one thing at a time is not enough.

▸ Be adaptable. Every Mixer has his or her own way of working.

▸ Be a good listener. Keep an ear open for information beyond your department.

▸ Be respectful. Manners go a long way.

▸ Be confident. If you make a mistake, say so, apologize, and move on.

▸ Be a constant learner. There's always something to learn.

▸ Be discreet. You'll be privy to very personal information or moods; keeping personal stories private is an important part of the job. Trust is a precious commodity.

▸ Be a "Yes" person if possible. But know when to be a "No" person (I'll talk about this later).

What Mixers Look For

I surveyed award-winning production sound Mixers *Stuart Wilson, Chris Munro, Peter Kurland, Mark Ulano,* and *Simon Hayes*; here's what they told me:

1. Punctuality is extremely important!

2. Prepare with the Mixer regarding each individual show; they are all so different. The same goes for the requirements from Production.

3. Read the script, break it down into how it will affect your work as a Utility; consider cast count, background extras, everything that will affect your expendables order, and anything that will require ordering additional equipment.

4. Liaise with the boom operator to discuss requirements once he or she has read the script.

5. Ask the Mixer to request pre-calls for large cast and background extras days.

6. Understand the importance of inter-department relationships; we rely on so many departments that can affect the outcome of our job and the tracks recorded: Camera, Costumes, Set Design, Lighting, and Transportation.

7. Plan to see costumes/fabrics ahead of time to establish wiring techniques. A conversation ahead of time with the costume designer and supervisor is always recommended.

8. Once the camera's rolling, and if you are not required to boom, you should be listening to see what can be done to better the scene for the Sound Department.

9. Idle conversation is not part of the working day; 100 percent of your focus should be on the department and what can be done to make the track better and to anticipate the next setup, scene, or next location.

10. An even temperament is crucial to deal with stressful situations.

Given a choice, most professionals would prefer someone less skilled but with the right attitude over someone with greater expertise but a difficult personality.

What Do You Need to Know? (Department Expectations)

▸ You should have a working knowledge of film production and know a bit about the specifics of every other department and what they need from Sound and USTs.

▸ You should understand what the Sound Department needs from the other departments.

▸ You should be familiar with basic types of microphones, their polar patterns, accessories, and how they connect.

▸ You should know how to operate the boom and be able to step in at a moment's notice.

▸ You should know protocols and how to communicate with actors, especially if they are "A-list" and have entourages.

▸ Your conversations should be short and to the point.

▸ You should become film literate. Many references to other films are expressed during the work and knowing them promotes a giant leap in being respected; film knowledge represents a shorthand form of describing essential information and elevates you in some hierarchy positioning.

▸ You should always keep up to date with hygiene and safety protocols.

As in every other work environment, you'll need to have social tools to help you work closely with coworkers whose personalities may test your limits. Not everyone on a set is able to manage the behaviors necessary to effectively communicate and collaborate with a multitude of personalities under constant stress. Those with any history of experience will have made some self-discoveries and moved either within their craft, to other crafts, or to less social positions or even altered their careers.

CHAPTER 3

The Business Side of Art

Filmmaking is both an art and a business. Narrative moviemaking and television costs can run $700—$3000 per "on-production" minute, so every minute counts. As of 2019 (pre-Covid-19), a rough gauge of budgets is that lower budgets are considered under $15M, medium budgets $16—$55M, and larger budgets are $55M+ (above-the-line costs are a significant factor). High-concept or action pictures or big tent-pole movies can have budgets as high as $200M or larger. When you're in business talks with production managers, use words that show you are considering costs in your discussion; it's the beginning of them building trust in your opinion.

And when the Mixer is speaking with the production manager about the cost of a UST, it is necessary to address a common misunderstanding about the staffing of the Sound Department. Any staffing requirement tends to raise a red-flag response on the part of the employer, who often assesses the situation on a presumed budget rarely discussed with the department in advance. (This is true of any size project and any department.)

There is no personal financial gain to any other party in the Sound Department to make sure we have the team complement we need. *What really happens is that the value of production time is being protected.* Here's how: high-priced talent can be quite an expensive budget item, independent of the costs of production. If the talent must wait to be wired 2—4 minutes two times a week because the Mixer and boom operator are understaffed and busy with their own jobs, at $2500/minute of production time, the production has just spent $10,000—$15,000, *not* including the actor's salary (possibly as high as $500,000 per day). The cost of hiring a (non-union) UST in the US is approximately $2500 for a 50-hour workweek (current US Covid-19 recommendations), thereby *saving $7,500—$17,500 per week*! In truth, some productions do not require a UST for every situation, but the production sound Mixer (PSM) is not asked to provide input.

This is borne out even without knowing the math and the costs by simply listening to the assistant directors (ADs). They will constantly pepper the Sound Department with questions like "How much longer?" "Are we ready yet?" "Can you wire them now for the next scene?" "Can you make that adjustment on the next take?" "Can you just wire everyone so we can just go right to shooting?" and so on.

Questions and comments like these serve as ample proof that production is a balancing game of trying to stop the cash hemorrhage of the typical shooting day by crunching time into an ever-shrinking envelope. It is the job of the PSM to make them slow down for a moment and see the real cost of actual versus perceived efficiency as it relates to hands on the job.

How Other Experts Do Their Job

The *Harvard Business Review*'s article "The Making of an Expert" is an interesting read: **https://hbr.org/2007/07/the-making-of-an-expert**. In essence, the article states:

> Consistently and overwhelmingly, the evidence showed that experts are always made, not born.

Expertise is a combination of focused practice, opportunity, and luck; and luck, after all, is when opportunity and readiness come together. Crews work efficiently and at a high level of competency. Know your stuff; it takes dedication, discipline, and focus to perform at high levels over many hours each day. Every shot is handmade; it's never happened before, and it will never happen exactly the same way again, so you'll always be contemplating scenarios—Plan A, Plan B, Plan C—and adjusting your approach to the work based on changing parameters. Your attention span will be put to the test. You will be concentrating on an activity and yet also must have the capacity to integrate new information from different sources (what you see and what you hear) in real time.

There are countless opportunities from which to learn every day on a set, and if you use every moment to be mindful, you can't help but succeed. Ask yourself:

▸ What are all the options?

▸ Which options didn't work as well as I'd thought?

▸ What could I have done differently?

▸ How do others solve this problem?

When you actively pay attention to improving, you will focus on perfecting your skills. If you think that people on a set don't notice this type of commitment, *stop now and think about* work; assess each person, and be honest about your perception of how far they'll go in the business.

If you can answer that question, you'll realize that *you* have been operating on that higher plane. And once you are mindful of it, you'll be more focused, and people *will* notice. And part of any job is what *you* make of it. I see some USTs who conduct their jobs as gophers and lowly assistants; you can feel that vibe from them. And then I see USTs who are filmmakers; this is how they choose to contribute and that's how people see them.

Get into a business mindset. Put time into maintaining your gear, your professional contacts, and building your outreach to the sound community. Sound professionals tend to be rather social creatures and offer one of the most inclusive and supportive networks in a professional arena. Take advantage of the gift that it is. Rather than being competitive, be collaborative. This business values personal attributes, not just knowledge or experience; therefore, *no one is taking a job away from you.* Be the kind of coworker you'd like to work alongside 15 hours a day.

Set a goal for yourself *now.* (To rise in a competitive business, you must do the work that will set you apart.) Use the Goal Worksheet in the Appendix.

NOTES

CHAPTER 4

Education & Training

Y ou need instruction; this is not a job you can just step into, although learning new things is certainly a component of your day. Learning should be considered a lifelong pursuit, particularly in the entertainment industry; the technology changes at a dizzying pace, and this can affect how projects are crewed, shot, and edited. The nature of film work is to create something new—a unique creation that has never been done quite like this before, and we create it in real time.

Many people want to help you become successful, and you'll see a multitude of YouTube videos and tutorials claiming to teach you techniques used in mainstream industry work. I've watched several of them myself, and they can be informative. But if you're just starting out, it can be impossible to know what is valid technique and current practice, and what will get you passed over for the next job.

I can't comment on all the online offerings available, but I've listed some reputable sources to get you started with reliable training in the Appendix.

You can also check out my upcoming companion books, *Behind the Boom Pole* and *The Blue Collar Guide to Filmmaking* for in-depth practical guides.

School vs. Interning vs. Mentoring

How do you choose between gaining experience and knowledge through school, internships, or mentoring programs? Here's the scoop:

Schools

Very few schools in the world actually teach production sound for film. If you're in one of them, you're lucky. Based on my interaction with film school students and graduates from around the world, most film schools focus on the theory and history of film but are woefully short on craft.

In Hollywood, it's not necessary to go to school first to obtain a film position. Many Mixers will tell you that it's more important to have the right attitude and disposition, and they can teach you the particular way they like to work and their preferred equipment. But it is *very useful* to be familiar with how most (if not all) of the equipment being used operates. Read and know the user manuals (most are available on manufacturers' websites). If you can, take classes in how to build cables, solder connectors, troubleshoot electronics, or use a Fisher boom (which is making a comeback in Hollywood). Being a "quick study" is important to keeping your job. Consider taking a first-aid course, particularly if you work with small crews or on low-budget shows where medical personnel are absent.

Interning

Interning is a great way to get an overview of a job to help you decide on a career. The practice of interning varies in different areas. In Los Angeles, productions that are amenable to inviting interns usually require the intern be currently enrolled in a learning institution, have proof of liability insurance from the school, and limit time on set to 8 hours on any given day. Interns cannot perform work; these rules satisfy the requirements of insurance companies. To find opportunities in the L.A. market, you can approach a production Sound Department member (via Facebook or your own sources).

Mentoring

Your career will progress quicker if you can find someone who will take you under their wing. Mentors can offer personal experience, interpret some confusing interactions, and give some perspective, which might take you years to acquire on your own. They can also be available if you need urgent advice from the set or the support of a coach.

A combination of all these options will give you a well-rounded understanding of their benefits. Some people mistakenly assume the UST position is a glorified PA job, and they want a more "important" job with a higher profile. After reading the list of duties and responsibilities the

UST position comprises, it's impossible to think it's just an entry-level job. You will be on the set, listening intimately to the director and actors, and actually contributing.

Physical Health & Training

I make no claims about being a qualified fitness instructor, and the information provided here is not intended to be a substitute for professional medical advice, diagnosis, or treatment. After reading content from this book, you are encouraged to review the information carefully with your professional healthcare provider. Rather, I serve as a mentor and guide who strives to help you reach your own health and wellness goals.

Most people assume they aren't strong enough to hold a boom pole, so they immediately write off this job, as it usually requires the equivalent booming skills as the primary boom operator. Yes, there will be minutes when the boom is a strain, and you'll have to muscle through. But boom operators have that as a main concern, not you as a UST. You have carts to push up hills, onto ramps, through doorways, and maneuver into elevators. There's a good amount of lifting, twisting, pulling, and squatting, so having a general fitness plan is a must.

I also lift weights, concentrating on the upper body; shoulder and back strength will do more to support you than just concentrating on your biceps. I always do some kind of *wakeup* exercise in the mornings as well, because you just don't know what will be asked of you in the upcoming day's work. I found it wise to buy a treadmill, so I can always get in some cardiovascular exercise before *call* (a scheduled work time).

I find yoga helps with both flexibility and mentally resetting from the stresses of work. Muscle soreness is a side effect of the stress you put on muscles from working, and yoga can alleviate some pains and pulled muscles by releasing muscle tension and improving flexibility.

Dance has helped many a crewmember with agility, coordination, strength, endurance, flexibility, and posture. Try a ballet or jazz dance class and see for yourself; Steadicam operators and dolly grips need to move gracefully for the camera moves, and they are proponents of dance.

Asking them for a recommendation may also be an "in" to having more of a relationship with those crewmembers. Often, someone in the Grip Department has brought workout equipment onto their truck and, Covid-19 protocols aside, she may be willing to have you join her at lunch.

There are so many exercise choices available to you locally and online. Find a plan that keeps you flexible, warmed up for the day's work, and has a core strength element to keep your back healthy. Some kind of stretching every day is a must to prevent being hurt. Stretch before work and after work. It's OK to stretch during work, even on set; sometimes you'll see dolly grips or boom operators stretch before a particularly physical move. Here are two programs that have worked well for associates:

Chris Hemsworth (famous for his "Thor" character) trained hard for his Marvel role and created a terrific online site of exercise programs, nutrition, recipes, and meditations. Together with his varied team of professional trainers and nutritionists, programs are now being offered to everyone. At the time of this writing, they offer a free trial period and a yearly plan or low monthly charge. The site offers several body-weight fitness programs (meaning that you need no equipment, just the weight of your body to provide resistance).

https://centr.com

I have heard good things from colleagues about Nike's Training Club. They offer trainer-designed workouts for everything from all-around fitness to yoga, currently free.

www.nike.com/ntc-app

Don't forget your ears! Have a regular hearing test and keep a copy of your results in your truck bag; you'll have something to compare with if there's an accident on set and you need to see a doctor. On *Pet Sematary*, an actor had consistently whispered his dialogue in every take until he suddenly decided to scream! The Mixer had increased the volume from the microphone for the actor's low voice, and that scream was physically painful for me. It necessitated a visit to an audiologist who was a 2-hour drive away, and I was off work for a day and a half. The pain was exhausting, and nothing but time alleviated it.

On another show, the director wanted the actors to react to the story point's "dangerous location" authentically by surprising the crew with the firing of a gun near the camera. Consider yourself forewarned.

Just a quick word about physical build, specifically *height*: Over the years, I've had guys comment that they're surprised to find I boom when I'm only 5' 4" (1.65 meters). There is some assumption out there that boom operators should be tall people. I don't *feel* short, but I have noticed that being vertically challenged has meant that I have had to strain a bit or limit my mobility a teensy bit by needing to use an apple box for height. No one ever makes needing an apple box or ladder an issue on the set!

I recently did a six-month long movie with a 6' 4" boom operator, and I came to appreciate the Mixer's point of view; he had chosen both a tall male boom operator and a short female UST—someone for any situation. You can always put me on an apple box, but you can't always scrunch a tall boom op into a forest of C-stands or hide him under a table.

While booming *Jocks*, a movie about college kids in a tennis competition, I remember needing to boom four tennis matches in a row. I ran back and forth for three of them, and our Utility offered to take one match to give me a rest. He was a kickboxer built like a chimpanzee—dense and all muscle. He boomed for about 3½ minutes, and then I heard pole rattling. He didn't have the strength to steady the pole, and I had to take the pole from him mid-run.

Emotional Training

Working in TV and movies is stressful, and that feeling doesn't entirely go away no matter how many projects you do. One does learn to make friends with stress, and even use that energy to assist and support your work, but you'll return home drained.

And when you're starting out, there's the fear of not knowing something, of getting something wrong that has consequences, of making a public spectacle of some sort. And to top that off, there are the irrational fears that only you have imagined!

Part of staying calm on set is to feel comfortable with unexpected verbal exchanges or changing circumstances. Until you feel you've mastered that, here are some suggestions for things to say in various situations.

A common fear is that you'll be criticized publicly or will have done something wrong in a big way. When panic sets in and you can't think straight, the following will get you out of that hot seat quickly and with your dignity intact. Take a breath, and then say, "Thank you." And nothing more. Or say, "Copy that." Or "Got it."

That is enough to convey that you received the message, and, unless someone is a bullying personality, it's enough said and everyone will move on. Practice keeping a neutral facial expression—not everyone can, and it'll be important at this moment. Everyone has been in that hot seat at one time or another, so don't get stuck in the moment; work is not going to stop unless there's been an accident.

You need some tools to use now and when you're at work. Try some of the following:

▸ Breathing: Use controlled breathing to lower your anxiety. Breathe in through your nose counting 1-2-3-4, hold a second, and then release through your mouth 1-2-3-4. Wait 1 second and repeat for 2 minutes.

▸ For body tension: 1. Stretch and bend. 2. Try tensing one body part (for instance, your shoulders) for 10 seconds and then relaxing. Dancing and/or listening to music may help and can be done during lunch. Some sound crews play music through their comm. systems during work. Tucking in some physical activity during the day can help.

There might be a time when what you've been told to do may conflict with another department or crewmember's task. If you reach an impasse, try saying something like: "I'm delegated to do [a task], so please talk to the Mixer about this." Or "Let's explain this to the Mixer."

If you believe there might be some gender bias, take the high ground and always keep it professional. Decide not to engage at that level. Many times, I have experienced people's views changing when I stand my ground by just doing my job and not engaging.

On my first union show, one of the first shots was to bring a truck into a parking lot and follow it to the bank. We rehearsed three times: it was a dolly back and then a pan. My action was to take three steps back and swing the microphone. The rehearsals went perfectly. On the first take, I took my three steps back and stepped on the director of photography's (DOP) foot. I completed the swing wondering why, since he hadn't been anywhere near me.

When we cut, I apologized to him. He said nothing. I watched him all night, thinking this was going to be something: he was tall, bald, older, and carried a swagger stick that he used from time to time to slap his black knee-high boot—I heard he was a former drill sergeant. Oh! And his name was Duke. I don't think it could have been any worse.

He made it clear that he didn't like women; I'm not sure he liked anyone other than "his boys." After the first week of being distracted by him, I couldn't stand the stress, and I gave up trying to second-guess him. I kept a professional relationship with the camera operator and first AC. In the last week, the extras coordinator told me he complained to the script supervisor: "You should learn to be professional like Patrushkha!" Go figure....

When you're hit with a series of curve balls, just keep moving forward.

NOTES

CHAPTER 5

Communication

D ifferent levels of communication occur on a set, and it's up to an individual to become aware of them. It's certainly an optional activity but has the potential to change the trajectory of your career, giving you a completely different experience of working on a project and perhaps adding an immeasurable boost to your standing.

There are some productions in which the Sound Department is regarded with less respect than the Camera, Grip, or Electric Departments. In my experience, it is because our department does not directly add support to the Camera Department in working the shot, nor is it dependent on the Camera Department for the next job. Also, in the past, as well as currently with some Sound Departments, the Sound people wait until everyone has finished setting up the shot to begin their own work and then ask for collaborative compromises and/or modifications to other's work. I'd be annoyed, too.

Verbal Communication

The most basic level of communication is *verbal*. You might think that because this is basic that it would be widely used, but that's not necessarily the case.

In the 1980s, directors came to work prepared. They would map out the work to the 1st AD and the crew, often handing out shot lists and diagrams, and then everyone could configure their department's work to most efficiently prepare for the shots. It also gave the crew a chance to suggest a shooting order that could make the work more efficient. Directors listened to their crews and there was a mutual respect.

And there was always time for a good story. I remember a short, spry director told me about his early days of being a stuntman—or should I say stuntwoman?—for Bette Davis and other actresses, because women didn't do that job. He dressed in high heels and wigs and shaved his hair—"everywhere." Directors talked about "script clerks" as they originally had come out of the secretarial pool. Directors appreciated their crews and understood the value of sharing, and crews made the director's vision happen in the time allotted.

In the 1990s I saw directors begin to stop communicating with the crew about what the work would be, and then stop coming in with shot lists. I saw 1st ADs move from commanding sets and directing the crew like air traffic controllers to not knowing themselves what was going on. Fast-forward to the 2000s, and I worked on a feature film for which the director told me not to ever listen to the 1st AD because he didn't know what was going on...there's even a mantra about it: "Don't listen to (*name*)!" There's been a shift away from telling the crew what the work is, and it leaves everyone expending energy trying to figure it out *on top of* doing their job.

For strategies for working on dysfunctional sets, see Chapter 12, "Running the Show."

Visual Communication

There is a fundamental process to organizing labor and equipment to create the environment necessary to shoot a scene. After understanding core filmmaking concepts and the process the project you're working on has set in motion, you can *visually* assess where the company is in the process without needing any words.

Departments that need large amounts of preparation can help signal the timing of the shoot—e.g., if a location needs a certain amount of dressing or some alterations that take a long time, *and* you see the progress from the Art Department, you can determine some logical outcomes and make adjustments in your own department. Watching dolly track being laid can also signal a moving camera, and the length or track configuration may tell you something about the coverage for the scene. An area being lit outside of what you thought the actor's set would be should raise a question in your mind, and a quick conversation with Lighting could explain enough to know what you need to be ready for the scene.

Utility sound technicians must be excellent communicators and detectives. They must understand the Mixer's expectations as any interaction may have potentially significant consequences, and the Sound Department may not be able to recover from a misstep for the rest of the show. And it's possible to lose a substantive contact for the rest of the Mixer's and your career. A case in point: On a long-term project, it became obvious that the UST and director had incompatible personalities. Rather than being able to discuss the situation quietly after work with the other Sound Department members and create an alternate information flow, the UST felt completely confident that the trouble lay in the director's propensity to jump to conclusions about the tone of the UST in the conveyance of information. The Mixer was unable to help the UST disengage the production's politics from personal righteousness, and after 11 weeks of doing every other thing well, the Sound team was ultimately never asked onto any of the director's future projects—it did not matter that the UST was replaced immediately after that project.

Film Literacy

Literacy is the ability to identify, understand, interpret, create, and communicate using materials associated with varying contexts. And having film literacy means that you understand referential comments or instructions to other films by the filmmakers you are working with.

Being film literate while on set can establish connections. This is a higher level of communication and requires that you be something of a film scholar; the players of this game are a diverse group. Acquiring film knowledge requires a longer commitment of time and memorization, but it can bring you closer to directors, producers, camera people, and actors and move you into an elite category. Examples of film literacy include:

▸ Being able to label slates for coverage using a film category (for instance, horror movie makeup artists or directors). For example, slating scene 35 AG as "SCENE 35 Abel Gance." It also helps in the case of overhearing a director telling the director of photography he'd like to do an "Abel Gance" for scene 47 (Abel Gance was a French film director, producer, actor, and writer known for his pioneering use of montage in the silent era).

▸ Playing the Name Game: Who was the first director to make a "Titanic" feature film? How many directors were there on *The Three Stooges*? Who was a nuclear physicist before he became a movie producer?

Who replaced Fred Clark (Harry Morton) on *The Burns and Allen Show* in 1953? It was Larry Keating, because Mr. Clark felt television was a disreputable venue and he wanted to return to Broadway. The producers were perplexed as to how they would replace a main character in a very popular, live televised show. It was the brilliance of Rod Amateau, one of the show's producers and directors, who, at 25 years old, came up with the plan: In the middle of Fred Clark's last episode, on live TV, he said his line and waited. George Burns turned to the camera and told the audience that Mr. Clark was leaving to return to Broadway. Fred stopped and bowed to the audience and left the stage. Larry Keating took Mr. Clark's place, George introduced him as the new Harry Morton, and the rest of the episode played out. Done!

I can't profess to be a scholar, but I did pay attention when I was fortunate to work with Rod, and I delighted in his stories!

Emotional Communication

There's an emotional level of communication on the set, and if you choose to engage on that level, it can be very satisfying—and make the difference between dreading work and making it through the day with your energy level intact. At the same time, it's important to stay conscious and mindful about emotional connection, as that can *distract* you from the work. There are many private dramas taking place during the making of a movie, and you must be actively aware of whether you are getting drawn into someone's drama, and then try to avoid that.

The positive side of an emotional connection is that others who operate on that level will connect with you and that can add a level of sanity to the day. It can manifest itself in sharing jokes, a running gag, getting a heads-up about a change that wasn't announced, a look that says, "I understand," or more overtly as in playing musical instruments together at lunch.

Understand the Players

If filmmaking were only about being able to do the job, we'd all be inter-changeable. But it isn't, and that's why some people's careers are stuck in lower-budget movies or smaller projects and others are on an upward trajectory. The most successful film workers shape their information to the recipient. When you can change your perception about the set, you become a different person and the set behaves differently and then reacts differently to you.

How People Receive Information

Each of us has developed information pathways that help us interpret and share that information (receiving as well as transmitting). The more pathways we can learn, the more productive we become. Here are several information pathways:

1. **Visual (Spatial):** These crewmembers use an image or cue to help them process information. They:
   - Have good spatial sense and sense of direction
   - Can easily visualize objects, plans, and outcomes
   - Like coloring, drawing, and doodling
   - Have good color balance
   - Are good at using maps and rarely get lost
   - Prefer pictures, images, and mind maps to help process information

2. **Aural Learning:** These are crewmembers who respond primarily to sound. They:
   - Find that certain music invokes strong emotions
   - Enjoy listening to music in the background while learning
   - Have a good sense of pitch or rhythm
   - Find that songs, jingles, and themes tend to pop into their heads without prompts

3. **Verbal (Linguistic):** Some crewmembers do best with verbal instruction and writing. They need to read content aloud to learn something or prefer to have someone speak the information to process it. They:

   ‣ Enjoy reading and writing

   ‣ Like tongue twisters and rhymes

   ‣ Have a large vocabulary and enjoy learning new words

4. **Physical (Kinesthetic):** Physical learners are extremely animated and always need to be moving. They learn best by going through the motions of what they are learning. If something is bothering them or they are trying to wrap their head around a concept, they would rather go for a run or walk than sit down and figure it out. They:

   ‣ Notice and appreciate the physical world around them, such as textures

   ‣ Enjoys sports and exercise along with outdoor activities and working with their hands

   ‣ Tend to use and pick up on body language

   ‣ Enjoy making models or doing jigsaw puzzles

5. **Logical (Mathematical):** Most logical thinkers end up being engineers, mathematicians, or pursuing the sciences; they want to understand the reason behind content or skills and tend to enjoy games like chess and solving brainteasers. They:

   ‣ Classify and group information together to better understand it

   ‣ Perform complex calculations

   ‣ Create procedures for future use after coming up with a solution to a problem

   ‣ Plan agendas and itineraries and even rank and number them

6. **Social (Interpersonal):** Social learners are natural group workers; they are individuals who like to be engaged with others, work on teams, and ask their peers for feedback in order to learn. They:

   ‣ Prefer to socialize after work or class

   ‣ Bounce ideas off others and work through issues in a group

   ‣ Listen well

   ‣ Are often trusted by others for their advice

7. **Solitary (Intrapersonal):** Some people are extroverts in social situations but prefer to be alone when they are trying to learn. They:

   ‣ Spend time on self-analysis

   ‣ Are concerned with goals and outcomes

   ‣ Think independently

   It's generally assumed that sound people are predominantly logical/ mathematical thinkers, but in fact, a good many come to film sound from a music and/or art background.

How People Transmit Information

1. **Directive:** This Mixer makes a decision, and everyone must follow his orders; there's little room for error. He isn't afraid to deliver ultimatums in the face of failed standards.

2. **Authoritative:** This Mixer will explain the vision they have for the work and give you fair and constructive feedback.

3. **Affiliative:** This Mixer will put people first, job second; it may lead people to be less focused on striving for excellence. On the other hand, this nurturing attitude can bring out the best in people.

4. **Participative:** This Mixer listens to the boom op and UST and reaches a collaborative decision.

5. **Pacesetting:** This Mixer sets a high-functioning pace, and the crew is expected to work at that level.

6. **Coaching:** This Mixer will use teaching to encourage boom ops and USTs to learn new skills, expects them to exercise more responsibility and independence, and may even expect his team to teach him the new things they learn.

Conflict is inevitable when people come together, but there are strategies for working through issues without damaging relationships. Try to remember that because people give and receive information differently, conflict or disagreement is normal and unavoidable. Don't jump to conclusions and do try to think of the situation as one in which both parties are working toward finding a resolution. Remember that conflict could be as simple as someone not hearing you correctly or a case of semantics—you are both in agreement on the issue, but the words conveyed something different to each of you.

If there's a real disagreement, try to understand the other person's side adequately by giving yourself time to process it. Saying, "I'd like to think about that for a bit and consider it" shows respect and thoughtfulness and everyone gets to save face.

Saving face is as important as the actual issue and can definitely affect your career. Saving face signifies a desire—or defines a strategy—to avoid humiliation or embarrassment, to maintain dignity or preserve reputation. You may rightly think that you know your friend on the crew, and you always have a certain fun way of cutting each other down; but in work situations, where there are dozens of people you don't know, you have no idea whether they will interpret your words and actions in the way your friend would. And if you speak negatively about your friend in a professional situation, it will be interpreted by some as you being a mean person—and that can manifest itself in you not being asked back for future work.

Sometimes you must say things to someone who might interpret your communication as being something that could cause him or her to lose face. How can you know the right thing to say or do to defuse that potentiality? Well, you can't know for certain, so you do the next best thing: you make an extra effort so that it's harder for your interaction to be seen negatively.

One strategy is to use tact. You employ tact by using words that are not negative yet convey the intent of something said in a brusque manner. For example, to tell a production assistant (PA) that he or she did not handle something and it's still a problem, you might say: "Can you show me how you shut it down? We still have some noise on set that I'm trying to locate." Or "Everyone coming onto the set knows to wait while we're rolling, even the producers, so don't worry about asking them to wait; they'll understand." Or "Grip, our microphones are picking up that work you're doing. Is it something you can take further away, or could I ask a PA to be stationed here to call rolls and cuts?"

It can be a little trickier with Camera, as they often feel some inordinate comfort making suggestions for Sound Department situations. You might say: "Camera, thanks for your suggestion, but the [issue or situation] makes that not a viable solution." You don't have to give a reason, particularly if you're being bombarded with other people telling you how to do your job—something other departments don't have to contend with. My go-to answer that shuts things down successfully: "Thank you."

Another strategy is to use an indirect "no." For example, "We considered your idea, but other factors lead us in a different way." If you're not sure how to respond, think about how you turn down someone who wants to take you out on a date, but you know you have to work closely with him or her. If it's appropriate, you might try good-natured humor.

Considering a different perspective can help you grow and may even bring you closer to someone, or at least you may appreciate the myriad ways people have devised to cope with problems.

NOTES

CHAPTER 6

Pre-Production

There are three basic phases of making a movie: pre-production, production, and postproduction. However, from our craft department standpoint, our three phases are pre-production, production, and wrap. A good amount of the important thinking and preparations regarding production sound is realized during the *pre-production* period. *Production* is the time of the ongoing shooting of the movie. *Wrap* is the period immediately after shooting, when a department cleans and returns the equipment to its home, turns in all materials and any paperwork, and cleans the workspace.

> *I describe departments and the processes in the order you will generally encounter them on a production.*

The Pre-Production Process

There is an adage known as "The Seven P's of Production":

> **P**roper **p**re-**p**roduction **p**revents **p**iss-**p**oor **p**erformance.

If you take away only one lesson from this book, this word says it all:

Prep

Make it your favorite four-letter word. I would argue that doing proper preparation could solve 70% of all the problems you might encounter on a job.

Your job as a UST starts weeks before the actual shooting begins. Your first contact will be with the Sound Department, as you likely have already worked with them previously, and they liked you enough to invite you onto their team again. If you've worked together before, pull up your Notes page and review it; don't leave it to memory for all those little details. Be sure to ask if they need any assistance right now.

If you get a cold call, though, you'll need to do more. A cold call means receiving a phone call out of the blue, from someone you don't know. Most often, it will be from a Mixer, but a boom operator or a production office staffer might also call.

Questions to Ask About the Project

These questions will give you important information to design an approach to the new project:

What is the title of the project? Then you can research the project in the trade papers. **Who is the director?** Knowing who the director is will give you an idea of the style, pace, and the expected visibility of the project when it is released. **Who is in it (main actors or a notable person)?** If the big-name actor is in a lead role, there will be a certain minimum budget and level of experience of the company. If the big-name actor has a cameo role, it denotes a smaller, lower-budget movie. Budgets do not necessarily correlate with a particular level of professionalism, but they provide pieces of information to help you anticipate what kinds of issues may come up during shooting and how they might be addressed. The intended budget may be listed on IMDb, or you can ask the Mixer.

Is it a union or non-union show? Which rules are in force? Remember that in the US, in the absence of union rules, there are governmental labor laws. Whether they are followed is is a point you'll need to pay attention to as you work. **What's the name of the production company?** Often, it is an entity put together solely for the purpose of this specific project. One reason is because if there's a lawsuit against the company, it doesn't affect the other assets of the principals. Who the principals of the production company are may be an indication of their longevity in the industry and may indicate a possible long-term client.

What are the start and wrap dates? If you have a scheduling conflict, should you speak up right away or wait until closer to the conflict date? It depends. Is it a one-day scheduling conflict or a week? A wedding or a surgery? Because of the particulars of personalities and timing, you must make your own call. Sometimes the scenes you miss will be minor, and your absence may not be noticed; sometimes, the opposite happens. I let the people I am working closely with know when I'll be gone in advance;

how far in advance depends on the nature of my work. If I'm responsible for helping get an actor into a spacesuit and connecting her communication system, I will make sure to let everyone associated know a few days in advance, providing them time to think of any concerns they may have and again the day before leaving. If possible, I'll introduce the person taking over to everyone—but not to the actor as she is being called to set!

How many days a week are we shooting? How much is working at night? Will it be on location? Are there any difficult or unusual locations or sets? I know from experience (especially from work on the film *Shy People*) that I can get motion sickness on boats or aerial craft, so I ask about these elements and am honest about my ability for the work.

You'll also want to have conversations with the members of the Sound Department if you don't know them.

The Mixer

Do an online search and read any articles by or about the Mixer. Ask others for notes on work preferences and any possible difficulties or pet peeves. Look up past boom operators and USTs and ask them. Keep everything they say in confidence if it's personal or uncomplimentary.

Don't feel shy about asking the Mixer how he or she likes to work and be sure to have a paper and pen ready to take notes. Listen for clues about the Mixer's workstyle or personality; you'll have a better understanding of how to represent the department in harmony with the Mixer's branding and present a consistent face to the production. If you disagree with the Mixer on some fundamentals, follow them anyway: there will be plenty of time for the crew to learn about *your* values.

It's possible that the Mixer could use help dropping off or picking up gear from the rental house or repair shop, cleaning the gear, building something for the upcoming shoot, or running to the production office. Mixers often can use help organizing and will appreciate your offer to rework and label the cases and/or space. This will give you a chance to get to know each other without the stress of production, and you'll get familiar with the Mixer's gear, connecting and testing everything in a relaxed atmosphere. You'll also have the benefit of having organized equipment the way it will make sense *to you*.

Some questions make sense to ask when the gear is in front of you, and some questions when getting ready for the shot. Don't overload anyone with too many questions ahead of when the information will be used.

Boom Operator

The boom operator and the utility should support each other, but they have independent job responsibilities. Do the same prep as for the Mixer. Find out how collaborative they are; some operators don't want to touch the carts, while some are total team players. Discreetly seek some input on this from the Mixer. Sometimes the show moves so fast that they don't have time. Build in an idea of how you'll handle everything, and the time needed—you may need to commandeer a PA to help with an equipment move.

Boom operators will have ideas on how much of their time is devoted to general department duties and what they consider to be their territory. Find out if they intend to help you with wiring when possible or never at all. Will they move the antenna or carts when you're wiring? I find it most helpful to have some thoughts in mind and then work out the actual process during the first week when you all see what the company pace is—the ability of the director, the speed and temperament of the DOP, and whether there are clear directions and information flow from the 1st AD.

A boom operator may want to get together for coffee or a beer so you both can talk about preferred ways to work. Take notes about how he or she likes to work and have some questions prepared, but focus on the work at hand or you may be thought of as underqualified. Trust that a lot of dialogue between both of you will happen during the first workdays.

With these questions answered, experienced USTs will know whether the job is a good fit for them. Once you've accepted the job, the task of getting to know coworkers begins. Ask for any production materials available now: Crew list? Schedule? Is a script available?

Departments and Interaction

With the name of the movie and names of the actors or the director, you can access available Internet research (IMDb, Google searches, *The Hollywood Reporter*, *Variety*, Deadline.com) and begin talking with coworkers. The Internet Movie Database (IMDb) is an online database of information related to films, television programs, home videos, video games, and streaming content online—including cast, production crew, and personal biographies, plot summaries, trivia, ratings, and fan and critical reviews. The free database is **www.imdb.com,** and the paid subscription service, **https://pro.imdb.com**, also provides production company contact info and in-depth industry activity.

Who will be the director of photography (DOP), camera operator, 1st and 2nd assistant camera (1st AC, 2nd AC), gaffer, key grip, costumer, props master, script supervisor, first assistant director (1st AD), and second assistant director (2nd AD)? These are the main departments you'll work with, and you may know someone from previous shows. Your working comfort is partially based on how good your working relationship is with these main contacts. Call your friends and colleagues to get an idea of what it was like working with those crewmembers: their quirks, pet peeves, and personalities. **How soon after call was the first setup ready? How quickly did the setups take place? Were there always multiple cameras? Were the cameras placed wide and tight or were there two sizes of complementary coverage from the same direction?** Ask anything you think will help you imagine how the work will play out. If you're just starting out, these questions might not make sense. Write them down in your Notes page under the movie title and answer them when you can; the questions and the meanings of the answers will soon become clear.

Researching the gaffer and key grip (Lighting and support departments) will tell you about the Camera's support crew and how inclusionary they are. If possible, ask someone you know from the gaffer's and grip's previous projects about how they light and how they communicate with other departments during the day. **How do they respond to requests for flags, cutters, or altering a light? At what pace do they work?** If there are seven grips, six electricians, and two full camera packages with full staffing but only two sound people hired, you can count on your day being hectic and your department being understaffed. Once you have read the script or received notes from the Mixer, there may be questions to sort out as soon as possible.

What is the budget and scope of the production manager's previous projects? These answers may be a good indicator of the budget for your department. The budget can help you understand the expectations of the production manager (PM) concerning your department's staffing, the number of prep days, whether Sound will be asked to attend the location scout, how easy it will be to order expendables, and whether you'll get pre-calls. There are, however, elements that can skew your expectations, creating large money expenditures that can cause the rest of the production elements to have decreased budgets. Some of these include casting celebrities, having many producers attached to the show, using many visual effects (VFX) or special effects (SFX), or an exotic location or using large numbers of animals or specialty talent. **If there are special effects (SFX) or live music, ask how much prep those departments are being given.** This shows an understanding of the true work involved and could be an indication of whether the budget is realistic.

How many producers are there? What is their experience and budgets of previous projects? The more producers there are, the more likely things may slow down while a committee decides on shots and coverage. And the more finances for the film will go toward management.

How much prep is the Sound Department being given? Most of the bigger-budget shows allot x number of days for prep, and the Mixer doles them out as needed. **Will the Sound Department be included on the tech scouts? What are the particulars of the deal memo, and do they differ from your expectations?** Once you have some experience, you'll be able to read a script, look at the schedule, and know whether it is realistic. An unrealistic schedule is a red flag—a cause for concern because it is untenable and someone in charge either does not realize something will need to change or is aware but must play a silly game to appease some higher authority in the organization. Whether that means extending the schedule, cutting scenes, or making the crew work longer hours or longer workweeks, the fact that it is not addressed openly means something is dysfunctional.

You may come to understand that the Sound Department might need to have a larger prep period or earlier call times. There may be unusual elements that could affect your work, such as a difficult-to-access location. **Does the equipment always need to be carried up flights of stairs? What about difficult topography? Will we need to be shuttled or given a Gator to traverse the area? Are we shooting on water, sand, or at a high elevation? Extreme weather?** As you learn more about the specific details, visualize how they might affect your day-to-day work. While the Mixer will also be asking these questions, having two people thinking about the issues will help make sure nothing is missed. And you'll be primarily responsible for moving the gear and Sound members.

Will there be a music supervisor or choreographer? What about a rehearsal schedule? Will there be a postproduction sound crew hired before the end of shooting? Is their contact information available? If they're not hired or haven't started on the project yet, is it OK to check in with them? If it isn't a priority for the production, then it's possible that production sound will not be, either. **When will they start work?**

As the production gears up for shooting, you'll interact more with the Production office staff, the crafts departments, possibly the actors, and production materials to help you understand the adventure that will soon be your life for the foreseeable future.

Find out what you can about anyone connected with the project. **How many projects has he or she done?** This gives you an indication of their experience. **Have those projects been recognized with awards or articles?** Maybe the individual is on a path of accelerated celebrity. **What was the scale of their previous projects? Were they only small, low-budget movies?** Maybe the crews are inexperienced and do not know the working processes to be able to allow someone to contribute their best work. **How many camera packages is the show carrying?** This will give you an indication of shooting style and the budget allotted for Camera—and their staffing. **What genre is the film?** Genre will influence the budget—i.e., horror movies and kid's shows are generally lower-budget productions, while big action films have larger budgets.

If you have an established relationship with anyone on the crew list, contact him or her first to say hello and share any information. Otherwise, your first call will be to make contact: introduce yourself and your department members. Exchange contact info if the crew list is still being created. If the director is well established, contact his or her assistant to see whether there will be a special headset or equipment request and have it ready for the first day of shooting. Make sure you have doubles on hand! Chat up the assistant to learn what you can about how the director works and his or her temperament.

I should note that all this deep background research is terrifically important but should be viewed through the filter of the personalities sharing it with you.

There are times when the negative experience of another is not your expe-rience at all. Remain objective. **It is also important to note that you will often receive exceptionally privileged information. Whether or not an NDA (non-disclosure agreement) is required of you, it is imperative that any information you receive be treated like Presidential secrets. Careers could be at stake if you act foolishly and share things you should not.**

The Script

It is essential to read the script, production schedule, and one-liner as soon as possible. Initially, it's more important that *you* read these pro-duction materials than the boom operator or Mixer. From these materials, you'll create a list of expendables and specialty equipment that may be needed. It also steers you to the departments that may need more inter-action during the pre-production phase. How soon can you get a script to read? Even just borrowing one so you can start a list of questions is valu-able and can jumpstart your planning.

This has become more difficult in recent years as many productions have become very security conscious about the story elements of their scripts being leaked to the public as a major liability. The result has been that many productions are limiting access to their script during pre-pro-duction. Most often, this restricts the reading of the script to heads of departments (HODs) or even just some of them. This is very counterin-tuitive, for without knowing the actual material, it becomes much more difficult to prepare, forcing a kind of generic approach.

How to Break Down a Script

The script's cover page lists the version or date, so always check that you have the latest copy. The script will be white, but as changes occur throughout the production phase, colored pages will denote changes. (A chronology of color changes is provided in the Appendix.) The changes may concern a change in setting or dialogue or omitting or adding a scene. Colored pages should replace only the pages for which the change occurs. Make sure that you read the ending of the last current page before the change and the beginning of the first current page after the change to make sure it follows logically.

Most scripts start with the words FADE IN, and most end with the words FADE OUT. Information on the scene setting and time of day are always in capital letters. Each scene describes the location (e.g., INT. for interior, EXT. for exterior), site, and time of day—e.g., INT. BEDROOM - DAY, EXT. ROAD - NIGHT, or EXT. BEACH - DUSK.

Be careful with scenes such as those dealing with vehicles: INT. CAR - DAY vs. INT. CAR - NIGHT. Shooting the interior of the car during the day might entail a tow vehicle and driving on the freeway. Shooting inside the car at night might mean it will really be night *or* that a black "tent" will be made around a car on a stage *or* that it will be a green-screen scene or synchronous video panels customized to the particular scene with pre-recorded locations. Shooting outside the car at night might mean actors are standing next to the car or even just walking away from it silently. Each of these choices requires different equipment and setup time. Note the scenes on either side of the scene in question to help determine what time of day is meant and whether there is a time jump—and therefore an actor has a costume or hair change.

Established Mixers, and certainly the high-end people I work with, invite and expect me to be a full-thinking member of the team. With that view in mind, I offer these notes: read the script through the first time to understand the story and tenor of the show (comedy, drama, romance, high-concept, gritty, etc.) and get a feel for the pacing. Your second read should be with paper and pen. If it's your copy of the script, you can mark it directly (in pencil if you think the script may later be valuable).

As you look at each scene, underline what you think may be noise or sound or weather references: anything from train whistles to background music, wind, rain, snow, or fire. (Did you remember to note the aquarium tank filter?) Write questions in the margins near the scenes. Have a conversation with the Mixer about the notes to address, whether she has information on how they're to be addressed, and which questions each of you will be responsible for. I then like to transfer those notes to my one-liner, as newer revisions will replace those original script pages. When those scenes come up on the Advance section of the call sheet, I confirm the resolution previously discussed with the affected parties.

When you read the script, the more you can imagine the movie, the more you'll be able to anticipate what sound elements may need attention.

Maybe it's not sound per se, but a prop or costume or vehicle; make a note and follow up with a question to either the Mixer or that department. Start with a department assistant and work your way up the department, until you get the information you need. You may be able to interject something helpful or possibly stop something that would have made your work more difficult. Whether or not you are getting paid, you're expected to have things worked out by the shoot day, and ultimately, if you haven't, you'll have to deal with it in front of the crew, while they wait.

Not everything that may be in your purview will be an obvious sound element. For off-camera dialogue, some directors use a script supervisor to read during the take, while some want playback. (Will it be a pre-record or happen on the day? Will it be a temporary track?) Some directors want the actual device (telephone, radio, or TV)—vintage or not—working practically. What about hearing the off-screen (OS) dialogue through the phone? *Never assume.* Talking with crews from previous shows comes in handy! Remember: working TVs or monitors means there will be a video playback person or two.

Once you've read the script, you're ready to talk to the other departments and learn about their challenges and what solutions you could possibly be working toward together.

Start with the department assistants. Whenever you communicate with people, no matter by text, email, or phone, be respectful and polite. The questions you ask and the way in which you deliver them helps the recipients form an opinion about your level of experience. When appropriate, use the collaborative word "we," as it conveys a feeling of being part of the team and that you are open to others' points of view to solve the collective issues.

If the person to whom you're asking questions must keep checking with someone else, you should ask for that person's direct contact info, rather than relaying information through a chain of people. Most people will not be shy about handing you off to someone better suited to answer your questions. Make note of the department's chain of command and follow it in any future dealings.

SAMPLE SCRIPT BREAKDOWN

Woods: Practical location or stage? Will we see both sets of actors in the same frame; pg. 61 continues, with 2 distanced groups of actors speaking.

Will there be actual music? Live or pre-record? A band or a DJ? Thump track? Will someone choose the song(s) before shoot day? Will the speaking actors be in the same frame with musicians (double continuity)?

```
                                                        59.

    CONTINUED:

    She accepts.

    He smiles as she rises and they make their way to the
    dance floor.  They're both aware of the eyes following
    them.

    He holds his arms out stiffly to her.  She takes his
    proffered hand but moves much closer to him than his
    locked elbow had invited.

                        MAGGIE
             You might as well hold me close.
             They're all looking anyway.

    And he does.

                                               CUT TO:


    EXT. CLEARING IN WOODS - NIGHT

    Gus and Ernest watch transfixed...  Never, in their
    wildest dreams...

                                               CUT TO:


    INT. AMOS' HOUSE - NIGHT

    Amos and Maggie reach hungrily for each other, removing
    each other's clothes, kissing deeply, pulling each other
    down onto the bed.

                        AMOS
             Are you sure -

    Maggie interrupts him, covering his mouth with hers as an
    answer, rolling them over to place him on top of her...

                                               CUT TO:


    EXT. LIGHTHOUSE - DAY

    An infamously thick pea-soup fog hangs on the quiet sea.

    The light is faint as it sweeps the dense white mist.

    The horn booms a muffled warning.

                                               CUT TO:
```

House: Closed set. Possibly replace (male boom op) with (female UST) for this scene.

Lighthouse: MOS? Should we have a sound effects session while there?

Costumes

The costumer may be an established professional, which will likely tell you that he or she understands the interconnectivity of their department with Sound (sadly, though, this is not always a guarantee). In pre-production, you'll meet with the building/supervising members of the Costumes Department, and during production you'll have day-to-day interactions with the on-set dressers, known as *set costumers*. Though technically incorrect, the term "Wardrobe" is commonly used on the set.

Set up a time with the boom operator to meet with the costume representatives and review the fabrics and, if possible, finished costumes. Wash your hands just before meeting with the Costumes Department and leave drinks in your car. Note the opacity of clothing, the noise it makes (or doesn't) in your hand. Don't just look at the obvious outfit; also think about the undergarments, the time of day, the time of year the outfit will be worn, and whether there are overcoats or sweaters standing by as alternative choices or if there might be inclement weather. Ask about any underwear or underclothing to be used. **Sexy underwear? Thermal underwear for warmth?** Ask about accessories such as hats, purses, or shoulder bags. **Has the actor decided on across-the-body or on-the-shoulder bags?** And the obvious jewelry: bracelets, necklaces, earrings, brooches, and/or scarves. Consider brooches or exterior ornamentation for hiding lavaliers. Make sure you look at shoes and check their soles, as noisy heel clacking will need to be addressed, preferably during pre-production, when professional treatments can be applied.

Have the set costumers worked with these actors before, or with big-name actors? If so, then they know how to approach A-list talent and entourages and are aware of the extra demands that entails—and they're more likely to have knowledge of Sound Department concerns. Perhaps the dresser always accompanies the actor; it makes sense to make an extra effort toward a good relationship with the person who can facilitate wiring or will do the actual rigging of the wire and can let you know about moods or temperament so you can adjust your interaction with the actor.

Props

Interaction between the Sound Department and the Property (Props) Department is frequent and ongoing. There are parallels in terms of the size and dynamic of both; they are generally three-person departments and are constantly improvising in real time in response to the unexpected. Many long-lasting friendships often form between the people in these two departments as there is a constant need to work together solving mutual challenges.

Your reach out to Props will be dictated by the script. For example, if the script is a western, a host of prop decisions will have impacts on the sound work (guns, belts, spurs, etc.). **Are the spurs on their boots real metal ones or plastic ones?** We might like both, to capture the cool sound but to have a silent option if needed. The same is true for items like metal chains. The more you can anticipate and discuss before production starts, the fewer problems you'll have on the shooting day.

Are there scenes with grocery shopping or bags? Many prop masters will have cloth shopping bags in their kits that are silent but look like paper. If they don't have them or can't get them, ask if they can spritz the paper goods with water to lessen their noise. **Are there scenes with ice cubes in drinks? What type of ice cubes will be used?** Often, plastic ice cubes are used to avoid having to constantly replace real ones melting. **Will Props use the hard polycarbonate kind (imagine 50 extras with relentlessly tinkling cubes in their glasses) or the soft silicone kind (silent)?**

For courtroom scenes, we often work together on getting practical period microphones that we will handle and use for the dialogue.

Often, though, issues don't reveal themselves until we're on the set. In this case, a good relationship with the Props Department can become critical; think padding under food dishes, padding in the sink for scenes of washing dishes, etc. A multitude of noise mitigation issues will arise, and a team attitude between the departments is the most successful strategy to work these things out.

There may be special "character" items. **Inquire as to what these "character" items are** and if they have jangly or noise-making attributes. You may not know what questions you should ask, so don't be embarrassed to ask a blanket question: **"Are there any props you think my department should be aware of?"** Besides sounds or music or handling noises, maybe a prop gets turned on (blender) over dialogue or even might create radio mic interference. Telephones or courtroom scenes with desktop or

podium microphones must be coordinated well in advance of the shooting. **Are they period microphones? Does the script call for televisions? Radios? Guns?**

Actors

Your prep for actors should be the same as for crew: research their past credits, watch their movies (especially the more recent ones), look for consistently used dressers and/or hair and makeup people; ask them about the preferences of the actor or his or her personality traits. Pay attention to the entourage members; their attitude will give you hints about the demeanor of the actor and possible attitude toward this specific project. Ask if they know of any sound procedures the actor likes to follow, what type of radio mic rig is preferable, and his or her comfort with wearing wires.

The salaries of actors who will be cast for a particular project are not necessarily in line with the budget of the project. What do I mean by that? For example, you could be hired for a first-time directing project with little money for crew salaries, but the project will have high visibility because of who stars in the movie. *That* could be the entire reason a project is being done or because the actor has a personal relationship with the director. It's also possible that the actor will have only a cameo (small part) yet that might be impactful to the buzz surrounding the very modest shoot.

As Shakespeare wrote, *a rose by any other name would smell as sweet.* How do you address an actor? When we are all working together, we are co-workers, and actors expect to be called by their first names. So, whether it's "Hi, Michelle (Pfeiffer)" or "Marty (Sheen), do you have a minute?" it's all appropriate. If you work with an actor who has a title, absolutely use the title: "Sir Ian, I'm going to Craft Services. Would you like something?" unless you are told otherwise.

There was only one time in my 40-year career that the crew was instructed to address an actor in a formal way—Joan Collins. She was an aging soap opera star playing an aging soap opera star in a movie of the week (MOW). We were all gathered for a meeting in which we were told we needed to address her as Miss Collins, after which she would say, "Call me Joan."

A-List Actors (Celebrities)

Listen to what everyone says about a celebrity but keep an open mind. I've worked with celebrities who reputable sources told me were horrible, abusive people, but they weren't when it came time for us to work together. Putting your best foot forward means to begin politely and low-key, studying them. Notice whether they are chatty with the crew or if they are reserved. Follow their lead. **Discretion is paramount!** You will sign non-disclosure agreements (NDAs) as part of your project start paperwork package, and any indiscretions you make may run through the industry and damage your reputation. More importantly, we in Sound feel a fiduciary duty to protect; we are entrusted with personal access to someone, and we take that very seriously. Remember that everyone is busy living while working and things happen; people are doing the best they can at that moment in time. That goes for *every person* on set or on the production.

For *The Hateful Eight*, Kurt Russell has a scene in which he talks through his action of emptying bullets from everyone's guns into a bucket. On the first take he completely cleared his dialogue while seemingly effortlessly doing his action. Mixer Mark Ulano went up to him in awe and learned he'd practiced for hours the night before. It's called an "A-list show" because *everyone* brings their "A" game.

Transportation

The Transportation Department, or Transpo, can add constant stress or make things flow on a set. Try your best to get on their good side by being respectful, following their instructions explicitly, and keeping them in the information loop with enough time to schedule drivers and time efficiently. You'll be the point person with this department for their placement of your sound trailer or truck. They handle runs such as specialty gear/ personnel arriving (like a playback operator or a Fisher boom or repairs to and from suppliers), shuttling you to actors for wiring, and moving you to the next location. You may also need them to pick up people from basecamp at unscheduled times or perhaps make a run for a last-minute needed item. They decide where your truck parks in relation to the set, so how much time you'll lose running to the truck makes a difference in your stress and to a lesser extent, your safety (don't *run* across the street, but using the crosswalk can add 4 to 6 minutes to your trip).

If your truck needs plugging in to charge equipment every night, work it out in advance. If you need a run for compressed air, coordinate with Camera to share the tank. Think efficiently and give Transpo a heads-up every chance you can. Ask them about their procedure for the lift gate, as rules vary by location. (On US IATSE shows, members are forbidden from operating the lift gate for insurance reasons.) Some drivers run the gate so that the crew can use both hands to secure the carts. Sometimes drivers are needed elsewhere, and you'll have to manage the gate by yourself. Because it's considered part of the Transportation Department's venue, try not to use the lift gate controls until you've asked them for their preference and have learned the proper operation.

Art Department

The Art Department dresses the practical sets or builds the sets necessary to tell the story as the director envisions it. The art direction sets a mood, a historical period, and an indication of the tone of the movie (comedic, contemporary, fantasy, etc.).

Some pre-production concerns for sound include: **If it's a practical set, how low are the ceilings? Is this a working business (printing press, factory, airport)? Will we have control over the workers, bells, and machinery? Is there an elevator, or must equipment be carried up stairs? Is there more than one elevator available for equipment? (If not, you could wait almost an hour for all the gear to make it to the set—and the same at wrap.) Does the elevator generate noise that will bleed into the set?**

On a built set, "wild walls" are sections that can be removed easily so that the crew has more room to work during the subsequent shooting of the scene or that facilitate camera and light placement. After a master shot or the biggest move, the Grip Department can remove the section to allow a wider work area. A telling sign of non-professionalism is if a built set has no option for flexibility during shooting. Along with flexibility options, professional Art Departments often make small holes at the bottom of set walls, called *mouse holes,* to allow for cable runs. If there isn't one, coordinate with Art and Grip to install one if needed.

Are there open ceiling areas? Movable ceiling pieces allow overhead room for the boom and lighting when coverage shots are made. **Are windows gimbaled? (They have pivot points providing the ability to tilt so that crew reflections are eliminated.)**

An unusual effect can be achieved by *gimballing*, or spinning, a room, like in *Royal Wedding* with Fred Astaire tapping his way over the walls and across the room's ceiling.

www.youtube.com/watch?v=CNSHjZmvZTM

If you have the delight of working with a gimbaled room, think carefully if you need to lay cable and manage it, as the cable may become tangled and pulled. I worked as the boom operator on *Electric Boogaloo*, and the following movie clip is of "Dancing on the Ceiling."

www.youtube.com/watch?v=PZ93GNHBHsE

Are there mirrors? It can be quite difficult to find a boom position that is out of frame, out of the actors' way, away from light stands and C-stands, *and* out of a mirror reflection. Low-budget options are to wad a piece of paper tape and tuck it behind a mirror to angle it away. Ask the grips if they can use dulling spray lightly to take down the shine of some objects.

Don't forget the set dressing elements: **Is there furniture that creaks or squeaks?** A leather couch or noisy director's chair may be a disaster! If you can hear it, the microphone will pick it up as well as possibly being distracting to the actors.

Grip Department

My favorite definition of the Grip Department is that they are a service department. Grips supply the apple boxes and flags, ladders, and Duvetyne (or Duvetyn) you may need as you work through the day. When you need to ask for any department's equipment, be sure to know exactly how that particular department works.

Some grips tell you where the item you want is, and you get it yourself; the A-list grips bring the item to you and insist on picking it up. If you need a ladder, get/ask for a sandbag if the ladder is taller than a four-step ladder; the leveraging of a long pole usually needs a counterweight on the ladder. If it's a very long throw (pole extension), I'll ask someone to stand on the opposite side.

Grips set up the scaffolding, move the camera, and lay track; take care not to walk over the track unless necessary, as you can knock it out of alignment or leave dust/grit on the rail when stepping over. Be sure to let a grip know if that happens. Grips can answer questions about vehicle scenes— e.g., whether they will be towed and what kind of vehicles will be used.

UST Doug Axtell as ballast on the shoot for *Long Hot Summer*.

Electric Department

You'll get electrical power from the electricians if you're not using the house power ("house" here means the location's actual power supply). Again, the more professional shows will have an electrician who brings you a *stinger* (electrical cord). You may also need power for other carts too far away to take an electrical feed from the main cart or for music speakers or Voice of God (VOG). *VOG* refers to a simple microphone and speaker system, allowing either the director or first AD to give direction to a larger group than just using their voice or a megaphone. You'll be responsible for setting it up, breaking it down, and explaining how it works and then monitoring their use with it.

The Mixer usually positions his cart off the set, and it may require power and a light; always start your request by asking the best boy and ask his or her preferred procedure.

The AD Department

The Assistant Director (AD) Department is the production arm of the shooting company and manages the crew for maximum efficiency and to handle day-to-day problem solving on the set.

2nd 2nd AD

You'll have the most contact with the 2nd 2nd AD or a PA (production assistant) in charge of moving actors. You'll go to said person to get updates for actor availability, wiring and de-rigging, coordinating with Hair, Makeup, and Costumes, and any other off-set departments. You'll also get miscellaneous actor/timing notes and coordinate errant equipment through them.

If there's a specialty wardrobe—spacesuits or cockroach costumes—or complicated props, the 2nd 2nd ADs coordinate the time needed so everyone can work without slowing down the shooting. For off-set music rehearsals, coordinate with him or her. If children are actors, the studio teacher will coordinate with the 2nd 2nd ADs. They also can advise you about whom you should talk to regarding a particular issue or if you want an unofficial production opinion on a situation before using official channels.

2nd AD

The 2nd AD handles the higher management functions of the timing between the actors and the crew. This person, with more authority and more influence, can become an intermediate for advocacy or problem solving. The 2nd AD oversees creating the call sheet and should be notified if your department feels changes need to be made. Call the 2nd AD if you need to coordinate specialty gear or personnel coming to the set. Also contact Transpo and, if applicable, the production office for a studio/lot drive-on pass. If you need a pass, be sure to have the full name and contact number of the person and let them know they will need to show ID. The 2nd AD manages the production report.

1st AD

This is the key management person on the working set who controls the scheduling, call times, actor movement, and safety meetings and protocols. How she works tells you what kind of information you'll be getting during work, and how much you will be kept in the loop of information. Get information on her work style from the second assistant director (2nd AD).

As a UST you won't have much direct contact with her during the normal running of the day. However, it changes in some situations like these: there are car tow/driving shots, and you need to interact with the 1st AD for timing issues, actor notifications for the shot ("I need time to show [actor] where the mic is when she first arrives," "I need to hardwire the actor when they arrive," "I need x minutes to show the actor how to start this music playback machine") or if you are a 2nd boom operator and have a need.

When setting up for stunt shots or when your work affects the actor's space: If your work for the shot is anywhere near the actor's work area, coordinate with appropriate stunt people to approve where you'll be and where any plant mics or other sound equipment is being placed *and* let the actors see where and what you have working for the shot. When Rick and Cliff enter Musso and Frank's in *Once Upon a Time...in Hollywood*, a partial wall prevented the camera from seeing them after the door swung open, so the grips laid down a runway of apple boxes. The sound of their heels on the wood was loud, so I was tasked with quieting them, which I did by placing small pieces of carpet on the boxes, taped around the perimeter of each.

When Leo DiCaprio and Brad Pitt came on the set, I found a moment to invite them to see the runway and showed them the neon tape strips I provided at the edges to make sure they knew their boundaries.

Script Supervisor

The script supervisor works closely with and sits beside the director and is primarily responsible for the implementation of the script on the set. The script supervisor is the main liaison between the director and the editor and the script supervisor's duties include, but are not limited to:

Continuity: "The actor had the cigarette in his left hand ; the cigarette is now 2 inches shorter than it was on the last take; the actor needs to shave."

Timing: "This scene is expected to take this much screen time. This scene's pacing is much slower than when the actors shot the beginning of it."

Screen direction: "His look to her should be on the other side of the camera. This shot angle will not cut smoothly with the shot you wanted from the roof."

The script supervisor protects the director by keeping track of dozens of important details as well as the consistent tone and temperament of the actor's character arc, dialogue, and line readings. The script supervisor makes sure the film shooting stays in its chronology; the actor who just drove a convertible through a rainstorm has a consistent look next month when she enters the hotel lobby.

Throughout the show, you'll get or give scene and take numbers, so find a comfortable banter; if you have a question about when an actor moves, you can either ask the script supervisor or the 1st AC. Along with the boom operator, these are people whose job entails watching and memorizing actor movement.

Camera Department

During pre-production, the camera people will be at the rental house checking lenses and running tests. The Mixer may ask you or the boom operator to make contact. Be sure to introduce yourself to the second assistant cameraperson (2nd AC)—on the phone is fine—and inquire what make and model of cameras and how many cameras are expected on the show. **Will there be handheld or Steadicam work? Do you know about any driving shots, off-speed work, or underwater work? Does the DOP operate his own camera? Who will the "B" camera crew be?** (The principal camera crew is the "A" camera team.)

Director of Photography

If the director of photography (DOP) is not the camera operator as well, it is usual for him to sit on the other side of the director from the script supervisor. There is not much interaction between the UST and the DOP, although the DOP may request an IFB (monitoring headphones) or want to listen to a music selection for an upcoming scene. If you are not getting satisfaction resolving an issue with the others in the Camera Department, then approach the DOP quietly and respectfully (check with the Mixer for the protocol).

Camera Operator

The camera operator may need an IFB to coordinate a camera move with dialogue or to listen to a music selection for the scene and match its tempo. If you'll be booming along with the boom operator, it's good manners to let the camera operator know that there will be two booms operating. Check any pole or body position if you're not sure what the frame line is, especially if there's a dolly move or camera height change. Ask the Mixer to watch the monitor first as you go through your moves, but if that doesn't answer your question(s), ask the camera operator. If you think you may have entered the frame, mention it as soon as possible and definitely before the setup is broken.

If you don't know the exact frame but you've picked a place and it turns out you're very close to, but not invading, the frame line, good job! If the operator says, "You're very close to the frame line," some people may think of it as an admonishment; instead, I thank him. That's an indication that you are good and know your lens sizes. You may not always know, but don't imagine that they are criticizing you, nor should you let operators bully you. Every communication either brings you respect or dismissal. Being confident builds your standing and you'll feel more comfortable on the set.

1st AC

You won't have much interaction with the 1st AC in the course of your day. However, they may need batteries or to borrow a tool.

2nd AC

This person is responsible for the care of the slates and Lock-it boxes, and other equipment as needed from the Sound Department. You and the 2nd AC sometimes need to coordinate the scene and take numbers.

Negotiate a system for the handing out and return of gear each day. For instance, if you cater to them too much by handing them a slate wherever they are, you will soon find that you spend 60% more time having to track them down and where they left each slate. You've allowed it to become *your problem*. I have had good success in suggesting that I put each slate on each camera package's cart (have them choose a spot) and that I drop it there at each call and pick it up from there each wrap. If your wrap is earlier than theirs, you can ask them to keep the slate overnight in the bag you supply after shutting it off *or* shut it off and return it to a particular spot. Impress upon them the gentle constitution of electronics.

Create the same system for lunchtime and re-jamming. When jamming needs to happen during the day (e.g., if they accidentally turned off the timecode), instruct them how to re-jam. "Come to the cart. This is where the cable is." Or "Hand it off to me; I'll get it back to you". When first handing out the slate, show them the toggle switch positions and explain how *not* to turn off the timecode (TC). Show them the high/low light and explain the sensitivity of the battery door. Remember that along with the Sound Department needs, they are at the bottom of the Camera Department hierarchy, and that can be an exhausting place.

Studio Teacher

When children under the age of 18 years-old are acting in the US, a studio teacher manages their day, balancing school, relaxation, and work time. Pay close attention to the child's workday, as there are strict work schedules based on age. Make sure you have the time you need to rig and de-rig and include the stage parent in all interactions. It's also good practice to have the on-set dresser present while rigging the minor. Parents and their children who haven't worn a radio microphone before need extra time to understand what it is, how it works, why it's important, and basic care instructions.

Locations Department

The Locations Department assembles a portfolio of locations to show the director, producers, and key crew department heads for the purpose of deciding where to film the movie. The Locations people liaise between the owners of the property and the film company to negotiate such items as temporary construction, painting, and mitigating negative factors (quieting noisy AC systems or removing animals, for example).

Location scouts are a key resource for information, especially on shoots where information is scarce or nonexistent. Most often, a specific problematic location will be included in the scout, but if not, the Mixer should arrange with Locations to get in for a look. If scouts are not possible, get the name and phone number of the contact to a have a brief conversation introducing yourself and communicate what concerns you may have. Make a point to meet the person early when arriving to the location on the day of shooting. Make sure they have a walkie-talkie or phone to be able to reach them (ask Locations for their department's procedure). Have the person walk you through the switches or plugs for turning off things and how long they can be off without problems. *Do not* take sole responsibility for this. Make sure that at least one representative from the Locations Department is fully aware of on/off issues, and it's a good idea to let someone from Production know as well. This can save a lot of grief later. You may be sent off on another mission, precluding your ability to close out the set properly, or a sight representative may be required to engage AC, heating, or refrigeration equipment. That said, don't forget to turn things back on when lunch is called, at wrap, and per the schedule given to you.

Some productions erroneously think they can save money by excluding Sound from a scout. Nothing could be further from the truth, yet it happens frequently—even on big shows or those with experienced production managers. Many of the problems associated with location choices could be addressed, and many resolved, during this relatively inexpensive period.

If the Sound Department is included, usually only the Mixer goes. The Mixer will pay attention to the relationships—watching how people are feeling each other out, getting an understanding of the director's and DOP's values, seeing how Grip and Electric relate to the DOP: Have they worked together before? The Mixer will research their credits to find out *before* the scout—and then watch.

You'll want to get a copy of the location scout notes from the Mixer to have a heads-up about the particulars. In general, Mixers just don't focus on the details we'll be dealing with during the scout; they are analyzing the bigger picture. Imagine there's a beach scene: the Mixer will make sure to understand the number of actors, their proximity to the actual surf, and the time of day. You'll want to understand where the carts will be, whether you'll need a piece of plywood to place under the carts, tents to protect the gear from sun/heat, sand, wind, or rain, whether you'll need to change the cart tires to off-road tires, where to safely stage the follow cart, and more.

While you usually won't go on a scout, there may be a situation where you need to represent the Sound Department. If you are invited to attend, go! Listen carefully to everything that's said (for content and to see how everyone relates to each other) and think about how you'll work at those locations. Listen for motors, generators, schools, fire departments, hospital emergency rooms, airports, freeways that you can hear but not see, etc. Look for low ceilings, construction nearby, existing generators, or discuss with Electric their own generator's placement, etc. You'll be able to settle on a staging area with a good DOP right there, along with Grip, Electric, and Props, and that will speed up morning setup on that day of shooting.

If you'll be in a refrigerated room or have winter exteriors, look into having a staging area and keeping the gear in the space so there aren't condensation problems. You'll need layered clothing for yourself, and you might need to trade off more with the boom operator.

Many Mixers will run a frequency spectrum analyzer at each of the locations to understand what radio microphone frequencies will probably be available on the day of shooting. Adjustments might be needed in the gear considered; the Mixer will discuss these.

NOTES

CHAPTER 7

Company Tasks

C ompany tasks include meetings, reports, and various forms of paperwork.

Production Meetings

A full company meeting is usually held near the end of the prep period. *Full company* means different things to different productions. Valuable information will be shared about how the group will work collectively, and other departments may have questions about how something will be done that will answer *your questions*. You'll gain an insight into personalities. If you're invited to the production meeting, be sure to go. If you are not paid for this time, go anyway.

If the Mixer is unavailable, I attend the meeting as the representative from Sound. Within the agreed-upon parameters, I make notes of the important conversations and watch the politics of whose questions are given time and whose are relegated to "We'll talk about that after the meeting." I don't get too deep into issues that would normally be handled by the Mixer. I inquire whether there will be a separate meeting for all the affected parties to discuss the issue (music and workflow are popular topics) and when it will be, and pass that on to the Mixer. First impressions are very important, so let the Mixer make them for the department; Mixers seem better tempered for that.

The meeting usually starts with the director giving a short welcoming speech, possibly followed by a producer welcome. Everyone sits around tables arranged in as large a shape as possible, to allow everyone to see the others. Actors do not attend this meeting, but crew department heads and appropriate department members associated with the actual shooting will be present. Where you sit makes a difference. (This is a recurring theme to note.) The director and production people will be grouped together wherever the head of the table is. The DOP is usually on the other side of the director. The key grip and gaffer sit near the DOP. Then others sit around those positions. Sit near a department that you may need to have sidebar chats with (or pass notes, which is less disruptive). Sit with your department if you are not the sole representative.

The 1st AD will introduce himself and open his notebook. He will read through either the script or the *one-liner*. The one-liner describes the work by calendar date, in the order the shooting will take place. I prefer production meetings that proceed scene by scene, as I find them to be more thorough and the chronology easier in which to make mental connections with the story.

Example of a One-Liner

The one-liner columns, reading left to right: scene number, interior /exterior, location, and one-line description of action, day/night, page count, and character designation involved in shooting.

The AD reads the description, adding a note or two if there's additional information at this point—for example, "A postal carrier has been added to this scene" or "This train scene will now be moved to the train platform." If any department has a question about the scene, it can be asked now. Usually the Sound team I work with will wait to hear what questions the Grip and Lighting Departments have; the answers often give us more information and answer our questions. For a question that should be heard by other departments, the Mixer will bring it up in the meeting. If a Sound question is very specific, it can be addressed after the general meeting.

Do remember that many times directors cannot answer questions at this point because they don't yet know the answers themselves. Sound might ask questions in the meeting concerning music (live, pre-record, etc.), the use of certain vehicles, distant locations, and hotel accommodations. If the Mixer chooses, this could be a time to announce interest in coordinating frequencies on the set between departments.

If it's a question for another department, ask it privately; there will be time to expand the discussion with ADs or the director before shooting. Questions for individual departments might relate to things that make noise: Costumes: "Are those cowboys wearing spurs as they walk down the boardwalk? Are they silent, film-ready spurs [rubber, realistic-looking quiet ones]? Will Costumes or Props be handling them?" Props: "Will the shopping bags at the market be noise-suppressed bags?" Get the contact name and number for a specific problematic location and have a brief conversation introducing yourself and what you'll need on the day. Transpo: "Will the cars be tuned up, so they are operating as quietly as possible? Are you installing spark suppression? Please *do not* use Armor All on the interiors (because none of the tapes we use will then secure mics and transmitters)." A common question concerns how vehicles will be moved during shooting: "Are the driving scenes tow, poor man's process (PMP), or free driving?" These types of questions affect multiple departments and will be answered during the meeting without you needing to ask. If you did not attend the meeting, have a conversation with the Mixer to get his notes and follow up on concerns.

Week Eleven

Labor Day - Monday, September 3, 2018 - Day Off

Scenes 79	INT	Playboy After Dark		Night 2	1/8 pgs	3, 36, 77, 78
		Flashforward to Sharon, Roman and Mama Cass on Hef's show				
Scenes 127	INT	Playboy After Dark		Night 2	1/8 pgs	3, 36, 77
		Hugh Hefner interview with Sharon and Roman				
Scenes 126	INT	Playboy After Dark		Night 2	2 4/8 pgs	3, 36, 77
		Sharon makes Roman ask if she wants to have a pool party				

End Day # 56 Tuesday, September 4, 2018 -- Total Pages: 2 6/8

Scenes 44	EXT	Playboy Mansion		Night 1	4/8 pgs	3, 8, 36
		The Polanskis are greeted by Jay Sebring and Steve McQueen				
Scenes 46	INT/ EXT	Playboy Mansion		Night 1	1 pgs	3, 6, 8, 36, 40, 77
		Steve & Connie Stevens admire Sharon, he never stood a chance				

End Day # 57 Wednesday, September 5, 2018 -- Total Pages: 1 4/8

End Day # 58 Thursday, September 6, 2018 -- Total Pages:

Scenes 7pt1	INT	LAX - Baggage Area		Day 1	1/8 pgs	3, 36
		Sharon and Roman collect Dr. Saperstien and luggage				
Scenes 7pt2	INT	LAX - Hallway		Day 1	1/8 pgs	3, 36
		Sharon and Roman walk thru LAX as Paparazzi shoot photos				
Scenes 146	INT	LAX - Hallway		Day 3	6/8 pgs	1, 2, 35
		Rick's rockin 70's hair, things are different in America				

End Day # 59 Friday, September 7, 2018 -- Total Pages: 1

End of Week Twelve

Scenes 69	INT/ EXT	Polanski Residence - Guest House		Day 2	2 4/8 pgs	31, 44
		The Shaggy Stranger pitches Paul				
Scenes 28	INT/ EXT	Cadillac Driving - Benedict Canyon		Dusk 1	1 pgs	1, 2
		No one forgives Rick for that last season of Bounty Law				

End Day # 60 Monday, September 10, 2018 -- Total Pages: 3 4/8

Scenes 46pt	EXT	Polanski Residence - Back Yard		Day 2	6/8 pgs	36
		Roman Polanski enjoying the morning				
Scenes 153	EXT	Polanski Residence - Back Yard		Day 3	3/8 pgs	36, 39
		Voyteck Frycowski dives and splashes Abigail Folger				

Day Out of Days (DOOD) Report

The Day Out of Days schedule charts the actors' workdays in a concise form. The value to a UST is noting when actors will begin and end their work on the show, to help the Mixer remember to get wild lines before an actor leaves or to know an actor's availability to pre-record anything before a set workday or if an actor requires some kind of prep involving Sound.

Aug 9, 2017 6:57 PM					LIMA PROJECT Day Out of Days Report for Cast Members		OFFICIAL WHITE			Page 1 of 16 8/9/17 ONE LINER	
Month/Day	08/10	08/11	08/12	08/13	08/14	08/15	08/16	08/17	08/18	08/19	08/20
Day of Week	Thu	Fri	Sat	Sun	Mon	Tue	Wed	Thu	Fri	Sat	Sun
Shooting Day	1	2			3	4	5	6	7		
1. ROY MCBRIDE	SW	W			W	W	W	W	W		
1x. ROY MCBRIDE PHOTO DBL.							SW				
2. H. CLIFFORD MCBRIDE											
3. HELEN LANTOS											
3x. HELEN LANTOS PHOTO DBL.											
4. COL. PRUITT					SW	W	W	W	WD		
4x. COL. PRUITT PHOTO DBL.							SWF				
5. LORRAINE DEAVERS											
6. DONALD STANFORD											
7. CAPT. LAWRENCE TANNER											
8. WILLY LEVANT							SWD				
9. FRANKLIN YOSHIDA											
10. MARIA SODERLUND											
11. SGT. BELLO											
12. ADJ. GEN. VOGEL	SW	WF									
13. BRIG. GEN. STROUD	SW	WF									
14. LT. GEN RIVAS	SW	WF									
15. LESLIE CORTEZ									SWF		
16. GRACE											
17. CAPTAIN FUJITADA											
18. FEMALE FLIGHT ATTENDANT											
19. ARJUN KAPOOR											
20. EVELYN (M.)											
21. SILHOUETTED WOMAN											
22. WOMAN IN WHITE PANTS/SHIRT						SWF					
23. MARS OFFICER											
24. MED TECH #1											
25. LAUNCH PAD MEDIC								SWF			
26. SAL											
27. SERGEANT ROMANO								SWF			
28. TECHNICIAN ONE											
29. MOON TV HOST											
30. MOON TV GUEST #1											
31. MOON TV GUEST #2											
32. JULIANNA ANDRADE											
33. CHIP GARNES											
34. JANICE COLLINS											
35. SPACECOM EMPLOYEE						SW	H	H	H		
36. YOUNG WOMAN IN FATIGUES											

Production Packet and Start Paperwork

After the production meeting, or when asked, visit the Production office to introduce yourself and pick up a production packet and start paperwork. Be sure to take any identification necessary for government or tax purposes. Some countries require original documents, so check first. If your country allows direct depositing of your salary into your bank account, make sure you have all the appropriate documents and account numbers as well.

Complete your paperwork for the production. *Never* leave a space blank; either write "N/A" (not applicable) or draw a line through it so no one can add text after you turn it in. I've learned that it's best to get a copy of your filled-out deal memo before you leave the office if the project seems a bit too unprofessional, even before the company signs—unless that will happen immediately. You can request a copy or simply take a picture on your phone.

If it's a United States IATSE show, determine under which contract you will be working. Investigate the specifics of the contract and find out from your Local if there are any special side letters affecting your wages and conditions. If it's a non-union show, don't assume the show will remain non-union throughout its production; knowing the key crew players will give you an indication of the likelihood that things may change, or the production may convey their intention to sign a union agreement before principal photography commences. Remember that even if a show is non-union (non-IATSE), there are state and federal labor laws that the company must abide by. Between the end of the production meeting and the first day of shooting, all departments should have a very clear idea of the bulk of the work and should have met or at least contacted the other departments needed to clarify any points and address any concerns. Because of this interaction ahead of shooting, there should already be an evolving sense of camaraderie and collaboration.

Production Office

If you haven't had time yet and your schedule allows, make an appearance at the Production office to meet face to face. It's important to meet the production coordinator and accountant, as you'll have the most interaction with them.

The production coordinator runs the Production office and will be your contact person for coordinating approval and acquisition of additional elements needed. Either she or her team will be able to answer questions that come up during the course of the shooting. Look to the coordinator to maintain and distribute crew lists, schedule changes, authorizations for parking passes, and other paperwork.

During the start process in the US, you will fill out a packet of papers, including a Deal Memo (work contract), NDAs (non-disclosure agreements), and I-9 (Employment Eligibility Verification form). You'll need to show an approved federal ID (passport, driver's license, *and* Social Security card, or other options), and often have your picture taken for a production ID badge. Some badges are worn throughout the shooting; some are for a particular location only. *Always* remember to bring yours and wear it. Try hanging the lanyard on your car rearview mirror or putting it in your bag so you don't forget it. The same goes for any parking passes that may be in your packet. A small thrill is the first time you fill out the Credits listing—how you would like your name to read if you are given screen credit. ("Hey, everybody, my name is 5 feet high on the silver screen!"). Some productions have two Security Departments: one for physical production and one for intellectual property.

> *NDAs: Non-disclosure agreements are confidential agreements, creating a trust between you and the production company that you will not share any information about the production, usually in perpetuity (forever). They are legal contracts, so be careful about sharing details with your friends, family, or on Facebook or other social media.*

If you will work on location, a travel coordinator will schedule flights and hotel accommodations and car service. If you're being reimbursed, make sure you have the required petty cash slip paperwork, the receipt, and understand the specific procedure Accounting would like you to follow. Ask how *per diem* will be handled (after the initial payment, a US accountant usually comes at lunchtime with small manila envelopes that you sign for, and the same procedure is used for paychecks on location when not direct deposited).

Some points to discuss with the travel coordinator include how close you want your room to be to others in your department, and if you're a light sleeper, ask if your room could be far from the freeway side of the building or away from the elevators, pool, and game rooms. Can the company get special after-hours access to the gym? Or one nearby? Don't forget no-smoking rooms or first-floor rooms if you'll be carrying gear back and forth. A corner room is larger and quieter. If you have allergies, or need operable windows, or other considerations, be prompt about bringing them to the coordinator's attention.

Payroll Department

The Payroll Department will need government forms filled out and signed to be able to pay you. One payroll accountant is assigned to handle the actors' money needs and a separate one for crew monies. Not only will you have personal dealings with the payroll accountant, but you are responsible for any department issues regarding the timecards, kit rental invoicing, and any *per diem* or other monetary dealings for your entire department throughout the production period. When you're at the accounting office, you can fill out a direct-deposit form so that your paychecks will go straight into your bank account. If the Accounting Department has any re-occurring department-specific forms they want you to fill out, pick up a healthy stack of them now.

Craft Departments

Once filming has begun, check in again with Costumes: It's important for you to see the main characters' finished wardrobe (invite the boom operator) so that you can start formulating a plan for radio mic'ing that will facilitate wiring during the run of the show. Review *all* the items discussed previously to confirm that nothing substantive has changed: What are the materials and accessories? What will be worn in the chest area? Remember that cross-body bag? Have any specialty items for stunt work been added? Basically, cottons are quiet, but silks, metallics, parachute nylon, and corduroys are noisy.

Contact the specific dresser(s) for the main actors: Ask whether you can have their mobile numbers to text or reach while on set. Has the dresser worked with the actor before? What is the actor's process? (Does he dress himself, and then want a wardrobe person to rig the wire, or does he want to be wired on set only?) Because mic placement is so specific with minute variations that can throw it "off," find a way to be part of the process as much as possible. Ask about preferred placements for the transmitter (TX)—for example, the actor may prefer his own pack and ankle strap, never a waist belt, etc.).

Do the same for Props and any other department you identified as having potential problematic elements.

Postproduction

At times, you'll be asked to contact the Postproduction Department to relay messages for the Mixer or ask about a particular setup, scene, or effect. It's a prudent gesture to make a cursory call in to Pre-Production to make introductions and exchange contact numbers right from the start. You will be the secondary contact for Post people during the shooting period—the Mixer being the first contact.

While you're waiting for other departments to return your calls, it's time to learn about the Sound Department gear.

CHAPTER 8

Equipment

The Sound Department is in charge of capturing actors' performances and sound elements (sound effects, atmosphere, voiceover, recorded-only sounds) during the production phase. We do that by designing the soundscape using equipment and personnel in real time to capture the aural information in a way that reflects the director's intent.

When a movie is being shot, the actors' voices are picked up by the microphone(s), sent by cable or wireless transmission to the sound cart, where the Mixer's equipment receives the sounds, or signal(s). He or she then blends these multiple elements and creates a *mix*, which is sent to the Editorial Department. The editors create assemblies of the day's work for directors and producers to review, called *dailies*.

Simple, right? Let's look a little deeper, following the chain of the work:

Microphones

At the heart of our work are microphones. Microphone selection and placement are the first steps in capturing performances and interjecting our personal aesthetic into the movie. To be an excellent UST, you should be fully qualified as a boom operator in addition to being trained in a host of other skills. But for now, a basic understanding of the characteristics of microphones, their types of sound pickup patterns, and visually recognizing them will start you on the path to understanding the mission of the Production Sound Department and a solid sound career.

Microphones convert sound into an electrical signal (a *transducer*) that is recorded onto a recording medium and then sent to postproduction to match up (sync) with the picture. Often, there are multiple microphones used to capture all the dialogue and sounds of a scene. Each microphone corresponds to a channel on the mixing panel. The production sound

Mixer, or Mixer for short (or Recordist in the UK), controls each channel via a sliding lever or dial called a potentiometer, or *pot*, to alter the level of each of the inputs as the tracks are recorded onto the files.

Boom operators usually choose the number and placement of the microphones for the scene, in consultation with the Mixer and UST. When actors are performing, the boom operator manipulates the boom microphone by precision placement and movement of the polar pattern in the best ways possible to capture the warm, full qualities of the human voice, while at the same time maneuvering the microphone away from unwanted sounds (noises).

There are two main methods by which microphones pick up the sound waves and turn that signal into electrical energy. The way that happens has a direct effect on the quality and fidelity of the result—and that is where the Sound Department's artistry begins.

Dynamic Microphones

Dynamic microphones use a plastic membrane that soundwaves cause to vibrate. They are economical with simple construction, rugged and resistant to handling noise, and do not require a separate power supply. They also have the enviable qualities of being mostly unaffected by temperature and humidity. They can handle very high sound levels, making them a good choice for many musical applications and high-volume special effects such as gunfire or jet engines.

The following are two examples of dynamic microphones commonly used in narrative work:

For more about dynamic microphones:

www.neumann.com/homestudio/en/ what-is-a-dynamic-microphone

Shure SM57   Shure SM58

Ribbon Microphones

Ribbon microphones are dynamic mics that use a thin aluminum corrugated strip (like a paper fan or "ribbon") between two magnets. They are valued for their abundant low-end pickup and natural high frequency roll-off and are appreciated for capturing the warmth of the human voice. They can record voices and instruments much more accurately than any other microphone and are beloved by acoustic musicians. While traditionally they have a figure eight polar pattern, they can be custom configured with other patterns. Because of their fragility, they're mostly a tool of the recording studio rather than the tough environments of practical locations.

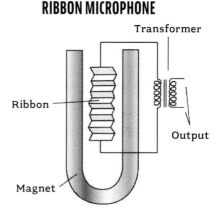

RIBBON MICROPHONE

Transformer

Ribbon

Output

Magnet

Condenser Microphones

Condenser microphones use a metal or metal-coated plastic diaphragm (a hardier material creating better fidelity). They are very good at capturing delicate sounds and capturing voices more accurately than dynamic microphones. They are more sensitive and have less self-noise than dynamic microphones. Their shortcomings are that their inherent electronics cause a small amount of noise, and they don't handle very loud sounds (sound pressure levels, or SPLs) well.

Condenser mics require an external power source. Enter the P48 — phantom power.

Also designated as +48V (volt), the power is supplied through a standard XLR cable to the microphone and most likely referred to as "phantom" since it doesn't require a separate external power supply box. There are several options for supplying the power to your condenser mics: you can use the mixing panel, the recorder, batteries, or a separate power supply.

Dynamic vs. Condenser

Condenser mics are generally more accurate across the frequency range and are particularly adept at subtle and soft (low SPL) sound. This is especially useful for dialogue and the constant potential for sudden and unexpected dynamic swings in volume—e.g., from a whisper to a shout and back. For on-set film work, the most common type of condenser mics are small diaphragm, directional types (cardioid and hyper-cardioid polar patterns). Large diaphragm condensers are applied more in the music studio environment, as they are larger and not really designed to follow talent around (mounted on a microphone boom pole or Fisher).

Dynamic mics are also an essential tool for on-set film production and can be most often applied when recording very loud or low-frequency sources such as drums, explosions, gunfire, engines, jet planes, etc. This doesn't mean they are delegated only to such use; they are also a go-to microphone in live music venues with challenging environments or loud sources, vocal or otherwise. They are usually designed with a boost to the upper midrange and produce a bass roll off. One company has for decades advertised their microphones being used to hammer nails!!

Microphone Patterns

Microphones have varying characteristics of directionality, called polar patterns or pickup patterns, and fall into three groups:

▸ Omnidirectional: all directions

▸ Unidirectional: one direction

▸ Bidirectional: two directions

These polar patterns visually describe the zone in which the microphone picks up sounds, identified by the "lobes" of the sound wave, or how well the microphone "hears" sound from different directions.

The most common types of microphones used in narrative, or scripted, filmmaking are omnidirectional and unidirectional. Unidirectional mics can be cardioid microphones, supercardioid microphones, or hypercardioid microphones ("shotguns") and are used most often for booming or as plant mics. Shotgun microphones, as their name implies, have a quite narrow pickup pattern and are used only by very experienced boom operators to capture sounds at a distance and/or to isolate sound in very noisy environments.

My friend Mark Ulano explains his method of finding a microphone's polar pattern: It's one thing to see a diagram of the microphone's polar pattern, but another to have an intuitive knowledge of a microphone's behavior under real-world conditions. An "old-school" technique for establishing the actual pattern of the particular specimen in hand is to power up the mic in a system, and while listening with reference headphones, quickly rub your thumb and forefinger as you move your hand in the approximate arc of the microphone's polar pattern. This can help diagnose the specific sweet spot as well as the edge of the pattern, which is so important to the placement or movement of the mic in question. Likewise, having a subject speak while experimenting with the mic's placement, distance, or aim really informs the operator of any coloring or inconsistencies that may exist.

There are variations from unit to unit in microphone manufacture just like musical instruments, so it becomes important to know just how the microphone you're working with is functioning rather than assuming it is performing to specification.

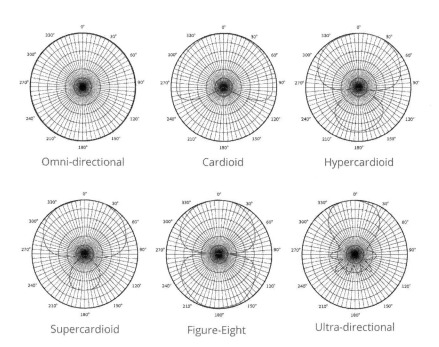

Omni-directional   Cardioid   Hypercardioid

Supercardioid   Figure-Eight   Ultra-directional

For more detailed or animated explanations of polar patterns, check out these YouTube videos:

▸ **www.youtube.com/watch?v=N0X7owMBICY**

▸ **www.premiumbeat.com/blog/6-microphone-pickup-patterns-every-filmmaker-should-know/**

▸ **www.youtube.com/watch?v=5ZEm1EvxL-E**

Several manufacturers provide a complement of microphones in these configurations, and I highly recommend that you spend some time visiting their websites to get familiar with their products:

▸ Audio Technica

▸ Countryman

▸ Deity

▸ DPA

▸ Neumann

▸ Rode

▸ Sanken

▸ Schoeps

▸ Sennheiser

▸ Shure

▸ Sony

▸ Tram

As far as microphones go, the popular brands with sound people who are starting out tend to be those models below the $600 (US) price range. The following are condenser mics commonly used in narrative work, reflecting a range of costs.

These are inexpensive microphones that production Mixers often buy as a first choice as they begin their career:

▸ Rode NTG-1
  www.sweetwater.com/store/detail/ NTG1--rode-ntg-1-shotgun-condenser-microphone

▸ Rode NTG-4
  www.sweetwater.com/store/detail/ NTG4--rode-ntg4-shotgun-microphone

▸ Deity S-MIC 2S
  www.trewaudio.com/product/deity-s-mic-2s/

▸ Deity S-MIC 2 (416 copy)
  www.trewaudio.com/product/deity-s-mic-2/

▸ Sennheiser ME66/K6
  www.trewaudio.com/product/sennheiser-me66k6-combo/

There are some high-quality, imitation Schoeps mics, like the Russian Oktava and some from China.

Common condenser microphones for
higher-end projects are below:

▸ Sennheiser MKH 50 60 70

▸ Neumann RM 82i

▸ The Schoeps Collette series and the
Schoeps CMIT, which is suitable for music
as well as dialogue and is less likely to pick
up wind noise.

▸ Sanken's CS3e has three elements. It has
several unique properties, including a zero
proximity effect and exceptional off-axis
rejection. For example, during a walk and
talk, if there are noisy leaves on the ground,
one can tilt the angle up slightly and lose
much of that noise. You'll still hear it, but
the noise is mitigated.

▸ The CMIT 5 has a very lightweight all-metal
housing, symmetrical polar pattern, and
is suitable for recording music as well
as dialogue.

Rode works excellently in wet weather,
as does the Sennheiser 416 or Sanken
microphones.

Colette   **CMIT**

The Schoeps microphones are sensitive to humidity, so you may want
some silica packets in the case to absorb moisture.

The boom operator must understand the types of microphones and their
patterns because she designs the approach to handling the sound coverage on the set. It's important for USTs to have a basic understanding of
the microphones and work toward being as proficient as the boom operator as soon as possible. For a more in-depth education on the subject,
consider my companion book *Behind the Boom Pole.*

Every job you do, no matter how short or how small, will build your repertoire of equipment knowledge and problem-solving skills. There just isn't
any way I can tell you about every experience I've learned from because
it's all based on the specific elements of those shoots, and every shoot is

different. In this microphone section, I want to show you the more common microphones you'll see in narrative television and film work, without reviews or opinions. Why? Because Mixers will have their favorite microphones, and those are the ones you'll be using. As you work with each one, you'll come to form your own opinions as well. For right now, concentrate on visually identifying them, their accessories, and their pickup patterns.

Wind Protection

Wind protection is essential for microphones unless there is no chance of air movement, and the subject is sufficiently distanced so as not to create any plosives. *Plosives* are consonant sounds that are formed by completely stopping airflow. They can be voiceless, like the sounds /p/, /t/, and /k/, or voiced, like /b/, /d/, and /g/.

Interior wind protection usually means acoustic or open-cell foam shaped to fit the microphone. Always think about the specific situation as you choose microphones and wind protection: perhaps the interior scene calls for a breeze outside the window; if the microphone placement is close enough for the FX fan to be a problem, an exterior foam or windshield (blimp) may be appropriate. Again, if a fireplace looks practical but is being operated by a noisy gas line from the special effects people, a more directional microphone than originally anticipated can filter some of the hissing by a talented operator understanding the polar pattern and using the edges of the polar pattern for the dialogue and letting the hissing fall away (called "playing the pattern").

The Journey

The two ways we get the signals from the microphone are: 1. By cables. 2. By wireless signal.

Hardwiring

When microphones are **hard-wired,** they have a cable that physically connects the microphone to the mixer or recorder. Microphones and cables can be terminated with many different connectors, but the following is a very basic scenario. The most common cable in the audio/visual workplace is known as an XLR cable, which stands for External Line Return. Cables are identified by their connectors, and a common XLR connector has a three-pin configuration.

Most microphones have a **"male" end** and connect with the **"female" end** of the cable. For boom mics, many boom poles are internally wired, leaving both ends of the cable available to make connections. There is usually a bit of slack at the top of the cable to allow for a variety of microphone sizes. Therefore, some sort of cable securing is necessary so that the cable doesn't slap against the pole and make noise. Some products are available to secure the cable; some mounts have pins built into them to wind the cable. *Do not pull the cable taut at any point; always make sure you have some strain relief.*

Interior wind foam

Boomed microphones for interior work are in a mount, attached to the boom pole. They have some type of wind protection covering them, as nearly any movement or light wind will be heard on an open microphone. Microphones for exterior work have more substantial wind protection, ranging from heavier foam to a zeppelin (windshield) with an additional covering. A windsock slips over the windshield to offer an additional layer of protection and a heavier, fur-like windjammer can handle heavy winds. They are colloquially referred to as a "dead cat."

A windshield with a windjammer

Plants

Any microphone can be planted; it depends on what you're trying to capture, the proximity to the source that you can place the microphone, and the area you have for hiding the microphone. I have planted a lavalier and wireless transmitter, and I have planted a Sennheiser 816 in a Rycote windshield. Always work to the shot.

For planted (fixed) microphones, the cable can be run right into the mixer and the cable secured along its route, either by paper tape (the tape recommended because the adhesive makes it easier to remove the tape afterward from the cable and surface) or, more professionally, by laying carpets or mats over highly trafficked areas where possible. Some exterior locations may require trenching and burying cables. On the first day of shooting *The Hateful Eight*, the UST was surprised to find himself on a Colorado mountaintop, in -10 degree cold weather, having to trench a 60' (18.3 meters) cable run in the permafrost using a pickaxe.

Traditionally, once a plan is agreed upon, the boom mics are set up, then any plant microphones, and then any wireless. Wireless are addressed last because the actors go through Hair and Makeup and then get dressed before they will be ready to be wired. Sometimes a costume necessitates that wiring be done simultaneously with getting dressed because there won't be access to an area once the costume is on.

On *Ad Astra*, actors in the Apollo astronaut suits needed to have their communication systems connected *after* they were in the suits but *before* their helmets were attached.

Wireless

More and more production Mixers opt to use wireless transmission from the boom poles to the mixer. Several manufacturers offer clips to attach to the side of the pole that hold a wireless transmitter; some boom operators prefer just to plug in a power supply/transmitter directly into the microphone and avoid cables altogether. Either way will yield the same result but having one less cable to manage does make things simpler and faster. On *Once Upon a Time...in Hollywood*, I first used a plug-in directly into the boom microphone, and although it added a bit of weight, I found it saved me a lot of time as I ran between wiring actors, pre-rigging cars, and booming full-time, making it a more-than-worthwhile configuration.

Recording Machines

These are recorder-mixers.

Zaxcom DEVA 5 recorder

Cantar X3 Multi-Track
Digital Audio Recorder

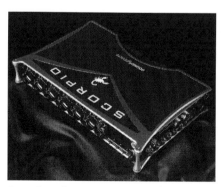

Sound Devices Scorpio recorder-mixer   Sound Devices 833 recorder-mixer

Mixers

Inputs can be used for boom microphones, radio microphones, plant microphones, audio feed from video playback, or music playback.

Outputs can be to a camera, the video assist operator, Comtek distribution, speakers, or VOG.

Yamaha 01V96i

Sound Devices 552

The Recorder-Mixer

The mixer is a self-contained routing device designed to give the Mixer maximum control over many aspects of the incoming sound. Similar to but not the actual routing devices itself, a computer control surface is an interface device used to remote the mixing capabilities of the nonlinear, file-based recorder; in general, the mixing panel and recorder are two technologies applied for the same outcome. The production Mixer has two options for where the signals from the microphones are directed: to the mixing panel (the mixer) or directly into the recorder. Most of the time, the microphone cables are inserted into the back of the mixing panel so that the Mixer can adjust the various sound elements (mix) in ways that are pleasing to his or her ear (another artistic consideration). Just like a recording producer has an "ear" for the music, the production Mixer has an "ear" for the movie's sound.

Sometimes, though, the microphone cables are connected to the recorder. A common situation would be when just a couple of inputs are needed or wireless gear is inoperable or there's a preference for "old-school" hard wiring to maximize quality potential through a minimal signal path.

Most Mixers like to put the boom mic on channel, or pot, #1 and the 2nd boom on #2. Some Mixers then

Production Mixer Kim Kylland with her one-man-band setup

put the lead actor on channel #3, and so forth. Other Mixers need more space between very active pots and put minor characters in between much-used pots. They'll all have a means of identifying which microphone correlates to which pot. One simple method is to use a small piece of tape under the pot with the name of the character (if this is the Mixer's method, make it as professional as possible by cutting, rather than tearing, the tape and using your neatest printing. Or, better still, make a label). Established Mixers use Velcro strips under the pots. Character names are put on labels that are attached to the hook side of the Velcro, and the loop side is on the mixing panel (so Mixers don't have their skin rubbed off when working!). USTs who love to label will find a warm spot in a Mixer's heart.

Equipment Package Sizes

When you are helping the Mixer put together the sound cart for a show, there will be some processes that remain the same and some that reflect the nature of the project. On some projects, the Mixer works alone in the Sound Department, and he or she is called a "One Man Band" (OMB). In this scenario, a Mixer will have a recorder, possibly a mixer, a boom microphone and pole, a couple of wireless microphones, and possibly an IFB system so others can hear. Many smaller productions—including interviews, documentaries, industrials, and some commercials—budget for only OMBs.

Bag Work

Sometimes the Mixer on a larger show will be going "doc," short for documentary style, which means she'll have the recording equipment in a gear bag or some type of portable, one-person rig, with a short pole or radio microphones. Then your job may be more of a "support" role in nature once the rig is built. Documentary style, bag rig, and OMB (one-man band) are names for the same rig.

When you're working as support for the Mixer on a narrative project, it's often because a camera car is being used or the Mixer is traveling and moving quickly. It's common for just the Keys (heads of departments, or HODs) to go with/on the camera car, while support crew from various departments pile into one or two "follow vans." Each department will send the minimum crew necessary to provide additional hands or support gear that the camera car had no room to store.

Support items for Sound to take in the follow van will be scene-specific and may include:

CASE 1

▸ Backup recorder

▸ Backup batteries for the Mixer's gear and radio mics

▸ Battery block and distribution cables

▸ AC strip bar, stinger, and tie

▸ Additional media and bubble envelopes

▸ Spare hard drive

CASE 2

▸ Small speaker, power cord, 50' XLR

▸ Antenna and cable (additional, in case something more than the fixed mount is necessary)

▸ Windjammers

▸ 9V and AA batteries

▸ Tape roll

▸ 2 space blankets, tarp

▸ Bungees/tie-downs

▸ Dust-off

MISC.

▸ Boom 1, Boom 2, as needed

▸ Radio mic kit

▸ Umbrella

▸ Folding cart, stool

▸ Furniture pad

▸ Comteks, as needed

Production Mixer Alan Holmberg keeps his bag ready to go while on the cart. Photo courtesy of Sound Devices.

IFBS

Whatever the size of your show, you'll need to manage receivers and headsets for various production personnel to be able to hear what the actors are saying. The most common of these units are from Comtek, and are simply called "Comteks." Units by Lectrosonics and Wisycom are also popular choices. The number needed will be determined on a show-by-show basis; the common recipients include the director, script supervisor, other sound department personnel, producers, background coordinators, and occasional grips, electricians, and camera operators.

Comtek PR — 67

Lectrosonics R1a

Sizes of a Sound Department

Low-budget projects often expect sound crews to consist of a production Mixer and boom operator, regardless of how the physical blocking and the movement of the actors is designed, the composition of the frame, the use of overlapping dialogue, or the number of cameras requested. Differences between modest-budget shows and large-budget shows really come down to numbers: a modest shoot may have one boom operator, 6 wireless, and 12 Comtek units, whereas a large-budget show could have two boom operators, 12 or more wireless, and 35 Comteks, plus additional personnel. The movie *Cats* had 17 Sound crewmembers, and the movie *1917* had seven.

There is often a misconception regarding the staffing of the Sound Department that one size fits all projects. A further misconception is that any additional staffing is unaffordable no matter what. The discussion in pre-production with the department head really should analyze the intended approach and expectation based on the unique aspects of any given project. Short staffing the Sound Department when there are built-in needs to accomplish the work can actually create a much more expensive and unintended waste of time and money.

Carts

Mixer carts can be standard or custom made. Here are a few examples:

Follow Carts

Follow carts carry the non-Mixer sound equipment: boom poles, microphones, antennae, batteries, radio microphones, tapes, and personal gear. Here are some examples:

Cases

All that gear needs to be safely stored and transported. Pelican and Thermodyne are two common case manufacturers for gear. Support cables and accessories are configured in tubs, crates, tackle boxes, and all manner of organizers.

Thermodyne

When you're asked to get something from the truck, think in terms of its whole unit. If you're sent to get a microphone, bring its corresponding accessories. If you are sent for more stock (recording medium), bring the envelope it will need to go in. If you're getting the soldering gun, bring the whole soldering kit and a paper towel as well. The more you can think in this way, the fewer times you will have to run back and forth, losing time and frustrating your teammates.

Pelican

What Gear Do I Need?

In the US, it's common to bring your own headphones or earbuds (the professional versions are called IEMs for In-Ear Monitors and produce superior sound quality), a tool belt with pouch or a fanny pack, a flashlight and/or headlamp, appropriate clothing, and sometimes a boom pole. It's normal to ask a Mixer whether he has boom poles for you to use, and most Mixers don't assume Utility people have their own.

A *pouch or bag* is necessary to hold several small items you'll need throughout the day. I picked up my current one from a hardware store. Valuable items to include are a small screwdriver, Swiss army knife, pen, black Sharpie marker, circuit tester, batteries for your IFB, batteries for the wireless mics being used, safety pins, items for wireless mic "touch-ups," a Lectrosonics tool, a couple of cable ties, work gloves, a small Maglite flashlight or headlamp, Moleskin strips, Transpore, Super Stick It!, lip balm, phone on mute or in airplane mode (if you use an internet app during work). I also keep two pens because I inevitably give one away to somebody who needs it, and it's not returned to me (*don't* be that person on set). Having a small notebook to record repairs, routines, or notes when you're too busy to handle things immediately is valuable; it's a detail that makes a difference! Write it down.

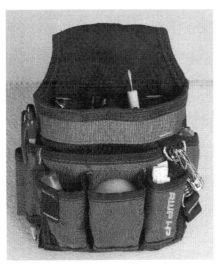

K-Tek's Hip Pack
https://ktekpro.com/product/
ksuhp1-stingray-utility-hip-pack/

The author's pouch

Most of us wear belts to hold the transmitter, receiver, our pouch, and gloves. Over time, I found that my waist gets pretty full of attached things and I'm now looking at the K-Tek hip pouch. The two bands—one at the top and one at the bottom—Velcro onto your leg so that when you run (which you shouldn't do but everyone has done at some point) your pouch doesn't bounce and things fall out.

Anytime I need to plug in power for the sound carts in a practical location, I use my electrical tester to check the outlet for proper electrical ground. Do not assume that power in an outlet is standard voltage, particularly when you're in abandoned buildings, warehouses, or buildings that are termed "stages" by the production; it's a good idea to have a small voltage meter as well.

You may want to keep breath mints or small candies for yourself. Altoids or the like are a nice gesture to actors (offer but don't imply they need them!) or crewmembers. If you will be away from the carts, consider getting a small package of baby wipes (unscented) to carry with you (hand sanitizer just can't wipe things down).

You'll also want to have a *kit bag*: a small bag to put on the follow cart. Possible items to include in your kit bag are lip balm, hand lotion, eyeglasses, hat and sunglasses, phone, your small notebook if you don't carry it in your pouch, and any medications you need to take during the day.

A *truck bag*. Bring a duffle bag with a change of clothing, including shoes, both rain protection and outerwear, sunglasses with a large lens area if you don't need them at the cart (boom operators look up at the sun all day; I find having a pair of sunglasses with a side "fin" helps wind or smoke from whipping across my eyes), and a hat that can stay on in the wind. Heavy boots should be able to keep you dry when standing in a puddle or protect you from cold; gaiters are a great quick-add for some locations.

A day's work can start at 3 AM or 7 PM (19:00) and go into the next day. *Always* have clothing that can keep you warm and dry. Because you may be working near actors, dark clothing will be less distracting, particularly if you have moves during the actual shooting. Keep a set of matte black clothing to avoid reflection problems. I call them "Blacks." If you work on small-budget shows or drive a good amount for work, consider purchasing a safety vest for times when you are working in or near street traffic, or if your car breaks down. On larger-budget, more-professional projects, they are supplied by Production.

First-aid supplies are never out of vogue. Keep a basic first-aid kit (and know how to use the supplies!) as well as items you personally may need, like medications or ibuprofen, etc. Think practically about the locations and pack accordingly. Disposable gloves and masks are now a must during the coronavirus pandemic. While the employer will be obligated to provide them in the US, it's a good idea to have some backups of your own. Consider taking a CPR class as a valued addition to your repertoire.

FILMMAKING IS DANGEROUS. FILM SETS ARE INDUSTRIAL WORKSITES, AND ULTIMATELY EACH PERSON IS RESPONSIBLE FOR HIS OR HER OWN SAFETY.

Items to bring to work: Depending on where in the world you work, you will either order these items as expendables, or you'll be expected to have the following:

Moleskin tape, Transpore skin tape, Allen keys (both metric and standard), battery tester, lavalier bullet, lavalier snake, scissors, mobile phone, Leatherman, Joe's Sticky Stuff, a small portable flashlight, jeweler's or precision screwdrivers, and the Lectrosonics app if using Lectrosonics TXs (available on iPhone and Android).

A laptop computer with Internet capability is handy for office work. For specialty situations, consider steel-toed safety shoes (required in some countries), your own headphones, and a short boom pole.

Clothing

Wear clothes that don't make noise. Do not wear corduroy, rip-stop, or nylon pants, or squeaky shoes—some treads on sneakers are notorious noisemakers, so bring an extra pair of shoes (or have booties or plan to go sock-footed when safe to do so). If you do find your shoes are squeaking on a particular floor, try roughing up the soles with sandpaper—but know that this is a temporary solution.

Clothing is by and large a personal decision, and witty T-shirts are enjoyed by the company. You might want to present a company brand—either literal logo designs or just a character trait. I have seen sound people dress like air-conditioning repair people with overalls (kind of a blue collar work ethic), a nicer style of casualwear, and I've also seen a lot of black, ninja-like branding from boom ops and Utility people because we want to keep a low profile and because we have something of a common work ethic about being stealthy.

We also do a tremendous amount of moving around, and whether you're a boom operator or a UST, it will involve walking, crouching, bending, twisting, lifting, reaching, possibly walking backwards, and all types of physicality. Because of that, the first thing you want to think about when you decide on your work clothing is range of motion: you must be able to make all those movements comfortably and without exposing your midriff or bum. You also don't want anything too formfitting or too baggy (which gets in the way). Again, black is such a well-regarded color because it doesn't distract actors during the shot, and often Sound crews are moving during the take.

I had the great pleasure of working with Chris Menges, DOP, on *Shy People*. We were shooting the inside of a tiny shed a girl was locked up in. It was such a small space that I was quite near the actor. He asked if I could change shirts, because my black was sucking the light from the room! He felt the white I had would've been too bright, so thankfully the Wardrobe Department lent me a brown shirt, which bounced an appropriate color on the actor's face.

Most people wear T-shirts and jeans or cargo pants, which we appreciate for their comfort and the many pockets available to put all those accessories we tend to keep. Many people also prefer shorts simply for the ease of motion (in Southern California, the weather is often suitable for shorts). As a rule, anytime you're in a public and professional work situation I would refrain from political slogans on your chest or anything that could be considered an offensive remark. That's just good business sense; when in doubt, always choose a low-key option. You don't want to wear any kind of jangly jewelry. Quiet-soled shoes with non-marking heels are a must. Some Sound people recommend steel-toed shoes, but that is not common in the United States unless at a construction site.

When choosing headphones, it will be a matter of personal comfort and aesthetics, but, in the beginning, something like a simple pair of Sony 7506s are common and will give you an introduction to learn what your personal preferences are. Once they're more experienced, several USTs and boom operators change to earpieces that have a lower profile. Also, hats fit better, and you feel less weighted down. It's a small thing, but sometimes that's enough to make a difference in your comfort. Think about chin ties on your hats so they stay on in strong winds.

When you're doing your prep, consider the weather: the time of year, the time of day, the location in the world you'll be working in, and whether you'll have rain.

Other water scenarios are discussed in Chapter 16, "Scene Elements."

Because we're often outside for many hours without a break, it's extremely important to remember sunscreen protection. Unfortunately, it's common to hear of sound Mixers getting skin cancer or melanoma, particularly on their hands. Some Mixers wear white cotton gloves for sun protection. Stay in the shade as much as you can and keep sunscreen applied.

When choosing gloves, make sure they are lightweight, comfortable, breathable, and flexible enough to be able to wrap cable and easily disconnect cables. I have become very fond of Gorilla Grip gloves. They are black with a fabric top and a type of rubberized palm, with a stretch elastic wrist cuff. They have a perfect combination of allowing for dexterity and keeping my hands clean and protected. A bonus is that for those times when you need to operate a boom, if you turn the gloves upside down and use the cloth side for your palm, they create a perfectly quiet slide. They're readily available and cheap in the US. ($3—$5 per pair on eBay, and at Walmart, AutoZone, Home Depot, etc.) You'll also want some kind of clip to attach them to your belt.

CHAPTER 9

Show Prep for Sound

While you're waiting for other departments to return your calls, you'll be busy prepping your department. Make sure to get any notes the Mixer made during the production meeting and transfer them to your appropriate schedule organizer. Will the Mixer wire the actors? Some insist on it. Will the Mixer hand off all communications with the Production office to you? How does he store his wireless system?

The boom operator will stay on set to watch the placement of lights by the Electrical Department, and the attenuation of lights by the Grip Department (setting flags and cutters and more), and she will also watch the camera movement and any refinement of the shot or action as it evolves. Sometimes boom ops will set the plant mics if the UST is busy with other work; how the work gets divided in certain situations is something that should be discussed in prep but is also worked out for each shot's design as needed.

IFBs/IEBs (Comteks)

Organize the production receivers and headphones in a way that suits you, as you'll be the one to distribute and manage them. Use a case or tote bag, depending on how many you'll need. Label all the ones you anticipate needing daily (I use a P-Touch labeler); have headsets or earpieces that go with them ready to use and have a variety of styles available for anyone you haven't had that discussion with. An IFB directory form is attached in the Appendix, or you can use a program like Excel to make your own. Label the dedicated holder pockets as well as the unit itself and always return them to their spot. After the third day, adjust your directory and print several copies. Also add a label and line in the directory for Guest 1 and Guest 2, so you can easily keep track of additional IFBs when there's a last-minute need.

When you (the UST), the Mixer, and possibly the boom operator get together for sound equipment preparation and loading onto the equipment truck, take notes of how the gear is set up on the carts, any mention of procedures the Mixer shares, and any timing preferred for morning setup. Now is a good time to compare mobile service providers; there are usually a few locations where one provider signal doesn't work as well as others.

On the higher-end shows, all members of the Sound Department have intradepartmental communications as well as some degree of interface with a walkie-talkie. During pre-production, confirm that the company has ordered walkie-talkie units for each person in your department and determine their intended method of distribution and maintenance. Some will give your department individual chargers; others will just trade out used batteries all day.

Channel 1 is the main production channel and listening to it will give you instantaneous updates regarding timing, movement of actors or vehicles, and all manner of information. Being able to communicate with each other is so important when you have gone off to wire an actor and there's a bit of a schedule shift that you need to let your department know about, or if you've been sent to the truck for one of hundreds of adaptors that Sound Departments tend to have, and you may need to ask a follow-up question. Take a moment to check the bullhorn; clean it if necessary and learn its functions and where the switches are. You may want to test the batteries if already installed or put in fresh ones.

As you go through your list of items to order, note whether each one is a production expense or if the Mixer will be putting items on his own account. Making a mistake and sending Production an invoice for personal gear or repair will create ill will, and some production managers have an extremely low threshold for errors. Likewise, establish early on the preferred method of reporting L&D (loss and damage) on the daily production report when something breaks or is lost in the course of the day's work.

Expendables

Along with recording stock, reports, and envelopes, there are pens, Sharpies, correction tape, 2" black paper tape, 1" black paper tape, 1" red paper tape (to identify broken/damaged equipment or alerts), cable ties, and unscented baby wipes. A basic list of expendables is included in Chapter 10, "Expendables." Consider the location you'll be working in; you may need unlubricated condoms for water situations or sweaty actors to protect transmitters from moisture, or Silica Gel packets to keep the equipment dry. A lighter comes in handy for shrink tape or making repairs. Using this list as a starting point, ask the Mixer as well as the boom operator for his or her additional items. Consider buying a basic first-aid poster for the truck (see the Appendix).

Batteries: Many Mixers use rechargeable batteries in 9-Volt, AA, and AAA sizes. Ask whether the Mixer would like to order rechargeable batteries and whether he or she already has a charger for the cart; that may need to be ordered as well. The other types of batteries are lithium and alkaline. Avoid using batteries that are not one of these types. A producer on a shoot once delivered a dozen heavy duty 9V batteries that a PA bought at the discount store, and then one Lectrosonics transmitter and receiver drained them all on the first day! If you don't use rechargeable batteries, you'll go through many batteries each day as radio microphone batteries are changed before they are completely drained. Discuss how the Mixer wants to dispose of them. To make them a bit more "green," offer them to crewmembers for their small electronics or children's games. Keep a box available on the follow cart for the used batteries. The common system for identifying batteries is: tips (positive pole) down = fully charged, tips up = needs to be charged.

Labels

The Sound Department loves labels! Mixers will usually have some type of label-making device. Consider the labeling tapes an expendables item and check your beginning inventory. Make sure all the cases have labels as well. Decide how the cases will be stored on the production vehicle (or in the Mixer's vehicle) and make sure the label is on the front-facing side. Label everything you can. As you do, take a look inside the cases to familiarize yourself with the contents. Some USTs take a photo of case contents for reference with their phones.

Frequency coordination: with more and more wireless devices being used on set, someone from Sound should reach out to other departments using wireless (Camera, Lighting, Grip, Video) to coordinate the frequencies proposed for usage. Mixers may want to do this, but they would most certainly admire a UST who is willing to take on the task. A simple form note to the 1st AC, Electric best boy, and video playback operators will help identify who is in charge of frequency coordination (Sound) and make sure all device coordination goes through our department. Suggest to the Mixer that the email note is cc'd to the PM, who will receive another lesson in the importance of having a UST and all the jobs they do.

Either the Mixer or you will schedule an equipment load-in with Transpo, if appropriate. For short jobs or small jobs, the Mixer might self-drive to the location in his own vehicle, and you'll off-load the gear and set up together. For longer-term or larger productions, Transpo will arrange to have your gear picked up from the Mixer's home or storage space. The equipment will be loaded onto a flatbed truck or something similar, and then you'll follow the vehicle to the equipment truck, usually shared with Camera (sometimes the Mixer has his own sound trailer). If you're working on a stage, the truck may drive to the stage for downloading *or* you and the Mixer may have an earlier call on the first day to handle the transfer. You might be asked to bring some gear on the first day or to charge batteries. Make a note in your planner and check it every morning before leaving for work!

Sound might be provided a room on the stage specifically for your equipment, called a *gold room*. Make sure the gold room can be locked and that there are at least two keys. Combination locks are more convenient, as no one will be held up waiting for the late arrival of a key.

Wrapping Cables

The Sound Department wraps sound cables in a specific way: the first loop is wound in a clockwise direction, the next loop is counter-clockwise, alternating until the connector is left. Put a cable tie around the mid-point of the hanging connector ends; some people connect the connectors.

Wrapping a sound cable:

www.youtube.com/watch?v=6duVvwdd5F0

Electrical cables, however, are always wrapped clockwise and form dense circles that fit in plastic milk crates (carrying cases) perfectly. When you return an electrical cable (stinger), make your loops the width of the crate and tie the cable in the same manner as the others.

At the end of your load-in, check that anything on the truck or stage that should be charging is indeed charging and that power will stay on through the night, that everything is put away securely, and that the truck/room or area is secured. Check with Production, Transpo, and Locations for any special instructions regarding security. If a security company has been hired, make sure the guard knows your gear is valuable, and try to get the name of the guard, if possible.

Review

Follow up on the work agreed upon with other departments and confirm that location issues were resolved, that an expense was authorized, or that modifications were completed, or understand where the bottleneck is and address it so that it is no longer an issue by the shoot day.

NOTES

CHAPTER 10

Expendables

There's a saying that movies are put together with tape. In this case, it's true. Tape is an indispensable item in the Sound Department, and that's where you should start your memorization of supplies. The following is a list of commonly used products; it's not uncommon to have crew-specific or show-specific expendables or procedures, so consider this a beginning list. Again, the script will help guide you for specific needs of the project.

Tapes

Note: Any tape left in place long enough will leave a residue!

Paper tape, black: This matte, low-tack, tearable tape comes in various widths (1" and 2" are most used). Commonly used for temporary securing, the tape is easy to tear away when finished. It blends into shadows when used to dress cables on the set.

Black paper tape

Gaffer's tape: A matte, cloth-based, tearable tape with a strong adhesive that leaves a residue. If allowed to remain on a case or piece of gear, the residue will eventually dry hard and require scraping to remove (and may alter the finish of the object). Sound commonly carries 2" grey gaffer's tape on their tape roll.

Gaffer's tape

Red artist's (camera) tape: The Camera Department uses two types of red tape: a cloth-based, 1" tape used to seal film cans containing exposed film rolls and a narrow paper tape used for marking actors' positions on the floor (and other uses). Sound Departments use red to denote items broken, in need of repair, or destroyed and put aside to follow the company's protocols for damaged items.

Red artist's tape

White artist's (camera) tape: A narrow, paper-based tape that's used primarily for writing on if label makers are not used. It is also used to dress cables against a white background.

Double-faced sticky tape: This tape is used for attaching two things together—for example, a teacup and saucer, to keep from rattling.

White camera tape

Double-faced foam tape: This tape often provides a bit of space between two items.

Joe's Sticky Stuff: This is an aggressive double-sided, 1" adhesive "tape." It is non-hardening and remains flexible but tends to melt at around 115 degrees Fahrenheit (46 C).

Double-faced sticky tape   Joe's Sticky Stuff

Double-faced foam tape

Foot foam: This is often used for quieting footsteps and can be purchased in pre-cut shapes or by the roll.

Molefoam: Moleskin with extra-soft cotton and foam padding.

Foot foam

Wiring Expendables

Hide-A-Mic, Bubblebee, Rycote, Viviana, DPA, URSA, and others make customized lavalier mounts and accessories. See the Appendix for a list of website links.

Molefoam

Transpore: A clear, plastic, low-tack surgical tape that can be torn in either direction, used for placing lavs on actors as well as non-human surfaces. Comes in different widths (since it can be easily torn horizontally, most people choose the 1" and tear it in half or double it to cover any situation). Most people have no allergic response to it, but for sensitive actors use a silicone tape such as Mepitac.

Transpore

Mepitac: A beige, silicone, latex-free tape requiring scissors. It's used for actors who have skin sensitivities. Leaves no residue. Breathable, repositionable, and moisture proof. The 1½" width is most versatile.

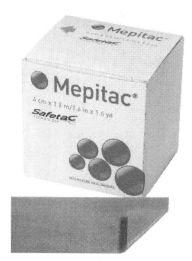

Mepitac

Tegaderm: A transparent, breathable yet waterproof tape. It holds up in water. To remove: Grasp one edge of the tape and slowly stretch straight out and down while supporting the skin.

Tegaderm

Coban: A latex-free, water resistant, self-adhering elastic bandage wrap that comes in different widths and colors. It can roll on itself with movement and become a tight mess, needing to be cut off. Other self-adhesive bandage wraps are available.

Kinesio tape: A latex-free, hypoallergenic, water-resistant tape. Stays put during movement. Comes in colors.

Coban

Nexcare tape: A beige, waterproof, latex-free, hypoal-lergenic, tearable, foam-backed tape for securing lavs or packs, when necessary.

Moleskin: A beige, latex-free, strong, 100% cotton adhesive-backed material. Cut with the backing side

Kinesio tape

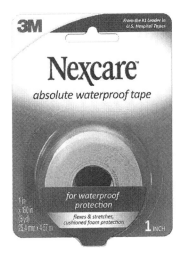

Nexcare tape

Moleskin

up for best results. If you have trouble with the Moleskin sticking (after cleaning and drying the skin), before removing the white backing, rub the moleskin between your fingers. This will heat the adhesive and allow for better sticking. Wrapping the lav in moleskin can significantly reduce clothing noise against the microphone. Purchase small packages at a local drugstore or an audio supply store for larger quantities. Comes in beige, white, or black.

Super Moleskin is thicker. When attaching a lavalier to clothing, you can cut strips to cover the wire so it isn't accidentally pulled when dressing.

Bunion cushions: Sometimes a consumer-use product does the job simply and cheaply; a bunion cushion can give a little amount of airspace around your lav. I haven't tried Zentoes corn cushions, but they look worthy of consideration.

Topstick: A thin, clear, double-sided adhesive tape traditionally used for securing toupées. It can be used to keep clothing from moving.

Super Stick It! strips and dots: A clear, high-tack, double-sided tape for clothing or attaching lavs to bodies.

Rycote stickies: Pre-cut, disposable, paper-backed, hypoallergenic mounting adhesives for lavs. Can be used on both skin and fabrics.

Bunion cushions

Condoms (unlubricated): To protect the transmitters from moisture.

Topstick   Super Stick It!   Rycote stickies

Body Straps and Pouches

URSA, Neopax, and Viviana make belts, straps, and pouches for securing transmitters and microphones on actors. Black, beige, and white options allow for blending in with the wardrobe.

K-Tek Heat Block pouches: Transmitters generate heat over time, and a heat block can make actors more comfortable.

Lav bullets: Several companies make a metal bullet-shaped weight that attaches to the lavalier cable connector to assist in running the cable down pants.

Lav snake: A very springy wire that does the same thing as a lav bullet, for tighter pants. Use caution when taking it out of its case.

Lav rod: A rigid solution for running a lav wire down tight pants.

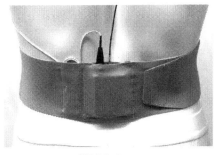

URSA strap

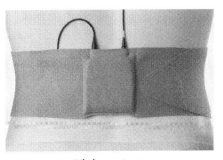

Viviana strap

K-Tek Heat Block pouch   Lav bullet

Lav snake

Lav rod

Wind Protection

Microphones need protection from wind, and several manufacturers create disposable, pre-cut material to secure over lavs, such as Rycote Undercovers, Rycote Overcovers, Bubblebee's Invisible Lav covers, and URSA Soft Circles.

Fur can be purchased in larger pieces for custom coverings.

Mounts and Accessories

A variety of clips and concealers are used to attach lavs to bodies, clothing, or hard surfaces.

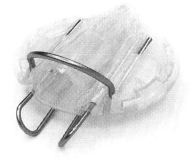
DPA concealer

Bubblebee concealer

IFB Headphones/Earpieces

Because these are personal use accessories, we consider them an expendables item.

General Items

Office supplies: Basics include pens and pencils, Sharpies, highlighters, paperclips, rubber bands, and notepads. Red Sharpies and pens are used to identify broken or damaged items or a caution.

Recording stock: Always make sure there is sufficient recording medium for the work.

Cases for protecting recording stock

Envelopes: Padded envelopes hold the recorded stock that is sent daily to the Editorial Department. A few regular office envelopes can come in handy as well.

Labels: (Various sizes, based on your label maker and department preferences.) Both adhesive-backed paper and adhesive-backed plastic are used.

Scissors: I find having both a small pair and regular size pair of scissors most helpful for cutting bits of tape, making custom wind protection, or sizing foot foam.

Medical scissors: Medical scissors have a snub-nosed tip to prevent accidentally cutting skin when used to remove tape from skin or clothing.

Batteries (single-use Lithium or rechargeable): Commonly used are A, AA, AAA, 9V, batteries for in-ear, wireless receivers (if applicable), button batteries, chargers, and battery caddies.

Cable ties: We use a variety of ties to secure cables. Order them in multiple sizes.

Adhesive remover: Goo Gone is the preferred product for label removal on many surfaces.

Canned air: Canned, compressed air is used to clear dirt off the equipment.

Velcro: Adhesive-backed hook-and-loop fastening tape secures small items to the carts as well as attaching character names on a mixing panel.

Cart accessories: Ask the members of the team for their preferences.

Cleaners: For electronics, cases, and all equipment. Hand sanitizer and baby wipes are staples.

Alcohol: Alcohol and alcohol wipes for disinfecting.

Uni-Solve Adhesive Remover Wipes: Several manufacturers offer products, and I find that Uni-Solve wipes work better than alcohol on lav wires without drying the cable.

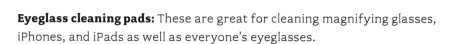

Eyeglass cleaning pads: These are great for cleaning magnifying glasses, iPhones, and iPads as well as everyone's eyeglasses.

Cotton swabs: For cleaning gear and ears (before inserting an in-ear wireless receiver).

Silver paste: For refreshing Lectrosonics transmitter conductivity.

Tents and tarps: Use these covers to protect the equipment and/or mixer and equipment from the elements.

Straps: A variety of webbed straps and tie-down hardware will secure the carts and equipment for travel.

Carpets: Carpets are small mats or runners used to quiet footsteps or placed over cables to prevent a tripping hazard.

Soldering supplies: Make sure the soldering kit has everything needed for making field repairs.

NOTES

CHAPTER 11

Production

O nce production is underway, your interactions will expand to include all the departments as well as real-time schedule shifts.

The Day Before

Review the crew list, actors' names, the map to the location, and all the information on your call sheet.

How to Read a Call Sheet

When you get your call sheet, the first thing to do is check the general crew call time and then your department's call times. If you're scheduled to come in before the general call, you have what is called a *pre-call*. The pre-call is scheduled when you need extra time to be ready at the same time as the general crew. Two examples for a pre-call are that moving the gear to a difficult location requires more time, or there is music happening first thing. Camera assistants often have pre-calls in order to have the camera built soon after call. A common practice is to have the UST call match the 2nd AC call.

The company information will be near the top: the producers' names, the director's name, the office phone number, the weather report, locations for crew parking and trucks, and shooting call. The shooting call is the 1st AD's best guess as to the timing of having all the necessary elements on set ready to film the first setup.

"NO FORCED CALLS WITHOUT PRIOR APPROVAL OF THE UPM" This is a standard notice and means that no one is to begin work before his or her con- tracted break time is over. Working on a forced call means that the worker will be paid an overtime wage, something productions are quite loath to do.

BOSS FILM PRODUCTIONS

Magnum Opus

PRODUCTION OFFICE:

Tel:

Director/Writer: Quentin Tarantino
Producer: David Heyman
Producer: Shannon McIntosh
Executive Producer: Georgia Kacandes

DATE: **Monday, June 18, 2018**
DAY: 2 of 102
Weather: SUNNY
HI: 71   SUNRISE: 5:40A
LOW: 58   SUNSET: 8:03P

SHOOTING CALL: **7:30A**

CREW CALL
6:00A
(SEE BACK FOR INDIVIDUAL CALL TIMES AND PICKUPS)

Work Trucks: AT SET

Basecamp: BEHIND STAGE 27

Crew Park: Carl Laemmle Bldg. - Bldg 2160
3900 Lankershim Blvd
Universal City, CA 91608

NO FORCED CALLS WITHOUT PRIOR APPROVAL OF THE UPM - **CLOSED SET - NO VISITORS ALLOWED WITHOUT PRIOR PRODUCER APPROVAL**
BREAKFAST WILL BE AVAILABLE BEFORE CALL- ALL CREW WITH A PRE-CALL MUST TAKE AN NDB **NO CAMERAS ON SET**

SET / SCENE DESCRIPTION	SCENE	CAST	D/N	PGS	NOTES
EXT. LANCER SET - WESTERN TOWN	52	5,9,10,18,50,54,55	D2	3 6/8	EXT. LANCER
Lancer Scene - The stagecoach arrives		56,59			
EXT. LANCER SET	53	1,2,5,9,10,18,50,54,55			
Trudi watches Rick arrive and send Cliff home		56,59			
		TOTAL PAGES		**4 6/8**	

Smoking is only permitted in designated areas. Look for the butt cans!

	CAST	CHARACTER	STATUS	PICK UP			REMARKS
1.	LDC	Rick Dalton	SW	11:00A	11:00A	4:00P	Bounty Law hair / makeup look first
2.	BP	Cliff Booth	SW	11:30A	11:30A	4:00P	
5.	Julia Butters (k)	Trudi Fraser	SW	7:00A	7:00A	7:15A	
9.	Timothy Olyphant	Johnny Lancer	SW	6:00A	6:15A	7:15A	
10.	Luke Perry	Scott Lancer	SW	6:00A	6:15A	7:15A	
14.	Scoot McNairy	Business B.G. Gilbert		12:00A	12:00P		Fitting at Universal
50.	Clifton Collins Jr.	Er		00A	6:15A	7:15	
54.	Monty Stuart	Stage		00A	5:30A	6:30	
55.	Ramon Franco	2nd		45A	6:00A	7:15A	
100.	Zoe Bell	Stunt Coordinator	SW	8:00A		6:00A	
x.	Mark Warrack	Stunt Double Driver	SW	00A		6:30	

					SPECIAL INSTRUCTIONS
1	LDC / Utility St		42A		
1	BP / Utility St		42A	6:00A	
1	Trudi St		42A		
1	Utility St		42A	6:00A	

BACKGROUND	SCENES	Report	Ready
2	Bankers	52/53	5:30A	7:00A
1	Boarding House Mistress		5:00A	7:00A
2	Clerks		5:30A	7:00A
6	Cowboys		5:30A	7:00A
2	Farmers		5:30A	7:00A
5	Horse Riding Cowboys		5:00A	6:00A
1	Inn Keeper		5:00A	7:00A
1	Post Office Clerk		5:30A	7:00A
2	Schoolmarms		5:00A	7:00A
2	Smithees		5:30A	7:00A
1	Stableboy		5:30A	7:00A
1	Stagecoach Large Man		5:30A	7:00A
1	Stagecoach Large Woman		5:00A	7:00A
4	Townswomen		5:00A	7:00A
1	Undertaker		5:30A	7:00A
1	Wheelbarrow Shit Boy		5:30A	7:00A
3	Widows		5:00A	7:00A
1	Trudi Double (k)		12:30P	1:00P
3	Cameramen		1:00P	3:30P
1	Costumer (f)		1:00P	3:30P
1	Costumer (m)		1:00P	3:30P
3	Electricians		1:00P	3:30P
3	Grips		1:00P	3:30P
1	Hair Rep (f)		1:00P	3:30P
1	Makeup Artist (1)		1:00P	3:30P
2	P.A.s		1:00P	3:30P
3	Producers		1:00P	3:30P
1	Scriptgirl		1:00P	3:30P

SJ" N.D. Horses (3), Stage Coach Horses (6),
Wagon Horses(2), Personal Carriage Horse, Beer Keg Horses (2)
Conoe Stagecoach, Marabella's Wagon, ND 2-Person Carriage
VEHICLES (Sc. 53): Golf carts (3) N.D. Parked Cars (10), Johnny Lancer's Motorcycle
Free-driving Rick's Cadillac with rear window removed (shot from trunk), stakebed
LOCATIONS: Set adjacent parking, studio tour ITC
PROPS (Sc. 52): Wheelbarrow and shovel
MECHANICAL FX (Sc. 52): Dust for horse team
SET DRESSING (Sc. 52): Scenic backdrop
GRIP (Sc. 52/53): GF16
MUSIC (Sc. 53): Love Child - The Supremes

We will be doing a prop photo shoot of Rick Dalton in Bounty Law look

ALL CREW PARKING IN BLDG 2160. ENTER THRU GATE 3. SHUTTLES WILL BE ON HAND.

Call sheet

"ALL CREW WITH A PRE-CALL MUST TAKE AN NDB" A Non-Deductible Breakfast (NDB) is provided free of charge by the company to align the crew meal lunch break without creating an overtime situation for pre-call workers.

The next section lists the locations, scene numbers, cast numbers, whether the scene takes place during the day or night, the page count of the script, and a notes section.

If you know what the location looks like and whether it's a day or night shot, with experience you can gauge how long the crew will take to make the set ready for shooting. Day interior scenes that will look like night in the movie mean that the windows will have to be darkened or closed in to prevent sunlight from coming into the room—an activity that will add time.

Next to the actor's name is his or her character name and status: H for hold, W for working, SW for start-work, and SWF for start-work-finish. When actors are on a hold, they are not currently scheduled to work that day, but that may change. When you see that an actor is finishing work on the movie, be sure to check that any wild lines or additional dialogue is completed before the end of the day. Knowing the timing of the actors through their morning process helps to coordinate the time for wiring.

When the page count for a scene is 1/8th of a page, it denotes that there is no dialogue...unless there suddenly is. Directors or actors can add a line or encourage ad-libbing. Whether to automatically wire actors without scripted dialogue is one of the early topics that will need to be worked out with the director. A good time for this is in the interview meeting with the Mixer, where discussions of art take place in less stressful environments. Even though there might not be dialogue, a Mixer will almost always want to record the ambient sounds alongside the camera and protect for the impromptu.

Always check the "SPECIAL INSTRUCTIONS" section for specific departmental notes—*all the departments*. On a call sheet I received, Sound will need to set up playback, the grips will be using a type of camera car, there will be misting fans, and Craft Services needs to move because they're in the direction that we will be shooting first. There's a separate note that we will be recording multiple vehicles in the parking lot. Knowing what other departments need to prepare helps one understand whether those departments affect your work schedule or add to a myriad of tasks. Now I know I need to get some details from the grips about the pursuit arm work:

www.youtube.com/watch?v=2GDfyX4gTu8

The recording of multiple sets simultaneously requires discussion in the pre-production stage. One scenario is to alternate between two boom operators if the company can be silent or if there is a long waiting period on one of the sets. On our film, the postproduction sound people chose to do a rather lengthy session with many cars and came to the location as their own unit.

The bottom section of the front page lists the *advance work* anticipated for the next few days. It also indicates the color of the revision schedule. Make sure you always use the most current version! You can get updated packets from the 2nd 2nd. The advance section is like a meeting-less production meeting—a heads-up that it's time for things discussed in pre-production to occur or that changes have been made and you have now been notified. Read the advance carefully, as if you are seeing it for the first time; changes are not always indicated.

The backside of the call sheet lists every crew person's name and specific call times. Compare your call time and your department's call time to Camera's and speak to the 2nd AD if you feel your department's time needs adjusting. Also consider the Grip and Electric call times, imagine their workload, and decide whether you can be ready at or before their set up time.

A 24-hour clock is used, and an hour is broken into ten 6-minute segments. A modest pre-call is considered 18 minutes before the general call time (6:42 AM for a 7:00 AM general crew call). Lunch is officially noted as 30 minutes, timed from the last person through the lunch line. A PA is stationed at the line to note the time. The time for which lunchtime is called has salary ramifications on an American union show: meal penalties (paltry as they are) are assessed after 6 hours of work. A concession was made to allow the company a grace period if a shot had been started but not completed. Productions abuse this constantly to keep the crew working.

Save your call sheets until well after the job is over. If you are on a USA - IATSE show, your hours will be credited to the Motion Picture Industry Plan, which manages health and pension services and various payouts. If you are not a union member, the call sheet with your name on it can provide proof of days worked. It's very important to make sure your *job classification* is not mislabeled on the call sheet or your pay stubs. If you are accumulating days to qualify for the Industry Experience Roster (IER), the call sheet and pay stubs may be needed to properly document days worked. They must be in the proper names of classification or may be rejected. This is strictly administered by Contract Services for the IATSE workforce in Hollywood. When replacing yourself or day-playing on someone else's show, make sure to have the 2nd AD record the name change on the production report and update the call sheet(s).

On the bottom right is a directory of walkie-talkie channels for contacting other departments. Keep your walkie-talkie on Channel 1 to monitor the running of the set. Use Channel 1 to request a conversation with a department, and then ask them to go to Channel 2—the open production channel; do not tie up Channel 1 with conversation. The channels listed for a department are for their internal communication. All departments monitor Channel 1.

Sound Attenuation or Noise Mitigation

A very significant task for the Sound Department is the location and control of unwanted noise invading the filming environment. It is increasingly common for productions to neglect taking a production Mixer on location scouts; therefore, noise issues should be one of the first things you think about when you read a call sheet. Be very careful to understand the protocols established by Locations: you will usually communicate items of concern to them and let them interact with the outside parties. Involving yourself directly with homeowners or stores may breach the process in the contract and drag you into unintentional dramas or worse.

To the extent possible, confer with Locations or the facility representative in advance if you have a major concern—e.g., a scene in a factory or power plant. Noise attenuation is one of the UST's main location responsibilities and should be addressed as soon as possible so that the appropriate support can be engaged while you concentrate on all your other jobs.

Upon arrival to the set each day, the UST should work through a check-list for discovery and coordination. Do a full walk around of the exterior perimeter of the location, looking for potential problems, (for example, sprinkler systems, pool pumps, decorative fountains, or wind chimes). Check in with the assistant directors to make sure the necessary police are on call for traffic control (ITC or Intermittent Traffic Control). Check in with the Locations Department to confirm control of air conditioning, heat, and refrigeration. The UST needs to check that the Transportation and the Electrical departments have placed the generator in a suitable spot, not too close to the set.

Likewise, do a full inspection of the interior location and all the spac-es and adjacent spaces. Keep an eye and ear out to confirm that all the agreed-upon elements are, in fact, under control and search for the unexpected: electrical cable runs that may compromise needed window and door closures, practical set dressing (such as room fans or noisy flu-orescent ballasts), placement of set-lighting ballasts too close to the set, ground and floor surfaces such as dry leaves or gravel. If a fireplace is to be used in the scene, check with Special FX for the proper muffling of gas lines and distancing of noise-making mechanics.

Some common examples of unwanted noise elements when filming in practical locations and some expected duties include:

▸ Air conditioning and heating systems. (Maintain control of them)

▸ Mobile air conditioning brought to cool the set. (Conduct oversight on placement and routing of)

▸ Refrigerators in kitchens and bars. (Locate, find electric or manual controls, and manage)

▸ Elevators. (Control and/or suspend their operation)

▸ Drinking fountains. (These often they have refrigeration, so it's possible to silence the motor by unplugging them. If not, ask the facility repre-sentative or Locations to handle it.)

▸ Plumbing noises from adjacent floors or neighbors. (Locate, isolate, and maintain control over)

▸ Leaf blowers, lawnmowers, snow blowers, and other gardener-generated activity. (Locate and/or have Locations deal with)

▸ Construction site close to the location. (Have Locations work out a plan)

▸ Ice cream trucks. (Have Locations manage)

▸ Marine traffic. (Have Locations manage/coordinate with the Marine coordinator or Marine representative)

▸ Air traffic. (Identify as precisely as possible the kinds of aircraft and direction and frequency, and then enlist Locations to contact the airport, if possible, to modify flight plans/routing)

▸ Trains. (Locations should have obtained train schedules, and a railroad representative should *always* be present)

▸ Schoolyard schedules and playgrounds. (Request a schedule of bells and recesses from Locations)

▸ Public Address systems. (Locate and have Locations manage)

▸ Telephones. (Silence them and coordinate a strategy with the building liaison)

▸ Doorbells or buzzers. (Locate and then suggest a suitable modification or refer to Locations)

▸ Muzak—either in the principal location or in stores nearby. (Identify the stores requiring accommodations and refer to Locations)

▸ Door and window closures. (Determine whether any need to be open for the scene and remind Electric not to use them for cabling if there's an alternate route. Check the area outside of windows for noise issues.)

▸ Animals in proximity to the set (dogs, goats, turkeys, chickens, etc.). (Locate, if possible, and alert Locations.)

▸ Squeaky door hinges or door closures that are too loud. (For squeaky hinges, work with Props or Grip to use a squirt of WD-40 lubricant and work it in by opening and closing the hinge a few times; for door closures that bang, many times a hydraulic closer is available that can be adjusted to alter the speed and velocity of the closing. Occasionally, a Props person may need to be enlisted to catch the door off camera.)

▸ Clothing or accessories that create distracting noise—e.g., jewelry, squeaky leather, noisy ties, etc. (Often, Costumes can discreetly secure chains by adding small safety pins to tie them together. Have an assortment of tapes and foams and a small pair of scissors standing by.)

▸ Excessive acoustic reverberation. (This attribute should have been discussed in pre-production and appropriate measures taken to treat the space with acoustic material if possible.)

▸ Automotive traffic. (Intermittent traffic control, or ITC, is used when sounds of inherent traffic will be intrusive in the filming environment. In the United States, off-duty or retired police officers are used to manually control the flow of traffic in the affected area.)

▸ Restaurants. (In restaurants, there will be multiple extras—all with table service, dishes, drinks, forks, knives, and spoons—who will need direction about quieting their motions. Discuss with the extras coordinator. There may also be icemakers, soda dispensers, coolers, refrigerators, and coffeemakers. Coordinate with Locations to get a schedule of how long machines can safely be turned off and follow that schedule. If the location warrants that you are busy booming or performing other tasks, enlist a PA to handle the machines—with the authorization of the 2nd AD.)

▸ Footwear. (Hard-soled footwear on principal actors or background artists may require padding of shoes or laying floor carpets. Again, this should have been reviewed in pre-production with Costumes and Art. If silencing is necessary in the moment, assess whether a carpet/floor mat can solve the problem. To adequately stabilize an actor, place Molefoam across the toe and ball of the shoe and another piece on the heel.)

You'll discover new and unexpected intruding elements on the filming day. These, too, will require coordination in a timely manner with the departments responsible for their control. This can include the ADs, Locations, the site representative, Grip, Electric, Sets, Props, Costumes, Camera, or Production.

The Night Before Day 1

Have the following positions' phone numbers in your phone: locations manager, assistant locations manager, on-set dresser, 2nd AD, 2nd 2nd, as well as sound referrals for additional boom ops, USTs, Mixers, playback people, and video assist operators. Have equipment houses' contact info and after-hours phone numbers and have numbers for a few people you know who might be able to lend/rent gear during an emergency. If your show doesn't have a medic (or even if it does) have some basic first-aid info on your phone. Download the Lectrosonics RM application if you will be using Lectrosonics wireless microphones. Check the weather for the next few days. Now is a good time to make sure your ICE phone number is input to your mobile phone. (ICE, or "in case of emergency," is an emergency phone number input to your mobile phone that first responders can call if you are unable.)

This is a good time to tell you about one of my early gigs: My first paying job was to shoot pick-ups on the Hawaiian island of Kauai. The feature had been shot in India, but they were looking for a more economical solution. We stayed in a lovely hotel right on the beach, had mid-morning calls, and were done working by late afternoon. The editor drove us to beautiful locations for an establishing shot or a small scene.

I remember the shooting of a dialogue scene near a waterfall, and I was positioned in between some trees while two people talked. I can't remember how long the scene was, but I do remember thinking I was having trouble holding the boom quietly that long. I heard some handling noise and was trying to will myself to hold out a little longer. I was still having some trouble when I felt someone behind me take hold of the pole, just enough to steady it.

When we cut, I looked behind me —an electrician had come up behind me and had given me a hand. I was embarrassed but thanked him; he was gracious and supportive.

When we start a new career, there can be a time when it is a bit more than we can manage. Someone else may be going through something similar in his or her own department, so when you have an opportunity, be the gracious coworker.

And try to get a good night's sleep!

Day 1

When you wake up, check your phone for any changes. These could include new call times, new work, or members of your department calling in sick. Wake up with enough time to react to the information. Eating breakfast at home or at the set is a matter of preference, but camaraderie is built in those minute exchanges and potential information garnered around the caterer or craft service tables. The Utility's busiest times are at call and at wrap.

Take your truck bag, kit bag, pouch, photo ID, and any favorite gear. Don't forget any gear you took home to work on or the script you borrowed. Check your planner for notes you made. If you haven't done your start paperwork, find time before lunch to get it in. In the US, you'll need several pieces of ID to verify your name and social security number for tax purposes. If you are completing start paperwork on set, the 2nd AD usually handles the verification because you are disclosing sensitive information.

Follow the directions given on the call sheet and allow for morning traffic, potential detours, or difficult weather. Have your phone available in case of a last-minute call. Pull over if you cannot safely talk and drive.

Where Are We?

The Locations department will have provided directions to accompany your call sheet. Look for the signs with arrows and follow them to the location if street parking is allowed or to the crew parking lot.

CREW PARKING

When you get to crew parking, keep an eye out for the ADs or camera people. Confirm the day's schedule and pay attention to any changes from the call sheet.

When working on a studio stage, things are relatively simple: You'll have directions for which gate and structure you'll use, and the guard will check your name and direct you to parking. Or a walk-on pass will be available at the guard booth. You'll show your ID or badge, if issued one, and proceed to the stage. Trucks will be placed around the stage building. If you're day-playing or dropping gear, there may be a drive-on pass at the gate; ask Sound or the company ahead of time how it will be handled.

If you're working in a warehouse or other similar structure known in Los Angeles as a "stage," your call sheet will have directions on crew parking, catering, and other truck locations, if they're not near the set. Sometimes there will be shuttles because parking is not allowed at the location.

Sometimes production companies need to spread out over multiple locations that are not within walking distance of each other, and there will be multiple truck areas.

WORKING TRUCKS AREA

At this location you'll find the hard crew trucks: Camera, Sound, Grip, Electric, Props, FX, Craft Services, etc. There is usually power at these locations and *most often* bathroom facilities of varying quality. Check with Transpo before choosing a shuttle van to get into so you end up where you want to go. When the Catering truck is placed here, a Honeywagon or smaller waste service facility will be as well.

BASECAMP

Like its non-film definition, basecamp is a point along the path to the destination. It usually has the AD trailer, the Hair, Makeup, Wardrobe, and Actor trailers, and a Honeywagon. The AD trailer is a common place to drop Sound files and paperwork at the end of the day (but occasionally the AD Department stations someone at crew parking to make the hand-off easier).

CATERING

Sometimes the Catering truck is just far enough away that Transpo provides a direct shuttle stop; always inquire when you choose a shuttle van. Figure the additional travel time into your timing so you get to the set when expected. A nice gesture is to pick up breakfast for the rest of the department to save time.

Once you arrive to the set: If you have any medical condition that may come into play, find and notify the medic. If there is no medic, make sure the 2nd AD is aware. If you might need immediate assistance or medication, such as an Epi pen, let the 2nd AD *and* your department know (so whether you're on set or working off-set, someone will know how to help).

When to start work: If you get to the truck early, it has become a practice in some areas to start work immediately, sometimes working for as much as 30 minutes before your call time. Many Sound people see the Camera Department (fully staffed, I might add) already setting up because the DOP wants to be ready to shoot at call. This is an unfortunate practice and could have drastic consequences. Local laws and regulations aside, United States insurance companies will not cover you for accidents that happen outside of the time you are asked to work. Morning time can be dangerous because of the movement of people from several departments working in one truck (Camera, Stills, Sound, Video, Playback, and/or Transpo), the constant operation of the liftgate, and the lack of light or low temperatures that create some slippery conditions. If you work in those situations, take steps to change your mindset, or at least have your call time adjusted so you are covered when you start work.

Be properly trained in the procedure for liftgate safety and teamster protocol. Confer with the driver of your truck for specifics. Generally, the driver or teamster is responsible for managing the liftgate for insurance or jurisdictional reasons. Make sure you know what the policy is before assuming you can operate the liftgate yourself.

If you *are* allowed to operate the liftgate, *always* announce that you'll be moving the gate: "Gate going up" or "Gate going down." The control box will be hanging on the right side (as you face the back of the truck from the outside) above the gate. Some trucks have three buttons (lower, level, lift), and others just lift and lower. If the gate does not automatically level, be sure to push that first when raising the gate, and then push it again last when lowering the gate. If the driver does not operate the gate, make sure you have adequately secured the cart(s) before moving. If you are the last one off the truck, leave the gate in a middle, level position so it can be used as a step (although some productions no longer allow this option).

If the area the truck is parked in is not safe or no security people are nearby, raise the gate up entirely and close the back doors. Make sure the Security person you requested from Production will always watch the open truck. *Did you check the call sheet and with Camera to confirm there will be a Security person at the truck at all times?*

When you arrive to a practical location on the day of shooting, the first thing you should do is walk around to detect any adverse sound conditions and notify the Locations Department. Sometimes you'll get the carts out and roll them directly to the set. Other times you'll want to scout the location for the best path to get to set or the staging area and carts location; it just depends on the location. However, *if you're shooting on a stage, first make sure the facilities person has brought the bell and light system cables and control box; plug them in and test them. Many directors like to block (work out the choreography of a scene or a move) first thing and will expect a means to quiet the set immediately.*

Find out what and where the first shot is. Get the carts off the truck as soon as possible, even if you just have them off to the side. Then get the gear you'll need and configure it (which we call "building the carts") and get your department IFBs and communications up and running.

Cables, cables everywhere: you'll be wearing multiple electronic devices *and* possibly have a lanyard around your neck identifying you as an authorized crewmember. The way we keep personal devices neat on experienced sets is to keep your cables under your clothing. Start by holding open the back of your shirt and dropping the cable down; reach up the back for the connector and attach it to the transmitter on your belt. You'll see the other departments—Grip, Electric, Camera—do the same thing. It's very easy to have your cables get caught on a C-stand knuckle, which is not something you want to happen if your hands are above your head working the shot.

Understand the set and shot. Once you know where the Mixer wants her cart and you've chosen a spot for the follow cart, use your ground tester for electrical outlets before plugging in any sound equipment into a wall in a practical location *or* check with Electric and plug in. Get the Mixer's cart up first, so when she arrives, she can start her prep as well. Then get microphones up and the minimum equipment you need to be shoot-ready. (For the 2nd boom pole, match the boom op's microphone.) Move the bell and light system to the Mixer's cart if necessary, the hand-off items to Camera (jammed slates, Lock-it boxes), get a video feed to the Mixer and send the audio feed to Video Assist and then video village, hand out key IFBs (Script, Director, 1st AD), set up additional microphones, and then begin wiring actors. Follow the procedures discussed with your department to be ready for the first shot.

Do not move anyone else's gear unless absolutely necessary. Find the person or department and bring it to their attention respectfully. If you must move something, tell the person as soon as possible, or tell an AD.

Unless the production is on a tight paper budget, the day's script pages (*sides*) will be handed out for the crew. If a PA has not come by with sides, get them now. Sometimes you will have a choice between full size and mini/pocket size. I have found that Mixers like the full size for their cuing, and set crew likes the minis to stick in a pocket (but ask).

Timecode

For a quick primer on understanding sync between Camera and Sound, see the following video:

www.youtube.com/watch?v=KpJql4ojm50

Because of the early capabilities of equipment, the Sound Department is tasked with controlling the synchronization of devices on a set and the Sound Mixer is the "keeper of the clock." Postproduction determines the frame rate in conjunction with Production, and Production will set an identical frame rate. A programmed crystal generator controls timecode and sync to a device. Placing portable timecode generators on each of the digital cameras ensures absolute synchronicity with the sound recorder. Having all devices operating at the same speed allows for a quicker time in the editing room. Timecode slates offer a visual backup reference and help immeasurably when the assistant editor conforms film takes to a digital medium. Ambient Recording, a leader in this field, offers tutorials:

▸ **www.youtube.com/watch?v=p7l7detTays**

▸ **www.youtube.com/watch?v=-7qQxjx4qF4**

There are multiple timecode (TC) products available: often the Mixer will supply the devices, but sometimes Camera will bring their own. Investigate who has the boxes and what the procedure on your specific project will be. Synchronizing (jamming) is a simple matter: turn off the device to be synced, plug in the connector, and turn it back on. After removing the cable, confirm that sync has held. Crystals do degrade over time and should be checked and potentially retuned for accuracy every couple of years or when combining Lock-it boxes of varying ages. Sound equipment houses offer a variety of products and may have manufacturer links offering tutorials on their devices. *Always check that the cable connectors are the proper ones for the equipment being used.*

Timecode Slates

Denecke makes a popular timecode slate, and their TS-3 runs on six AA batteries in a plastic sled. They are placed "in series," so be sure to check the polarity as you load them in. Depending on the brightness level, whether the sticks are kept closed, and the strength of the batteries, the batteries will last a few days at the brightest level and up to a week on the low setting. If the slate reads "00CODExx" after closing the sticks, it means the slate is running on internal timecode rather than external and is out of sync with the production devices. *If* an external power source is used for some reason, *remove the batteries first, or they'll explode.*

www.youtube.com/watch?v=N1OgbRygAWQ

After that, give Camera their TC sync boxes (work out with them a system for who installs them on the camera and how they will be returned at the end of the day). The same for slates: check the batteries at the start of the day, sync them, and deliver. I suggest to Camera that I will put the slates on their respective carts and expect to pick them up at the end of the day at the same place—it's much easier to find a cart than a lone slate left somewhere. Sometimes a less diligent 2nd AC will put the slate down anywhere; don't underestimate the likelihood of other departments taking your slate off their equipment and putting it on the ground.

Denecke TS-3 slate

On the right side of the slate as you face the back, there is a 4-pin XLR connector for providing external power (or timecode) and a ¼" female headphone jack for jamming.

There are two switches on the back of the slate: the left toggle is the on/off switch and the right is the high-standard-low light toggle switch. Explain to the 2nd AC that accidentally turning it off will require a re-jam. Sometimes a 2nd

Left side · Right side

AC doesn't know to handle the slate carefully and might hit the sticks too hard. Doing so can break the contact for the LED numbers, sending it out of commission. If the 2nd AC disregards your caution, you can tighten the sticks to make it harder to slam them. You can also make a label that says "Treat this slate like a lens."

On the left side, when opening the battery compartment, a tiny lever pops up. Take care to push that in when you close the door. The rotary dial on the left controls the frame rate—e.g., "0" = 30 fps, "1"= 29.97 fps. For other rates, see the frame rate chart pictured at right. Before handing off the slate at the beginning of a job, find out the frame rate and set it. The gray toggle switch above the battery sled should be in the up position to generate timecode, or in the down position to act as a reader.

0	= 30
1	= 29.97
2	= 25
3	= 24
4	= 23.976
5	= 25 PAL
6	= 29.970 (NTSC)
7	= 29d (NTSC)
8	= 30d P/PsF
9	= 29d P/PsF

Frame rate chart

Video Village

Start by finding out where the video village is being set up (look for a monitor, a set of director chairs, or ask the video assist operator). Run your cables or wireless feed and communications as needed. There are multiple ways this can be configured; how you handle it will be the result of collaboration between the Mixer and video assist person after conferring with the client.

It's become common for directors and producers to want to hear takes played back but not have the audio broadcast over a speaker where actors might hear it. The audio is always recorded and played back in real time, but there is an inherent time delay coming from the camera, and when playing back a correction must be made. This is usually worked out on the set when the director asks for audio playback through the headphones. The Mixer and video assist person work out how that correction will happen, but because the video operator has that capability with his gear, it is usually handled by having a transmitter (IFB) at the video assist's cart, and he handles the switching as needed between a live feed (for shooting) and a time delay (for playing back). The video assist person gets an IFB (Comtek), but not usually a headset (because he or she has their own).

IFBs

If you have a small number of IFBs, it's easy to manage. Give the same set to each person every day; it's easier to track damage, and it's a personal hygiene issue. With Covid protocols, you'll be labeling plastic bags for each IFB and assigning them to a particular person for the run of the show. A sample Comtek Directory form is provided in the Appendix.

Your IFB protocols will have two sets of procedures: how you manage the video village IFBs and those distributed around the set. In general, deliver the individual ones first because those are the people who need them first—Script, director, ADs, background coordinator, camera operator, video assist, playback operator, video engineers, music supervisor, and choreographer. At times, the action will necessitate other crewmembers needing an IFB. The producers rarely come at call so you have more time to set up the village.

I suggest making a sign (preferable) or tell the recipients, "Please notify the 2nd AD if you take the IFB away by accident—I'll be on the clock until I account for each one every day." A step up from the sign would be to design a screensaver for the video village monitors that display your message; ask the video assist person if that's possible as some display their company logo by default when not in use.

You'll place an IFB and headset at the director's chair, and when there's a moment, finesse where and how she would prefer her setup be placed. I advise against placing it *in* the director's chair pocket as Props comes through quickly during company moves and wraps; some Props people don't check the chair pockets, and you'll have to go through a rack of chairs to find that compressed IFB. Many directors use music stands, or sometimes there's a table for them and producers. I put labeled IFBs on the table, matching the chair location with the IFB and headset. I try to meet each of the above-the-line people and make sure they have the headset type they like—or I order it.

When you're starting out, you can wear Comtek headphones around the location but not on the set as the open foam nature of the headphones will bleed sound onto the set and may be picked up by the boom microphone. If you're on the set, notice if the director's or script supervisor's levels are enough to cause you to hear the bleed when your headphones are off.

If you find that to be the case, right after the take make sure that you suggest that they turn the volume down or be willing to trade out their headphones for a closed ear set.

Sometimes a director requests music on the set or in his headphones, and at times I'm asked to coordinate that and his comfort level. Sometimes a director wants to hear playback of a take, and the Mixer is too far away. I can relay communication between the director and the Mixer because I always wear a lavalier (mic) and headset.

If the director uses a VOG or megaphone, I hand it off and recover it. The UST is responsible for maintaining it and addressing any problems related to it. The most common problems for a bullhorn are that the switch was turned to "siren" (sometimes intentionally as a joke) or the batteries have run low. If the VOG is not operational, check with the Mixer for the level of the pot or check whether there has been a *kick out*—e.g., someone tripped over the electrical stinger and disconnected it.

The UST's job duties may vary wildly based on the director. At times, there will be a need to record some wild lines with an actor away from the working area. Sometimes the director will lead the session if available to leave the set, and on occasion an AD or editor will fill in. I've been asked to go to the actor's trailer and be the boom operator *and* director to get multiple, varied readings.

On *Ad Astra*, I managed the director's microphone to the actors and headsets; he usually bypassed the VOG microphone to talk to the Mixer and asked me directly to have certain music selections played in his headsets during certain sequences. I stayed physically closer to him on the set once I understood his preference.

On *Once Upon a Time…in Hollywood,* my main interaction with Quentin Tarantino was to hand him headsets for each take if we weren't on the stage. On Tarantino movies, there are always two boom operators working. If Quentin wasn't on headsets when the Mixer needed him to be, whichever boom operator was closer gave him info or made the request to put on his headset.

During the first day at the Spahn Ranch location, we had periods of plane noise and frequently had to decide during a take whether to cut or continue. Because the Mixer was off set, and the other boom operator was on the far side of camera, Quentin looked to me to give him an evaluation. With only facial expressions, I had to make judgment calls. And we conferred after the shots, sometimes including the Mixer, Mark Ulano, and sometimes just between us. Even if we settled things in that moment, I informed the Mixer of what had transpired so if there was a disagreement, he could speak up while we were still in the setup.

Once we realized that we were in the flight path of a small private airport, we took action: Mark contacted Locations and gave them suggestions for contacting the airport directly. We learned that the flights were mostly pleasure rides, and the air traffic controller rerouted the planes to another quadrant. We shot at that location for several weeks and could have had quite a bit of delay if Sound and Locations had not collaborated. One of the things crewmembers love most about working on a Tarantino show is that he makes it clear that *everyone* is expected to work for the good of the project. There's a lot of support and sharing, and it continues off the set with potlucks and birthday parties.

Try to time your setup process so you are ready to wire when the actors are ready: begin setting up the radio mics and checking frequencies.

Unless you need to be in the trailer when they're dressing, have the ADs bring the actor to the cart so you won't have to lug all your supplies, thereby taking them away for other actors' use. When actors are wired at the cart, you can instantly listen and make modifications to the mic placement. When reading a scene to decide whether to wire actors and which ones, also think about whether the actors or director like ad-libs. Don't assume that only the actors with written dialogue are the ones to be wired. Some characters make audible sounds, like sighing or chuckling, that need capturing. Think like a filmmaker; this is the kind of question that you can feel comfortable asking the director or 1st AD (*unless* the Mixer has described a different procedure for you).

Rehearsals

Chronologically, there are three types of rehearsals: a *table read*, a *blocking rehearsal* (director and actors, or director and actors and DOP, or director and actors and crew), and a *rehearsal*.

A *table read* is the first time the cast and director come together to go through the script and talk about the tone of the piece. They sit around a table and speak their dialogue.

During a *blocking rehearsal*, the director and the actors work through the action and dialogue on the actual set during production. There are several versions of this step depending on the director's preference: the director may want just the actors and script supervisor present, or the actors and DOP and Script, or the actors, their stand-ins, and necessary crew to witness the action to inform their strategy for achieving the work shown. Ideally, the actors will act out their movements as they speak their dialogue, and the 2nd AC will put down colored tape marks where the actors stop, and in the same orientation (tape is angled the same as the direction the actor is facing).

When crewmembers are invited for a blocking rehearsal, they should be silent and unobtrusive while the director and actors work out what the action will be and where the camera will be placed. A great deal of valuable information will be revealed to the departments if the actors perform their action and speak their dialogue as if the camera is rolling: what props are moved and will need to be re-set, whether wardrobe gets taken off, whether the camera needs to move far enough that track must be laid, what is the entire area in which dialogue will need to be captured, and whether that calls for one boom operator, two boom operators, a plant microphone or radio microphones, whether an actor will be particularly quiet or shouting. Every department will perform this kind of analysis for their own concerns.

Often the director and DOP stand next to each other and speak quietly to discuss the approach to be taken. How will we in Sound know the shot? This is one of the levels of communication that is unspoken. Here's a common scenario: When a blocking rehearsal begins, the DOP will be watching and deciding where the camera should be placed. He will walk a bit, here and there, watching the action. When he settles, 99% of the time that is where the camera will be placed. The director will move to his side to continue talking. The gaffer will stand on the other side of the DOP, who will quietly explain where he wants the key light and how he wants to light the scene. The key grip will be near, and he and the gaffer will coordinate their work. The dolly grip will be very close by to hear whether there will be a dolly move, how long it will be, and the route of the move. If it happens that no one says a single word during the rehearsal, by watching the movements of these key players you will have a relatively good understanding of how the shot is designed. Again, this is a *very common procedure* but certainly not the only way a rehearsal is processed.

Sometimes there's a marking rehearsal, and the physical blocking is not fully shown or shared with the crew. A *marking rehearsal* is a variation in which the actors go through the moves without acting, so that their physical positions may be marked for lighting and composition. If you need to place a mat over any mark to quiet the floor under the actor, *make sure* the 2nd AC is notified and be sure to help her transfer the marks onto the carpet without changing the location or angle of the marks. Make sure the carpet/mat is out of the frame, edges lay flat, and there is no possibility of tripping! When rolling carpets or mats, roll them so that the practical side is rolled *out*—that way the edges will tend to lay flat. If the edges do curl, either use a different mat or tape the complete edge with 2" paper tape— a double row if necessary. Fold over the first ½" of tape to form a tab, making it easier to remove the tape.

You may wonder why many directors refuse to do a full rehearsal with action and dialogue: the most common rationale heard is that the director is "saving the performance" for when the camera is rolling. After working on more than 80 movies and television episodes, I have come to believe it's likely the director doesn't believe showing this precise information to his team is needed, or he believes that it is overly time consuming. I believe this is a directorial lack of craft issue, often causing delays or misunderstanding by the departments in the earlier takes. It is certainly dismissive to the Sound Department, which garners information from rehearsals concerning pacing, physical range, and volume—key considerations when deciding how to mic the scene successfully.

Whatever the reason, many directors choose not to give information to the crew about the action they are about to shoot, thereby making an inherently difficult job even more difficult. One of the more complex skills to develop is the need to almost "read minds" and interpret the probabilities from the information that *does* exist. As every department must adapt in this way, it often results in the first and second camera takes being *de facto* rehearsals. Nonetheless, there is a very high expectation for the Sound Department to succeed in this environment.

Once the rehearsal is broken, the actors will be sent to makeup, costumes, and hair, and the crew will then work on the set. "The crew has the set" is usually called by the 1st AD and signals to the crew that it is their turn to work: ladders and equipment come in to make the set ready for filming. If the 1st AD fails to follow this protocol and you see the grips and electricians begin moving about, it is safe to begin your work. If you are not sure, it's appropriate to ask, "Do we have the set?" or "Does the crew have the set?"

Stand-ins will take the positions of the actors and be available for the crew. They are collectively called *second team*. If the DOP would like to rehearse with them, the 1st AD will call, "Second team rehearsal." It's prudent to perform your moves during this rehearsal to check for shadows or conflicting elements.

Anytime you are on the set, pay attention to what the crew is doing. Even if you believe you aren't working on the shot, and even if the boom operator and Mixer tell you that you are *not* working the shot, anything can change that, so keep current with where the lights are, where shadows are falling, where the camera moves, whether there has been a change to where the actors move, and where a possible 2nd boom position could be. Perhaps the boom operator becomes ill and needs to suddenly leave the set, maybe even for the rest of the day or the remainder of the show. A UST should always be ready to fill in seamlessly for the boom operator. That goes for the Mixer's position, too. If you are not involved with the shot at all, watch the Mixer and learn his procedure for communicating with the 1st AD to roll or discuss a problem, how takes are identified, how the machines work, and how communications with the director and script supervisor occur.

When the DOP is satisfied with the lighting and camera movement, he will return the set to the 1st AD, who will call for the actors and, when they arrive, will announce a "First team rehearsal" or "Picture's up!"

Room Tone

Once a staple of every sound team, getting room tone has mostly become unnecessary. *Room tone* is the inherent sound characteristic of a particular space and was recorded before a crew left that room or area. Its value was in providing the editors with a sound "background" to use as a transition when cutting in between shots.

Technology has moved forward in the editorial suite as well as in production, and editors are now able to take snippets of room tone inherent in
the takes themselves to use as needed. In fact, they prefer it to a recording made at the end of the location's work, which could be hours later,
when there might have been a change—in the traffic outside, for example.
If the room has a particular sound—say, a piece of machinery that cannot
be turned off—then a track of that sound can be helpful (boom it from the
location you were in during the dialogue). If you are asked to boom room
tone, use the main microphone that was used for the scene and place it in
the same spot as it was during the shooting. If the scene was radio-mic'd,
either have the actor be still or hold one lavalier mic in the general area
where the dialogue occurred. There are still Mixers who can't let go of the
habit of recording room tone in every location, and it's best just to say
nothing and go along with it.

Cabling

If you have to cable the boom operator, here's how: For a simple shot,
stand about 4 feet behind the boom operator, taking up the cable slack.
Prepare to move slightly faster than the operator, making loops with the
excess cable as the move is performed. Guide the operator if a collision is
imminent. Remember that bigger loops mean less loops and less twisting
of the cable. For very long runs, when two or more people are needed: put
yourself about 4 to 6 feet from the boom operator; this allows you to keep
from being run over but keeps you close enough if you have to steer her
around an object. (Think grips and Steadicam operators.) Space the others
about 6 feet apart. Then have everyone pick up only the slack behind him
or her, rather than one person having too much bulk and dropping the
cable, followed by inevitable tripping.

Running Cables

Cross electrical cables at a 90-degree angle as much as possible to lessen
the chance of electrical interference with the audio signal. Never make
a trip hazard when running cables; you can use a mat to keep a cable
secured, and it will be faster and easier to remove, rather than tape
that may be rolled onto itself and become a mess as people walk over
it. However, if you do need to tape down a cable, run your strips of tape

perpendicular to the cable; running a long piece of tape along the cable will not keep it secure—as soon as the first person's foot scuffs it, it will wrap tape around cable; trying to remove tape that's wrapped around the cable will take too much time. Another helpful suggestion is to cut a stronger piece of tape (i.e., gaffer's tape) for your securing strip, and cut a shorter piece placed in the center, adhesive-to-adhesive, to form a smooth surface against the cable. When you wind the cable, it will be clean and fast.

If there's a blocking, the boom operator will have a good idea of how many booms should work the shot. If you are needed at the beginning of the process, do your best to stay on set to watch the changing situation. Have several ideas in mind for positions and swings (Plan A, Plan B, Plan C, etc.). If you need to leave the set, make sure the boom operator knows your plan so he or she can protect your area. Let other appropriate crew know if you think there may be a conflict.

There will be times when the need for a 2nd boom is immediate. Always have your boom pole ready for action; the boom operator should fill you in on details as you make your way to set. Take a quick look around for any potential issues that you need to ask about *immediately*. Many times, things reveal themselves after the first take or rehearsal; work them out before the next take. Last-minute 2nd boom shots are often in awkward areas or positions or require a further swing than the boom op can manage. When you have *those* shots, your contribution is often of shorter duration but more difficult. If the last-minute position means that you'll be close to actors or a moving prop, dolly grip, animal, stunt, or FX, let all of them know.

Again, you may need to become the key boom if your height or weight and the boom op's size makes a difference in getting the shot, if the boom op has to leave the set or cannot do the shot because of allergies to something at that location, or some other factor. Your ability to fill in seamlessly is imperative. From Day 1, become a student of the personalities around the camera and the tone of the set.

One of the nicest DOPs I ever worked with was Paul Lohmann. He was of the generation I first learned from, and they believed that everyone had an important contribution to make and that we were all in this endeavor together. I remember booming a MOW (Movie of the Week) and once asking for a left-side frame line because I was fighting some element. He unlocked the operating wheels, spun them a fraction and said, "Nothing's set in stone." In that instant, the frame was just a couple degrees different, and my job was made easier. He was also a fun person to hang out with between shots, as my picture below shows:

DOP Paul Lohmann wearing a windsock

To assist you in honing your expertise in anticipating upcoming shots, watch the grips; they frequently break someone off to start on the next work. Or ask if there are rigging electricians (a separate crew that pre-lights the set).

Once the actors are set and IFBs are out, check in with the Mixer and boom op. If there are any runs for the day or next two days, get them to Transpo with the appropriate paperwork, and let them know the speed of that run and whether they need to wait for a repair. I made a run slip that shows the date, the drop-off location, whether it needs to go to a specific person, the purchase order number (if needed), the urgency of the run, whether it's billed to the company or the Mixer, any details the driver might need to make an instant assessment on behalf of the Sound Department, and my phone number for questions. When you're meeting the Transpo coordinator for the first time, ask if they have specific run slips and show them yours. The Appendix includes a sample run slip.

Lunch

Before going to lunch, attend to wired actors, power down the equipment, and cover the carts. Retrieve the slates (or have Camera trained to drop them at your cart). Turn on anything that was turned off for the shot. After lunch: power up equipment, re-sync camera hops and slates, replace batteries as needed, re-rig actors, and prep the next setup.

The Preliminary Call Sheet

A preliminary call sheet, referred to as the "prelim," comes out soon after lunch and reflects the anticipated work for the next day. It is produced on yellow paper to denote that it is not a final call sheet. Receiving a prelim helps you anticipate what the next day's work will be and prepare for it.

The value of the prelim is that it gives each department an opportunity to review the work and other departments' call times to assess whether their own department calls need to be adjusted, or if special equipment or additional personnel are needed. It comes out with enough time to call the equipment houses before they close.

The prelim is reviewed by the UST and discussed with the Mixer. Points to consider include, but are not limited to, the shoot time, the 1st AC's and 2nd AC's call times, the 1st actor call, Transpo vehicles, rigging times and crews, additional cameras, and any special props or stunts or sound items. The most common point to bring up to Production is the Sound Department's call times, and the most common adjustment is to move up the UST and boom operator times to align with the 1st and 2nd ACs.

The other main value is to work out potential noisy props or wardrobe that may need minor alterations. Larger issues for any department (e.g., FX equipment such as rain towers, gas lines for fires, heating water, or fans) should have been discussed in pre-production and mitigating measures already taken. A quick call to confirm those measures is worthy of your time. This is also the time to advise production of upcoming needs for an actor—e.g., cue aids and some rehearsal time or wild lines or information that requires coordination.

*** CONFIDENTIAL - DO NOT SHARE ***
*** ABSOLUTELY NO CELL PHONES ON SET ***

BOSS FILM PRODUCTIONS	*Magnum Opus*	DATE: Friday, November 16, 2018

PRODUCTION OFFICE:

Tel:

Director/Writer: Quentin Tarantino
Producer: David Heyman
Producer: Shannon McIntosh
Executive Producer: Georgia Kacandes

PRELIMINARY
CREW CALL

4:00P

DAY: 108 of 109
Weather: PARTLY CLOUDY
HI: 74 SUNRISE: 6:27A
LOW: 52 SUNSET: 4:49P

SHOOTING CALL: 4:30P

Parking: Universal Studios Frankenstein Parking
100 Universal City Plaza
Universal City, CA 91608

Basecamp: Universal Studios
LOT WEST OF FRANKENSTEIN PARKING
100 Universal City Plaza
Universal City, CA 91608

Work Trucks: King Kong South Lot
Catering: King Kong North Lot

(SEE BACK FOR INDIVIDUAL CALL TIMES AND PICKUPS)
11/10 Schedule Memo

NO FORCED CALLS WITHOUT PRIOR APPROVAL OF THE UPM **CLOSED SET - NO VISITORS ALLOWED WITHOUT PRIOR PRODUCER APPROVAL**
COURTESY BREAKFAST AVAILABLE BEFORE CALL- ALL CREW WITH A PRE-CALL MUST TAKE AN NDB **NO CAMERAS ON SET**

SET / SCENE DESCRIPTION	SCENE	CAST	D/N	PGS	NOTES
EXT. SUNSET STRIP	117		DUSK 1	1/8	"Ext Rick's House"
EXT. RICK'S HOUSE - BACKYARD	182pt3	1,22,100,101,1x,22x	NIGHT 3	2/8	

EVERYONE MUST WEAR THEIR CREW BADGES!!!!!

BREAKFAST IS OFFERED AS A COURTESY. PLEASE COME EARLY IF YOU WANT TO EAT.

| | | TOTAL PAGES | 3/8 |

Smoking is only permitted in designated areas. Look for the butt cans!

#	CAST	CHARACTER	STATUS	PICK UP	REPORT	MAKE UP/HAIR	READY	REMARKS
		Rick Dalton	W	4:00P Rnt.		4:00P	6:00P	
22.		Sadie	W		3:30P	3:30P	6:00P	
100.		Stunt Coordinator	W	4:00P		NA	4:00P	
101.		Fight Coordinator	W	4:00P		NA	4:00P	
2x		Stunt Utility	W	4:30P		4:30P	6:00P	
22x		Stunt Double Sadie	W	4:30P		4:30P	6:00P	
x		Stunt Utility	SW	4:00P		NA	4:00P	
a		Puppeteer	W	3:00P		NA	3:00P	

STANDINS		NOTES	Report	Ready	SPECIAL INSTRUCTIONS
1	Rick SI		4:00P	4:30P	PROPS: Gun
1	Utility SI (Sierra)		4:00P	4:30P	LOCATIONS: Heaters, separate green rooms

BACKGROUND	NOTES	NOTES	Report	Ready	
					PRODUCTION: Electric blankets
					SPFX: Pool heated, flamethrower, pool care, doors, blood in pool
					STUNTS: Fire protection, gels
					ART DEPARTMENT: Dino's sign
					COSTUMES: Towels

DRIVERS / CARS	NOTES	NOTES	Report	Ready	
					LOCATIONS

	SI.	2		
	BG	0	SAFETY BULLETINS
	DR	0	#1 FIREARMS, #4 STUNTS, #17 WATER, #22 LIFTS, #25 CRANES,
	TOTAL:	2	#19 FLAMES

ADVANCE SHOOTING SCHEDULE		SCENE	CAST	D/N	PGS	NOTES

NOTE - NEW ADVANCE SCHEDULE
(IF RICK'S HOUSE LOCATION COMPLETE) VFX PLATE SHOOT, SATURDAY, NOVEMBER 17th

INT. RICK'S HOUSE	TBD		NIGHT 3	•	
					BG: 0

MONDAY, 11/19 - WEDNESDAY, 11/21 - COMPANY WRAPS PER UPM / PROD. SUP.
MONDAY, 11/19 VFX PLATE SHOOT ON STAGE WHILE WRAPPING

INT. RICK'S HOUSE	VFX182		NIGHT 3	TBD	RALEIGH STUDIOS
	VFX183				BG: 0

TUESDAY, 11/20 - WRAP PARTY!!!
THURSDAY, 11/22 & FRIDAY 11/23 - THANKSGIVING HOLIDAY
DAY 109, MONDAY, NOVEMBER 26th - VFX REDUCED UNIT

EXT. GREAT ESCAPE - GREEN SCREEN	22pt	1	NIGHT 1		RALEIGH STUDIOS
EXT. MOVING TARGET	142	1	NIGHT 3	1/8	BG: 0

Prelim

Pay attention to the cast count and extras count; they could signal the need for batteries, additional radio microphones, or foot foam or mats.

There's usually a point in the afternoon when you can slip away to the truck to catch up on paperwork. You'll have an IFB distribution list, loss and damage reports, the Mixer's equipment inventory list, Certificate of Insurance for his gear, daily time sheets and weekly timecards, expendables ordering, POs and Transpo run slips, as well as your notes and housekeeping duties.

Consider getting a folder or two: one for contracts, insurance forms, and inventories, and the other for payroll forms. Two manila envelopes or pocket-type files work well attached to the truck wall. You may be asked to coordinate getting drive-on passes, department crew badges, a Starbucks run, or meal orders. I like to note the lunch times right away, as about 30% of people you ask at wrap won't remember...and if you ask too often, you appear less professional. It will only take seconds to fill out the weekly timecard as well as the daily, and you'll appreciate not having to do that at wrap.

This is a good time to check if anything will need charging on the truck overnight and discuss a plan for supplying power with the Transpo department and where the Camera truck (or Sound truck) will park overnight. Security for the truck may need to be worked out with Production.

There may be limited specialty gear you'll need to be responsible for at a particular location. On *Ad Astra*, we had foam and plywood panels for sound deadening that the grips built and carried to locations for several weeks. It was my responsibility to get them from the grip truck to the set, install them, break them down, and return them to the truck at wrap for each move. Lastly, I had to coordinate with Production how they wanted to handle the panels when no longer needed on set.

Some shots require traffic nearby to be attenuated. Intermittent Traffic Control, or ITC, is under Locations' authority. In the US, it is supplied by retired police officers; their job is to regulate the flow of traffic in the immediate vicinity of the set, either re-routing traffic or holding traffic as necessary to facilitate the movement of scene vehicles or actors or to abate traffic noise. *Always obey the instructions of the police* and let them know, via the AD staff, when Sound needs to adjust their work.

Making a Location Move

Location moves can be as minor as going into another room or as major as splitting the unit to travel across town. Learn whether the timing of the move is based on completing certain shots or on actual time (e.g., if an actor must wrap by *x* o'clock, we need to jump to that hour of setup). Wrap as much as you can before the time of the move. Depending on circumstances, you should consider making a reconnaissance trip to the next location: Where will you set up? Are Grip and Electric already working there? What's their ETA (estimated time of arrival, but in this case meaning when will their work be ready for actors)? If you can take some gear there and keep it secure, do so.

Always make sure there is security available before leaving equipment, and have someone at both sets. Speak with security personnel directly about watching your gear. Tarp or cover everything you can. Coordinate with Transpo for your shuttle as well as any flatbed or crew van necessary to transport the gear.

At Wrap

Start by de-rigging actors, as they will be the first to want to leave, and then return any gear that belongs to other departments (stingers you borrowed, apple boxes, or C-stands). Grab the slates and Lock-it boxes at the agreed-upon place. Collect *all* the sound equipment that may be out (IFBs, radio mics, music playback, bullhorns, etc.). Return all to the trailer/truck or the staging area assigned. Restore the location to its original state: turn on refrigerators or coolers (some USTs leave their car keys in the appliance, so they don't forget to turn it back on). Return any walkie-talkies you have or follow the protocol. Charge any equipment that needs it. Fill out the weekly timecard and the daily timesheet; doing both saves you time at the week's wrap *and* you won't have to worry about forgetting earlier times.

Preset anything you think you'll forget for the morning or write yourself a note about it. Lock up the truck or staging area. Let Transpo know when you're done in case they're waiting for you to finish before they move the vehicle or have been supplying power for the truck lights. Turn in the day's work along with the daily timesheet, noting times in your personal journal/calendar if you choose *not* to make weekly timecards as you go.

Another reason to do timecards as you go is that if you call in sick the department will have to call you to get that information! Some people take photos of weekly timecards, but you won't need to if you tear off a copy from the multiple-part timecard.

If you're wrapping at dusk or at night, work out a plan with the Electric Department *prior to wrap* to keep lights on for you. If you have equipment that needs charging overnight, make sure the teamster/truck driver knows and has a way to supply power. Having a personal light for wrapping at night is a must—a headlamp allows you to be hands-free. At times, a larger flashlight is great to cover a larger area when hunting for a piece of equipment. Sound gear is notorious for its number of pieces, and most of them are small and black and expensive—a fact you will come to be painfully aware of when one is missing at wrap.

Drive Home Safely

Drive home safely and do it over and over again for the run of the show. Driving home safely is not as easy as it sounds. Wrapping after a long workday, many crewmembers can attest to having arrived home with no memory of how they got there. Sadly, many have crashed their cars, and some have died.

Please take a moment when you get to your car and consider: How long was your day/night? Are you switching from days to nights or the reverse? Can you stay awake 50% longer than the time it takes to drive home? American productions have finally started offering hotel/motel rooms to crew who request it. Don't be an idiot. Never drive with excessive fatigue.

CHAPTER 12

Running the Show

S ome days you will wrap the gear from a location and the next day set up somewhere else. But sometimes you'll be in a location for multiple days and will get to have a "walk-away wrap." A walk-away wrap is when the work will resume at the same location, and the equipment is secured for the downtime. Most likely the microphones, including radio mics and the main expensive pieces of gear, will be put away and secured, but the rest of the gear will be returned to the carts. Power down the carts and cover them with tarps.

Turn in paperwork and media.

The Flow

There are many production worlds in the movie and TV galaxy: from *Gilligan's Island*, where we're all in this together and everyone helps make it happen, to *Mad Max*, where film is war and it's department against department...and everything in between. The hands-on producers, director, and certainly the 1st AD usually set the tone.

As you gain experience, you will get a handle on "reading a set." The sooner you can do that, the better. It involves watching what people do and listening to what they say—looking for inconsistencies as well as noting the general morale of the cast and crew. Be perceptive about your surroundings and pay attention to other departments, especially those you work closely with.

Learn to pay attention to the "vibe" on a set, and you'll soon learn to anticipate potential problems or a changing order of setups; this is the higher awareness of things that is so very valuable to your department. There will be ebbs and flows of the work pace, friendships, relationships, and company moods—it's all a normal part of the work process.

It's natural to have fears that you'll make a big mistake, and your confidence might be strained: just remember that *no one* has ever done this shot before, and everyone is reacting in real time. Stay focused on the work at hand, and don't give yourself the time to contemplate *yourself*; thinking in a team mentality will inherently guide you to make more appropriate choices as the work reveals itself.

A teacher's parable: On the journey to a new city, I met someone on the side of the road. "What are the people like in the town?" I asked. "Oh, they're horrible—selfish and jealous and manipulative at work." I continued and met someone else, waiting for a bus. "What are the people like in the town?" I asked. "They are generous and helpful and friendly." And when I finally reached the town, I saw for myself: the people were just as they were described.

When you expect that coworkers will be respectful and helpful and treat everyone that way, you'll find that they are (mostly). Know that everyone will have a hard day sometime, and that you can have a positive effect on someone's day.

Script Revisions

When script changes occur, there's a color order: White (original), blue, pink, yellow, green, goldenrod, buff, salmon, cherry, tan, ivory, white (this time known as "double white"), and back to blue ("double blue"). Make sure you always update the Mixer's script as well; the boom operator usually handles his or her own.

Camaraderie

Production companies set a tone for their projects early on, and there's a wide range of possibilities, from none at all to Quentin Tarantino's legendary 100 Roll celebrations. Some common activities include call sheets with daily witticisms or jokes, Friday night social time after wrap, $5 Fridays (a pool where participants write their name on a $5 bill, put it in the pot, and at wrap whoever's name is called gets the entire pot of money), going out to breakfast after a night shoot, crew movie screenings, kick-off parties, and wrap parties. During the shoot, some crews have dress code days: Hawaiian shirt day, Friday tie day, everyone gets their nails painted red (including any dogs hanging out in the trucks). Some crew people lift weights at lunch and invite others; some bring homemade Thai food their wives made, enough for a dozen people. Friendships made on sets are some of the deepest and longest lasting; take time to get to know the passionate people you're working with; they're a human rainbow of interesting personalities and talents.

Some sets lend themselves to serious fun: Playing the "Name Game" with slates can keep your mental faculties honed. Someone picks a category, and every take must be slated with associative words that start with the letter of the alphabet on the slate: for example, if the topic is exotic fruits, the 2nd AC would say, "Scene 15Acai (15A), Take 1."

On *Pet Sematary*, we had *a lot* of time to wait while shots were being decided upon and set up. The key grip was rebuilding a motorcycle he picked up on the weekend, I made a 7,000+ piece quilt and even brought my sewing machine just off set, someone else was repairing an 80-year-old piece of technology. For a reason that escapes both of us now, I presented a grip with a rubber chicken; it became the crew mascot. The grips would put it on every set; toward the middle of the schedule, the director noticed it and ordered it gone. The grips interpreted that to mean find a more creative way to add the chicken. The second time the director realized that the chicken was still part of the company, there was a stronger talking to. But these were no ordinary grips. The last production location was the side of the road, NIGHT. EXT. Denise Crosby's car stops, and she looks for a phone at the closed diner; if you look carefully, you'll see the shadow of a hanging chicken in the window. (A nod of appreciation here to Electric.)

EPK/ENG

If you're on a show of any visibility, an *electronic press kit* (EPK) crew will visit for a day or a few days. The Unit Publicist arranges for a crew to get behind-the-scenes coverage of the director and actors, and incidental crew. The Mixer should have been notified by the unit production manager (UPM) and a discussion should've taken place about coordinating frequencies and other possible requirements. Once the crew arrives, the UST will coordinate frequencies. Experienced EPK crews will have compatible equipment and know the protocols. The Mixer will designate the type of feed being given, usually a parallel program feed (they will hear what is being recorded by the Mixer). They may also have their own recording gear for doing actor interviews or other original material.

It is also possible that an *electronic news gathering* (ENG) crew may arrive. These crews are not part of the company and may be from a news station or entertainment program, rather than under the direction of the company's Publicity Department. Know which crew you are interacting with. They may not have coordinated frequencies ahead of time, may not have compatible gear, or may not have any gear at all and ask you to supply them in the moment. Their frequencies may interfere with the actors' mics, and you may have to be diplomatic in informing them that the production takes precedence, and they must be stopped. It has happened in the past, and it will happen again. While you do not have an obligation to accommodate them, it may be something that the production would ultimately want, and you will need to act fast.

They will ask for a feed from the production sound Mixer. *Never* give them a feed without having it approved first. And once they do have a feed and you know actors are wired, it's good practice to tell them the ENG crew has a feed and that the Mixer will keep their microphones down when not rolling. The publicist should already have notified actors and gotten sign-offs, but actors can forget, and they have always appreciated a reminder.

Usually, the Mixer will provide the feed via a cable off the mixing panel, and that may be hardwired to the crew or attached to a transmitter supplied by the crew. Sometimes they will want a Comtek. Get approval from the publicist or 1st AD before giving that kind of company access. As a courtesy, let the 1st AD know when those crews are present and have a feed, in the event it has been under the 1st's radar while concentrating on the day's work.

Physicality of the Work

We are one of the few positions that must have all their body parts working to be able to do our job, whereas a DOP can have broken arms and broken legs. As long as someone can roll his wheelchair up to a monitor, he has a job. If a camera operator has a broken foot, she can ride a dolly.

But as USTs, we can't. We can't even have a head cold (we'll have trouble hearing). From head to toe, we need to be in perfect condition. And that's why it's so very important to have a physical training program that you follow. What we do is so physically unnatural that we must train consistently so we aren't getting hurt.

Interacting with Other Departments

Electric: Check in with Electric to find out where the generator(s), or "gennies," will be placed. I also talk to the Electrical Department regarding their cable runs into the set. I always ask that they avoid running their cables through doors that lead directly to a noisy street and place lighting dimmer packs and light ballasts (both might use noisy cooling fans) as far away from the set as possible.

Grip: They will be the department modifying the light output with flags, cutters, and siders, or lending equipment to you or setting a ladder for you. Sometimes grips will "float" a flag that will be in your air space.

Their department also moves the dolly; dollies may squeak. You will find yourself needing to coordinate movement or, at times, even riding the dolly. If you work long enough, at some point you will kick a wedge from the dolly track. Make sure you let the Grip Department know immediately and point it out. They will make the decision whether to bring out a level to make the fix or just push the wedge back into position. Don't walk over the track; you could drop dirt from your shoe that could affect the smooth movement of the dolly.

Tips

▸ Being "boned" (negatively impacted) can come from *so many* places; have alternative plans in mind for every setup.

▸ Understand the frame. Many problems or questions can be answered by knowing what is and isn't going to be seen. Of course, this assumes that the camera operator can be counted on to set the frame and it will stay that way.

▸ On some productions, the director will never feel comfortable committing himself to the take, let alone the setup. You will need to figure this out fast and watch and plan accordingly.

▸ If there's a good chance that the shot will get bigger or you foresee running into problems for yourself, get them solved sooner rather than later (unless there are mitigating circumstances). Mitigating circumstances can be any of the following: 1. You will be breaking for lunch and need to change the actor's battery after lunch anyway. 2. You trust the DOP who tells you the shot won't be used (for a very good reason). 3. Someone has just gotten yelled at, and to bring up the issue will put you in the line of fire, and you decide the risk isn't worth it. 4. The actor is having difficulty, and you know the director will be doing another take.

▸ A UST might need to make sure the extras are quiet and do not interfere with the dialogue.

▸ When you borrow another department's gear, always ask how and where they'd like it returned...and then do that. Note the Electrical Department's cable wrapping is different from the Sound Department's wrapping. Make sure you return a stinger exactly how it was given to you; the loops need to fit back into a plastic crate, so be sure to note the size. If it's a regularly occurring "favor," it's not a bad idea to leave a small token of appreciation (e.g., homemade cookies or a little note or cleaning the cable).

▸ Sometimes you won't be happy with the work you or Sound is doing. You'll take it personally. You won't always be able to control the outcome of your work. Sound people take it very personally. After many, many years, I've learned that how you take it has no effect on the outcome. Do your best and move on. You must.

▸ Sometimes you can get flustered when trying to explain a mistake you've made—the words fumble in your brain. Practice what you're going to say—and your delivery—*before* you need it. Consider your audience and try saying one of these:

"Operator error"
"I can do better"
"I #@&%ed up"

The Production Report

The *production report* is an official, summarized account of the company's daily activity. It is sent to studio executives and is permanently filed to serve as a legal record.

Along with notes on production days, scenes, script notes, film footage, and crew call and wrap times, most production reports list any incidents: fire, theft, or accidents. Make sure to always notify Production of even the smallest incident, as many times the extent of a situation is not known until sometime in the future.

Production reports commonly show the In and Out times of cast and crew and usually provide space for noting any accidents or other incidents.

Daily Production Report

Production: _____ Production No: _____ Date: _____
Date Started: _____ Est. Finish Date: _____ Current Production Day: _____
Production Company: _____ Director: _____
Dir. of Photography: _____ Camera Operator: _____
Producers: _____ Unit Prod. Mgrs: _____

Production Days

	1st Unit	2nd Unit	Rehearsal	Work	Retakes	Test	Idle	Travel	Total
Scheduled									
Actual									

Set: _____ Location: _____
Crew Call: _____ Shooting Call: _____ First Shot: _____ Lunch: _____ End: _____
Post-Lunch: _____ Break: _____ End: _____ Camera Wrap: _____ Last Man: _____
Total Scenes in Script: _____ Total Pages: _____ Weather Report: _____

Scenes / Script

Scenes									Script								
Scene No.								Scene No.									
Additional								Minutes									
Retakes								Set-Up									
Sound								Previous									
Credits								Today									
Previous								To Do									
Today								Total									
Total																	

Film Inventory: _____ Additional Rec: _____ Approved: _____
Specs: _____ Previous: _____ Today: _____ Total: _____

Film

On-Hand	Video Tape	Recording Tape	Picture Negative	Negative Breakdown		
				Good	Waste	Drawn
Previous						
Today						
To Do						

Delays: _____
Notes: _____

Cast

Cast	Character	Status	Call	Lunch In	Lunch Out	Wrap	Hours	Travel	Wardrobe

Extras

Name	Scenes	Pages	Status	Call	Wrap	Rate	OT	Travel	Wardrobe

www.BusinessFormTemplate.com

The value of a production report cannot be overstated: While at work, this is the document in which you make an official report of an occurrence, be it accident or incident, to name the most common. Accidents, no matter how minor, and lost, damaged, or missing equipment should be noted on the report. *Remember to ask the 2nd AD to write down any little thing that happens to you.*

If the producer's 11-year-old son took a Comtek home, note it and ask the 2nd 2nd to contact the producer. If you cut your finger on the truck door, note it, take a picture, and go to the medic. If you notice gear missing after a security company has guarded the set, note it and report it. Get a copy of the incident report if possible or at least note it in your calendar. Don't forget to follow up.

Director Speak

When you have done your pre-production work, you'll know how the director really feels about the sound element in his or her movies; you will have watched and listened to at least a few of his or her films and spoken to previous crews.

Hopefully, your Mixer will have done homework as well, engaging with the director from a filmmaker's point of view, not from a Sound Department point of view.

What do I mean by that? The Mixer should discuss any character traits that could be manifested in sound; that could mean anything from someone's volume (e.g., a character starts off as a victim, but overcomes the incident over the course of the story) or a dialect or lisp ("Will there be a dialect coach? Would you like me to monitor the consistency of that trait and let you know if the actor is inconsistent?"). Children can be very quiet or timid and that may not be something that works for the scene or character. What about a teenage boy's voice cracking?

Something we always listen for is intelligibility. Often, the director is watching the overall scene and doesn't notice. And now is a good time to point out that some directors have hearing loss; it's good to find that out and adjust your delivery of information in a way that is very obviously supportive of the project and watching out for his or her back. It's all about building trust.

Strategies for Working in a Dysfunctional Environment

You must already understand the filmmaking process and put energy into trying to understand what the director and Production want out of *their* workflow and *their* vision. It doesn't matter the size of the project or the importance of the names involved; when you're in Sound, there's always the potential to have to navigate biased opinions against your craft.

All sets run on bits of talk and interruptions, and every set, no matter how dysfunctional, has a workflow. Listen to everything.

On shows, most of the communication necessary for understanding the immediate situation is not announced out loud, so every little bit of knowledge is a piece of the puzzle. Have a departmental communication system in place, just like the other departments. They use walkie-talkies or their own internal system, and it's a good idea to monitor those systems if possible.

Quickly learn where the authoritative power lies. Whose demands get met? Whose will is stronger? Whose ideas are ultimately the ones that are shot? Who has the authority to make changes?

Quickly learn how the work flows. Someone will decide the shooting order, when lunch is called, how often it's late, whether to shoot another take, and whether to wrap now or continue.

There are multiple hierarchies. You might find that the 1st AD determines the lunch and wrap times, but the principal actor decides the shooting order. Or the high-profile guest star controls the shooting order for those days worked, otherwise the director of photography does. On a movie I did recently, I realized it was the key grip who had scheduling power, and his determination of when the Grip Department would do certain setups or scenes controlled the day's work. Once I had that awareness, it was easier to coordinate the scheduling of when I should jump to working the car rigs or when to stay on the set or wire the actors.

Departments that need large amounts of preparation can help signal the timing of the shoot—e.g., a location that needs a certain amount of dressing or some alterations that are taking longer. If you have that information from the Art Department, you can garner some logical outcomes and make adjustments in your own department. Mixers and boom operators need to spend most of their energy focusing on the set and rely on the UST to keep them knowledgeable about all areas of production.

USTs must be excellent communicators and detectives. Understand the Mixer's expectations regarding the production day; any interaction that goes poorly may have potentially significant consequences, and your department may not be able to recover for the rest of the show. And you may lose a contact for the rest of your career.

Don't Do This

There are several things that you *should not do* as a UST.

Other Department's Gear

Do not touch other people's gear without their permission. Do not move other department's items; tell them what you need and let them figure out how to accomplish it (unless they ask for your involvement). If someone from the department is not around, move the item as necessary and find a representative immediately and let him or her know. Or tell an AD if you are leaving the area.

Apologizing

Is apologizing always the right thing to do, to be "very collaborative?" Yes and no. Yes, you must be very collaborative with everyone, but I have seen so many postings on Facebook from around the world—Sound people apologize a lot—and you have to stop that. It's not a good attitude, it hurts the credibility of the Sound Department, and when you get to work on the big movies, it can work against you by giving people the impression that you keep doing things wrong. So *stop* always apologizing!

Of course, if you've done something that warrants an apology, absolutely, own it; apologize and move on. But remember! Sound has every right to be on set; in the same way that an actor asks if he can have a mug instead of a glass—the point being that a request is made, and everyone just accommodates it.

This must be understood, and it must start with us. You have a job to do. Be pleasant, be professional, but don't apologize if you need to work through some kind of collaboration with another department so that you can get what you need for your work.

Obliviousness

"I've had some boom ops who always tried to correct the director in directing or DOP in placing camera or lights, and those were fired in a short time," a Mixer confided in me. Hopefully reading this surprises no one. It is not your place to correct anyone—unless it is a gross safety issue (e.g., moving an unconscious person who may have a spinal injury).

In general, don't ask someone in a higher authoritative position something that can be answered by someone in a lower position. If you need to talk to the head of the department, be succinct, get to the point, and don't be offended if you're handed off to someone else; that's information on the preferred chain of command. Memorize it and use it. Don't tell another department how to do their job. Don't suggest how they should resolve an issue; just state what the issue is. "I can't get my follow cart close enough to the set for the antennae to have good reception" rather than "I need you guys to move your gear cart so I can get mine close to the set." If they invite you to offer ideas, then suggest.

I worked with a seemingly sweet Mixer who had terrible self-awareness, several times even commenting negatively during the workday on my future ability to be a parent. One day we were shooting a kitchen scene after a move, and the generator had already been placed. Forty-five minutes in, we were ready for a rehearsal and he became aware of the slight gennie noise. I relayed a few rounds of conversation between him and the director-producer, but he wasn't satisfied with the responses.

He came onto the set in a huff, explaining that he could hear the generator. The producer (with decades of TV experience) had everyone quieted, took a listen, and decided it was low enough not to be a problem. The Mixer persisted, leaving the set but shouting, "You'll be sorry!"

I had my embarrassment to contend with, along with everyone staring at me. Thankfully, I was not held accountable for the Mixer's behavior...and I agree with the director.

Two Weeks Before the Show Wrap

Toward the end of the show, people are tired, some people are physically sick, the holidays are coming, and your family misses you. This is the time when, collectively, the company will let its hair down, and all those good deeds and that good work can go up in smoke. Tell yourself every morning that this is the most important time to maintain your integrity. Don't let short tempers get the better of you! If there's someone who has grated on you the entire time, know enough to stay away from him or her. Or bite your tongue and buy them a coffee. Make sure that any unspoken or unfinished business gets straightened out before the last week; then it's behind you when the 1st AD announces that shooting is done, and you don't have to avoid anyone during the show wrap reverie.

Show Wrap

During the last couple of days, clean and wrap as much as you are able. Assess the status of any loss and damage (L&D) items or any repairs at the shop. On the last day, make sure to get back all the gear that was given to other departments, anything left in the Production office, in storage areas, and anything Transpo may have—unless they are going to make a run for you. If any equipment now becomes the property of the company, make sure you know the process for handing it over. Some crews exchange gifts, and some actors give gifts.

The next day is usually the one wrap day given to the Sound crew. The Mixer and UST often wrap the package, cleaning the gear, inventorying and packing by case, and wrapping up paperwork. The truck is cleared out, and the equipment is transported back to its storage area. Final paperwork is turned in to Accounting and Production.

CHAPTER 13

Booming

Booms are not a type of microphone but the apparatus for its operation by a technician, much like a 1st AC who handles focus for the camera. Booms can be poles (boom pole) or a dolly (Fisher boom).

Courtesy VDB Audio

Boom operating is really about a duet with the actor, more than focusing on the dialogue and movement and beyond anticipating seamlessly whatever is coming, almost being an extension of the actor. That's how it felt working with Brad Pitt for nearly a year, essentially being his personal boom operator. It was a gift to study one actor for so long—and a singular honor to have both films, *Ad Astra* and *Once Upon a Time...in Hollywood*, be Oscar nominated for Sound.

This doesn't usually happen; you will need to be a quick study of all the actors in the scene and understand them to anticipate what they may do or say, even before they know it.

To focus on that kind of character study, you must have the basics and physics down.

> *Being invisible and at the same time gathering all the information about the shot is an important skill for a boom operator.*

Booming Basics

On American productions, stand-ins will take the place of the actors while the crew is setting up. In other countries, the actors may do this themselves. For the most part, stand-ins will remain in the actors' first position, but Camera, Dolly, or Lighting may ask them to make the actors' moves. In that case, be prepared to rehearse your moves at the same time if you need the rehearsal. Sound may also ask for the moves separately, if needed. Coordinate with Camera/Grip/Electric before asking stand-ins to leave their marks, as those departments may be in the midst of setting equipment to that position.

If you think of the pattern from a lamp as a conical shape, gradually widening out the farther it is away from the source, you will have an idea of the edges of the light fall. A boom should stay above that edge.

You should feel comfortable "poling" while the rest of the crew is working—that is, extending your pole, standing in the position you expect to boom from, and swinging your pole through the anticipated arc or whatever move might be necessary. Watch for hitting anything overhead as well as noting where the shadows fall on the floor or furniture or crew. If you must walk back or bring the pole back (when an actor walks toward you), remember to *first look behind you to make sure the area is clear.* When a pole-back move will happen during the take, make sure to let crewmembers know, using either the 1st AD on smaller sets or a PA or your spotter to keep the area clear.

There have been a few times when I've needed to make those moves and have hit someone. Over time, I have come to learn that sometimes, no matter how many times you tell people, they're not going to pay attention. In the beginning, I'd apologize even after looking behind and announcing it over and over. Thirty years later, I still announce it repeatedly before a take, but I don't look back, not even during a take (you don't want to be the reason the take is not good).

Reflecting on my youth, I was wrong to apologize all the time. I alerted everyone, I notified the AD Department, and I made sure that everyone around me was told my work for the shot; I am not responsible for the choices of others. I remember the *Pet Sematary* scene in the airport where many extras walked around me, and I had a walk-back. I announced it to the extras, they watched a rehearsal, and we all did two rehearsals at half-speed (often used when there are many moving pieces to establish possible collisions before moving at work speed). Sure enough, when the first take was up, I knew there was a good chance that some people would be surprised. I even told my Utility to prepare for extras bumping into us; I was not going to stop. I think I took out two or three extras crossing with the pole low—just like rehearsal.

If you realize that your pole has bumped into something behind you, don't become distracted. What happens next is up to you: after the director says, "Cut!" consider these options: 1. Turn around and see what happened while you were busy working. 2. Turn around and ask if that person is OK. 3. Move forward with the work. I'll say this several times throughout this book: *Don't needlessly apologize.* If you honestly aren't at fault, it really does make people think *you are making mistakes,* and people will subconsciously think that *you are responsible for an accident.* If that happens more than once over the course of a movie, you'll be perceived as not being ready to advance in your career.

Use your peripheral vision to follow crew movements so as not to hit anyone or equipment while swinging the boom. If you need to make a move during the shot and feel you need to practice, use a spotter so you can concentrate on the move and watch the problems on the set, rather than those around you. If the move involves coordinating with the dolly or another crewmember, request a joint rehearsal directly with the other party. If this rehearsal will interfere with any of the crew working, utilize the AD to control the set and stop work for you. Be accommodating if it doesn't happen right away, but *do not* wait so long that your own work and a possible alternate plan of action would be compromised.

If you find that the new position or move will displace other workers during the shot, coordinate with those departments and, if it affects a larger scope, involve the 1st AD.

Boom operators hold quite a bit of weight over their heads for very long periods of time and operate the microphone in subtle ways (often feathering the edge of the microphone pattern) to precisely target their subject, to deflect unwanted noises, and at the same time, moving around light falls that they must imagine, staying outside of moving camera frames they don't see while moving around a dolly and people, and anticipating any impromptu action or dialogue from any of the characters.

There are no shortcuts to getting proficient. Practice, practice, practice with a boom pole (or broom). Walk around your house booming your family, your pets. Even if you don't have a microphone plugged into anything, get used to moving with headphones and a boom held up; we use our eyes as well as our ears. Earlier in the UK, "old-school" boom ops didn't wear headphones or monitor the sound at all and performed purely on the visual. Practice walking backward. Make an overhead obstacle course for yourself. Practice listening to on-mic and off-mic voices and learn the microphone patterns by tangible experience.

Learn lens sizes and frame lines; if you have a camera, use it to understand what a 50mm shot looks like compared to a 100mm shot of the same subject. Check the framing of a 50mm at 15 feet and at 50 feet. See if you can borrow a director's viewfinder or rent one inexpensively for one day. Be able to imagine accurately the effect of changes in distance.

Learn the verbal language of shot descriptions:

▸ Head and shoulders: Archaically known as a "shampoo shot."

▸ 2Ts: The bottom of the frame hits an actor's chest.

▸ Waist up: Self-explanatory.

▸ Cowboy: The bottom of the frame hits the actor's thigh (where the western chaps would come to).

▸ John Wayne: A bit below cowboy (he hangs lower).

Terms currently out of favor:

▸ Sherwin Williams: A very wide shot, seeing just about everything. An older term I haven't encountered much these days, it refers to a paint company's slogan, "(We) Cover the Earth."

▸ Jack Lord: A 50mm shot named for the lead of the popular TV series *Hawaii 5-0.*

Let me preface my following comments by saying that *there is an exception to every rule*, depending on the circumstances.

The proper boom operator position is the one that works for the shot, but a good basic working position is to:

Face the camera. You'll be able to see when and where the camera moves, changes lens size, or if you need to get out of the way! If you are not wireless, clip your junction box to your belt on the away side of the action, so you're not looking through draping cables or tripping over your boom cable.

Keep your weight balanced. You will lessen the likelihood of a strain. At 5' 4" tall, I stand with 12—15" of space between my feet. A stance on the wider side of normal will give you an adjustment range as the shot progresses.

Keep your arms centered over your body. You'll have the most range from this position (rather than starting in an outreach and then finding you have less range). Aim for the weight of the pole to be centered with your body, letting the load be carried by your legs, not your forearms.

A good boom operator will always **plan alternative ways to work the shot**.

Boom from the opposite side of the camera from where the key light is (generally speaking).

Know the aspect ratio of the project you're working on. Know that the preview framing in film traditionally will be enough for the operator to see the boom about to creep into frame, and he can give you a warning—the aspect ratio being 1:85. If the project is being shot in widescreen such as a 2:40 aspect ratio, then there will be even more top and bottom room, but nothing on the sides. Increasingly more projects are being shot for television viewing, at 16:9, meaning that there is very little space in the top of frame before the operator can see the boom and no space on the sides.

Work out the communication with the camera operator. How will he let you know when you're hitting the frame (a hand signal or whisper)? How will you get his attention during the shot if you need to?

If you are positioned near the camera, keep your ear closest to the camera operator or 1st AC available, as they may need to whisper to you during the shot. If I'm in close quarters and sense that there will be conversation with the operator, I ask quietly which of his ears he prefers me to use in whispering to him. For an as yet undiscovered reason, many DOPs/operators are deaf or impaired in one ear. Always respect that information. Glance at the 1st AC for focus shifts. Watch the dolly grip for telegraphing moves.

On the film *Cujo*, quite early in my career, I worked with a DOP who liked to set a long length of track and operate the camera himself—with one hand on the fluid head and the other holding a zoom and focus control. He'd change his mind from rehearsal to rehearsal, take to take, *during the takes,* and wiggle a finger at the dolly grip to go one way or another...there was no way I could follow him constantly. When that became the method of the work, I imagined my own movie and boomed that. After that show, I was an ace boom operator.

A learning tip from the documentary world is to place a small piece of white tape on the lens's zoom ring as a visible marker of what focal length is being used or changed (provided by the 1st AC). It is wise to learn this trick, as overdependence on access to video monitors will stump you sooner or later. This way, you have a way of knowing the frame from more than one source. I worked with a very experienced boom operator who had mastered holding a phone in one of his hands while he boomed so he always knew the frame line. But one day the video tap went out, and he was frantic. It was only then that I realized he had no idea of lens sizes; he was incapable of doing the shot, and I was quickly preparing to take over when the tap was fixed.

In tight hallways, you might potentially ask to ride the dolly, either with the mic in front or riding in the back and booming overhead. It can get tricky with the camera booming up, and with obstructions in the ceiling or doorways that require you to scoop under the header without dipping into frame. Sometimes actors don't keep a consistent pace, and you must compensate with arm extensions or pullbacks. If you're tied down by riding the dolly, your ability to adapt to the unexpected may be compromised, not to mention the "coin" you're expending in your relationships with the dolly grip and camera operator. Still, there will occasionally be a situation where this is the best solution. As always, use common sense.

Terminology

▸ **Rake.** The up/down tilt of the microphone in its mount, the adjustment of the microphone away from a position pointing 90 degrees from the mount

▸ **Back rake.** To adjust the microphone to be less than 90 degrees

- **Pan.** With the boom pole, keeping the same level, and moving the mic horizontally from one point to another
- **Tilt.** With the boom pole, raising the mic/pole up vertically
- **Scoop.** Reaching under and pivoting to gain some reach in the mic's ability to receive a sufficient level of signal
- **Staying on mic.** Maintaining the sweet spot, where the voice is clear and full
- **Feathering.** Keeping the mic at the edge of the polar pattern to gently blend
- **Cue.** Rotating the pole so that the microphone is pointed toward the actor
- **Swing.** The pole is moved
- **Lead.** To precede the actor
- **Chase.** To follow the actor but using the microphone to chase or follow

To make things even trickier, not everyone uses the same terminology; what's important is that the communication within the department is agreed upon.

Basic Booming Tips

- Plan A, Plan B, Plan C. Boom operating is a problem-solving position, so always keep planning for alternatives.
- How to stay on top of the dialogue. Try color-coding the dialogue by actor. Try memorizing if you can, always being prepared for someone to miss a cue or improvise. If that's too difficult or you have actors who improvise a lot, then pay attention to their speech patterns and the back and forth banter rhythms. Also, watch actors' mouths; they often telegraph when they're about to speak.
- If you keep missing the non-sequiturs, find a key word in the line beforehand and pay attention to it. When people are around a table, you can back the microphone off a bit and have a wider area of useful microphone pattern that's forgiving.
- The shorter the lens, the further away from the subject you need to boom; the longer the lens, the closer to the subject you can boom. A core

skill set for booming is knowing the shot scales of lens focal lengths without needing the use of a video monitor. You need to imagine with certainty what a 50mm lens sees at an 8-foot distance.

▸ If your pole keeps crossing a corner of the frame, move your body closer to the camera or arrange some means of elevation. Apple boxes can be used individually or combined to make a small platform. They can be supports for a piece of plywood dance floor. If you need more height, ladders are available from the Grip Department. Use the smallest ladder necessary for the shot, and ask for a sandbag as ballast, if one is not brought. For awkward throws, it can help protect your body to lean against the remaining height of the ladder as you work. *Never* stand on the top two steps of a ladder; doing so raises the center of gravity and is exponentially problematic with an extended boom pole. I set my ladder perpendicular to the shot; that way, I can lean against the top portion and, if necessary, rest my elbow on the top as a pivot point.

▸ When you are asked to boom off-camera dialogue, the actor is often right next to the camera. Angle away from any noise coming from the camera, using the edge of the mic pattern so that noise will fall away as much as possible.

▸ When you need a cable puller when your department is busy, ask for help; 2nd ACs and electricians or grips have more experience cabling than PAs. If you have to run forward, cabled, without someone to cable you, lay the cable out ahead of you. If you have to run backward, cabled, without someone to cable you, run with your back to the action and watch behind you as you can. *Don't put yourself in danger*; use a more directional microphone to gain reach and slow yourself down.

▸ Always boom the slates, especially if they are quiet.

▸ Use the amount of wind protection needed for a scene but avoid using more than needed.

▸ You may need to ask someone to move because you need that exact position. Make sure that's true, then be polite and speak up soon, even if it means asking the director.

▸ Rest when you can if you're a boom operator.

▸ When you're waiting on the set, don't lean. Some people use boom stands to mark their territory. Be aware that if you leave the set, something could change in your stand's location and it may be moved without you being notified.

▸ If there is a large spatial split, use two boom operators or boom(s) with a plant or radio microphone or try a microphone with a longer reach.

▸ If there are dialogue overlaps, and all the actors speaking are mic'd, then it is a directorial decision whether to accept it (not yours).

▸ Doing a handoff: The main boom operator and you have to hand off an actor because the movement covers a larger area than either one of you can cover. If you have to do a handoff with another boom operator, find the point in the action or dialogue where a switch can be made. Most times there will be a consistent point at which the dialogue pauses, and you can move out quickly while the other operator moves in. Be quick and precise but avoid handling noise and wind noise.

On *Once Upon a Time…in Hollywood* we had a very tricky handoff in which Rick Dalton gets out of his car and walks and talks all the way to his front door. Cliff Booth was driving and follows Rick while responding. The handoff point was at a specific physical place because Boom #1 was stopped against the garage wall. While the actors were fairly consistent, the distance between them fluctuated enough that Boom #1 had to remain back for Cliff's dialogue, while there was a dead spot before Boom #2 could reach far enough to cover Rick if he started speaking before being in Boom #2's mic pattern *and* Boom #2 crossed the camera's physical path *just before* the camera moved left to right, so Boom #2 had to make the move based on Camera moving, rather than on dialogue. The scene ends at the front door under a low porch ceiling and required a plant microphone there.

That handoff point was a moving target based on our physical limitations and the delivery of the dialogue; the Mixer did not have a physical line-of-sight with us in order to know when the handoff would happen.

We found the solution to be that Boom #2 would be in the zone to get the dialogue sooner than needed but in a backed-off position, and then drop quickly if Boom #1 would not be able to capture those words. It was a very fast, intricate set of moves that ended up in the movie seeming to be quite a bit less than it really was.

If you are on a stage and are sent to boom from the green bed, you will most likely need to be spotted to set the right height of your microphone. Spotting will also be helpful because it's common to throw shadows onto part of the set that is not visible to you.

Steadicam

For Steadicam shots, introduce yourself to the Steadicam operator and explain or show your intended moves/route if there's any question of viability. Because they are essentially camera boom operators, understand that they are keeping track of many moving elements, too. There may be moves, transmitter issues, or unwanted footsteps to discuss; many experienced operators have quiet shoes and have taken dance classes to be able to make fluid, graceful (quiet) moves. Don't surprise them by doing something unexpected or getting in their way and causing an accident. Point out any potential shadows or uncertainty you have about a section of the shot. Ask them to let you know quietly if you dip into the shot; a nonverbal sign such as a look up can help you adjust immediately and potentially save the shot. *Be sure* to be looking at the operator at that dicey section so you can save the shot. See if you can boom from a position that diminishes how much you must move. If a ladder helps avoid some collision with the dolly grip, use a ladder and a longer pole.

Corrections After the First Full Rehearsal

Sometimes the *first full rehearsal* is called the *final rehearsal* or *first take*, and you find you may need to make an adjustment after the actors have finessed their action and/or movement. For plant mics, *if* you can make the adjustment while other departments are adjusting, make it! Let anyone whose department may be affected know what the change is; remember to ask the camera operator if your change might be seen.

Otherwise, if you need to stop the set from moving forward, let the AD know but don't wait, begin correcting immediately. You might be told to wait until after the next take; follow orders. Do not become combative, but also watch for a lull when you can slip in that adjustment sooner. Some ADs may say you'll get a future chance to make the correction but then forget or intend not to let you have that chance. Pay attention to whether that becomes a reoccurring issue and consider it nonverbal information and adjust your *modus operandi* (method of working) accordingly.

The joy of recording effects: For some reason, I find it very satisfying to get clear recordings of moving vehicles, such as drive-bys or trucks rolling down a dirt road into the horizon. When you need to track something that travels away from you, you need to compensate for the distance by raising the microphone up slightly, following the speed of the vehicle, in order to keep it in the sweet spot.

When you have to boom from below, back off the microphone a bit, give it an obtuse angle, and always inform all the actors (don't forget the actors or extras who will make crosses). Notify all the ADs working the shot and the background coordinator.

When you find that you're tired and straining to get the shot, change your position frequently. I suggest you try leading with the other arm, resting the pole on your head for a brief moment, or raising both arms and locking them. Make sure to rest or change positions any chance you get. If your pole is particularly long and you can't collapse it between takes, don't be shy about asking someone if you can hand it off to them briefly. Equate your situation to that of the Steadicam operator; there is no shame in taking the weight off to stay safe and ready for the shot.

Shadows

Get specific about what is seen: the mic, the pole, your hand, you. If you decide poling is not appropriate but you need information about shadows, there are several more discreet options. A lower-profile method is to walk through the actors' positions yourself, watching the ground—you can either note where your head shadow falls, or imagine *or* hold your hand over your head at the anticipated boom height and watch where your hand shadow falls. If you don't want to physically go on set, watch crewmembers walking in the area you're interested in and note where their shadows fall. Or notice how the stand-in's shadow falls. Remember, you could also ask stand-ins to make the actor's moves. With experience, you'll no longer need to use your raised arm, and, over time, you may not need to make that walk at all.

The time to modify lighting or request help from the Grip Department is while the crew has the set. Always stay on the set to watch the evolution of light placement and attenuation. It's far easier to ask for a flag to cut a light while the grips and ladders are on set; stopping once the directors and actors have the set is unprofessional and perhaps a reason on-set departments have a bias against sound crews. There's also a good chance you will not get that adjustment.

First, don't panic; pole around and determine the parameters for the shadow. Ask yourself: is it in the frame? Or potentially in the frame? When in doubt, ask the camera operator. Try to find a workable solution around the shadow area. Then ask for cutters or siders (types of grip flag placements to prevent the light from shadowing your boom in frame) from the Grip Department. Alternatively, perhaps just moving a chair six inches will let the shadow drop out of frame. Try backing away with a microphone that will give you more reach.

Burying Shadows

Many a boom operator has held steady and had a shadow in the frame, which went unnoticed, which is an acceptable option. Find a position that allows you to get the sound you need and where the shadow of the pole, boom, or your body can be discreetly blended into the background.

Reflections

Get specific about what is reflected: the microphone, pole, hand, arm, body, or foot. If you are seen in a reflection, try moving around to get out of the frame. If you use a piece of white tape around the edge of the foam to help the operator see the mic, take it off for the shot. If the foam is not black, change it. If you can be still and wear your blacks, that may take care of the problem.

If you have a *mic* reflection, move the mic until it's gone and then assess. If the reflection is a pole, start walking in an arc around the stationary mic position, like scribing a circle with a compass. Walk until the pole is out of the frame, and then assess that position for viability.

If the shininess of the pole is reflecting in glass, run a piece of 2" black paper tape down *the side of the pole being reflected*, being sure *not* to wrap it around the circumference—leave it flat, with edges floating in the air. Once you press the tape around the pole, the reflection will return.

Reflections can be a problem in mirrors and windows. These should be discussed in pre-production as soon as possible with the Art Department. Cars are particularly difficult. Try booming from below, very far forward of the shot and rake the mic back *or* boom from very far back and rake forward. Try double booming so neither one of you has to cross the problem zone. Wire the actors. Use a plant to fill in an area you can't access.

Eliminating a pole reflection

Problems

"There's a problem." I would never want to start by saying those words; that starts the conversation down a very different path than saying, "We have a situation" or "Someone is uncomfortable with...." Situations are neutral. In the end, whoever is paying for the movie should be comfortable with the decision made. As long as you've explained the situation and offered options, you have to be OK with whatever is decided. The relationships with the client and actor are more important than any one shot.

If you think you may have been in the shot, whether physically or a with a pole shadow: if you can recreate the position of yourself and the mic, show the operator immediately. And tell him at what point you think you got in the shot. If the company is moving, tell the 1st AD so they can halt the work and either check the playback or just do another take for safety; it's their call. If an actor changed their delivery or action, respectfully ask if the actor will be doing it the same way again, and then be prepared for the change. If the company wants to know why, don't say it was because of the actor; just say there was a change. Don't throw anyone under the bus. Everyone is human; things happen. Don't play the blame game.

The Fisher Boom

The Fisher boom is making a comeback in Hollywood because of the use of multiple cameras as well as Covid-19 proximity concerns. It's a great solution to being able to boom some otherwise impractical setups and is a good skill to practice during your down time. It's possible to book time with J. L. Fisher directly.

Their website lists the various boom models, showing the differences. A Model 2 base works fine for most on-location situations. You'll need to order the size base and the length of the boom that you anticipate needing—a 16'–18' is a safe bet—and the length of time you'll need it. (Don't forget to ask Production, in advance of your order, if they'll need a purchase order number attached to the rental.) SAFETY TIP: Always set the brake and make sure the wheels are extended *before* getting onto the platform.

Coordinate with Transpo for the pickup and delivery, as well as the location where you'll want it dropped off. It comes disassembled, so you'll need two people to at least set the boom height and lift the arm onto the base. Instructions for wiring and using the weights will be available at Fisher. *Wear gloves* when handling the weights, which are lead.

This is a handy introduction:

www.youtube.com/watch?v=e1MWT6nIaRA

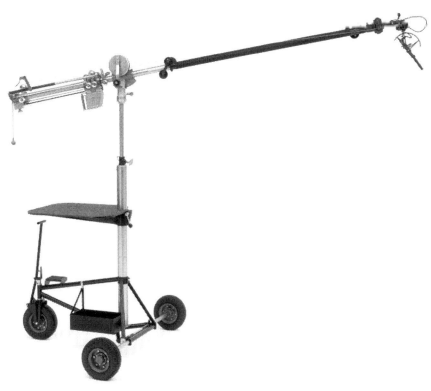

Fisher boom

CHAPTER 14

Plant Microphones

P lant microphones are microphones that are neither worn nor boomed. Any microphone can be planted; it depends on what you're trying to capture, the proximity you can achieve in placing the microphone, and the area you have for hiding the microphone. I have planted a lavalier and wireless transmitter behind a porch railing, and I have planted a Sennheiser 816 in a zeppelin (windshield) on a sandbag near a barn. Always work to the shot.

The Mixer or boom operator will have some rigs/mounts in their kits, and those are most likely what you'll use. Check them out during the pre-production phase. A good way to get familiar with a range of possibilities is to look at sound equipment websites to see what's available, and then check out the manufacturer's websites for tips on using the products. Also read grip equipment catalogs, motion picture and still camera catalogs, or websites for the same; don't assume that only sound products will solve problems. A nifty plant rig is to wedge a paint scraper with an adapter into the boards of a patio deck or any other possible place that can receive the flat end of a scraper non-destructively.

As you go through your day, be aware of items at the store or in your closet that may solve a work problem. Tinker—that's what the best USTs do.

Car Rigs

There are as many ways to rig cars as there are shots that involve using cars. In general, always try to understand the shots involved in covering the scene and create a plan that needs only minor adjustments, if any at all. Make sure you understand who owns the car and what can and can't be done to it. The car should come to the set without polishing agents applied to its interiors and in tuned-up condition (remember your pre-production work).

Review the scene to make sure you understand the action and take any business into consideration (opening the glove compartment or changing seats, for example).

Take into consideration the size of the actors. Is there space below the dashboard for a microphone rig, or is the actor large and an overhead rig makes more sense? How many actors are in the scene? Do they pick up anyone? Do they all have dialogue? Does the director encourage adlibs? Make sure you have sound coverage for any potential dialogue area.

Before starting any work in the car, do your best to understand how soon the rigged car will need to work and whether the company is breaking for lunch first. Many times, you can break for lunch earlier, come back earlier, and have some quiet space to secure your rig before everyone is back in.

Do not start work until you've talked to the Grip and Electric Departments. The Grip and Transpo Departments will load the vehicle onto any platform and, once secure, Electric will add cables and lights. Ask them politely to secure the gel frames, as the metal frames tend to rattle once the car starts to move. Let them rough-in their work before adding your cables; your cables won't get buried, and you can usually remove sound gear quickly and be on to the next set.

How you set up and rig for car work depends on the Mixer's preferences and gear. There's a Facebook group devoted to sharing information and talking about plant microphones.

To get your creative juices flowing, here are examples of some successful plant mics and rigs.

Check out the Appendix for a plant microphone Facebook group.

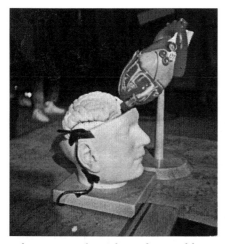

Schoeps capsule with a Colette cable

Multi-position arm

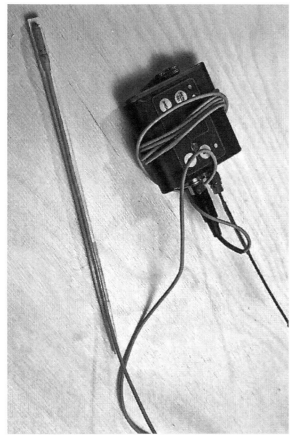

Lav taped to the backside of a light fixture

Dinkum fleximount with clamp

A single chopstick used for support

Hat rig

Eyeglass rig

Paint scraper mount

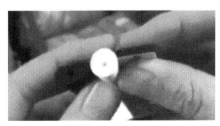

Lav foam comparison

Under a table rig

Two-microphone plant

A multi-position
clamp arm

A gooseneck lav mic

A quick rig

A low-profile
positionable stand

Car rig with multi-position arm

Cup holder rig

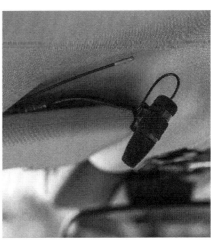

TX tucked onto a visor

CHAPTER 15

Wiring

When I started working sound in 1980, radio microphones were an exciting and exotic technology. The leading-edge technology was non-diversity VHF. Movies were shot on film and with one camera, except for stunts. As with so many things in life, it was a simpler time.

Fast forward to today, with not only the Sound Department having wireless microphones for actors and for boom operators, wireless transmission for video assist, streaming, video playback, and music playback, but the Camera Department now uses wireless focus systems, wireless transmission of image, electricians use wireless dimmer boards for LED arrays, the Steadicam operator has a wireless package, and so do the ENG/EPK crews—and the set is already getting crowded. In the United States, the Federal Communications Commission (FCC) manages and licenses the electromagnetic spectrum for both commercial and non-commercial users, *including broadcast television and radio*. In the United States, large blocks of public bandwidth were sold in a misguided attempt to reap large payments from private companies; now many different industries must compete in a much narrower bandwidth.

The FCC requires that anyone operating wireless equipment in the motion picture frequencies obtain a license. This becomes very important on a set when non-regulated wireless devices are brought onto a set without the forethought to coordinate with the Sound Department. Suggest that Mixers have their FCC licenses available and current—it has already resolved issues on sets (another thing to discuss during show prep).

An entire book could be written about the subject of wireless microphones on set. Here are some foundational lessons regarding the workflow, timing, and social interactions for using wireless microphones during production.

Given the opportunity, the Mixer will have tested his radio microphone frequencies during the location scout or at a private session. This doesn't mean you should stop running your receiver's scans when you arrive at a new location; it means now you know which frequency blocks you should be renting/bringing to the set. If you're on legally shared frequencies with a major broadcaster, they have priority, so retesting on the day and adapting to a changed wireless environment is a very common reality.

An important part of your radio microphone responsibilities is setting the frequencies of the transmitters so they don't receive interference from nearby transmissions already occupying the bandwidth or with the other transmitters. Each transmitter must be set to its own frequency within the government's accepted range for our industry. You can make a spreadsheet of all the RF frequencies in the area. Each location has its own signature frequency band activity.

This weblink provides basic information:

www.rfportal.app/resources/rf-basics/

Frequency Coordination

Coordinating the frequencies of the radio microphone wireless system ensures that each one will have a clean transmission. Once the carts are set up and powered, radio microphones should be tested as soon as possible. Make sure the transmitter (TX) frequencies and the receiver (RX) frequencies match. Start with the receivers.

On the receiving side: Make sure the receivers are getting power and that the antenna/antennae are connected to the individual receivers or receiver rack and turned on. The antenna cable is matched by impedance and length to the antenna system, so make sure you use the correct components together and *DO NOT use video cable by mistake*: Radio Frequency (RF) cable is 50 ohms, video cable is 75 ohms, and both cables should have factory-markings along their length. The higher impedance of the video cable will reduce the strength of the transmission and will be exacerbated by the length of the cable. Be aware of the line loss specification of the *antenna cable*. It is usually relatively short, around 10 feet, unless you are using specialized low-loss cable. The low-loss cable is usually heavier or bulkier and will allow runs of up to about 100 feet.

On the transmitting side: Make sure transmitters have batteries installed in them in the correct polarity and they are all turned off. Begin with the lowest frequency possible in your bandwidth and set the first transmitter. It's best to attach a lavalier microphone and walk around the intended area to test for any hits or dropouts. Listen with your own headphones on and the respective channels potted up or have the Mixer listen with you.

Once the first channel is approved, leave it turned on and put it down. Turn on the second transmitter, and walk the area the TX will be used in. Continue until all the transmitters have been checked and approved.

If time is an issue, turn on the transmitters one by one, and then take them all as you walk the space. The Mixer will be able to identify any transmission problems by watching the receiver screen and directing you.

Radio microphones: if one channel is having stability issues, you can "boom" the receiver by cabling the unit out from the cart and either placing it in a safe spot or manually holding it as close as you can get to the actor. This is particularly helpful when you have a walk-and-talk situation—one in which actors start at one location and walk to another during the take.

If the reception is sketchy for all the receivers, try moving the array closer, or move the receivers to a spot where the reception is better. If something is stepping on your frequency (something to take care of in pre-production or when you first get to the set), try identifying the source and asking for it to be shut off or shielded or increase the distance from the antennae or actors.

Other possible options include using transmitters that can simultaneously record internally, the digital remoting of the receiving gear from the sound Mixer's workstation through Ethernet-based Cat-5e cable, networking schemes such as Dante, and allowing very close proximity of the receivers to the transmitting subject.

Lectrosonics has tutorials to assist you:

▸ **www.youtube.com/watch?v=MurVgO_ppRU**

▸ **www.lectrosonics.com/wdsupport/WebHelp/freq-coord/ freqcoord.html**

Bags, cases, and toolboxes can be used to organize the wireless kit. On the left of the case shown in the image are small cases for the different types of tapes, wind protection and mounts, batteries, belts and straps, and labels identifying the model and color of the lavaliers. On the far right, transmitters are color-coded to identify individual transmitters for tracking channels that the actors are using as well as repairs (some Mixers use colors, some use numbers).

Organize your kit so that it makes sense to you. Courtesy of URSA Straps.

Lavaliers

A lavalier microphone (lav), also known as a lapel mic, clip mic, or wire, is a miniature microphone often placed somewhere on the actor's body, usually hidden from the camera's view. Clips, tapes, and various accessories are used for attaching them.

Sanken

COS-11. An omnidirectional, water- and moisture-resistant lavalier. The COS-11D specifically diminishes the instances where interference by digital transmitters is an issue.

Sanken COS-11 lavalier and accessories

Countryman

B3. The Countryman B3 is an omnidirectional lavalier mic that comes with field-selectable high-frequency response caps and extremely low handling noise. The B3 is an easily hidden weather-resistant mic.

https://vimeo.com/63437464

Mics hidden in plain sight

B6. The Countryman B6 is the smallest lavalier in the world and out-performs microphones many times its size. The changeable protective caps provide moisture resistance and color options and let you shape the frequency response to suit different applications or to match other microphones. With exceptionally low handling noise and rugged construction, the B6 is the ideal choice for theater, broadcast, churches, and general lavalier applications. With a diameter of only 0.1" (2.5 mm)—the size of a No. 2 pencil lead—the mic capsule virtually disappears when worn.

https://vimeo.com/65541958

Countryman B6 and accessories

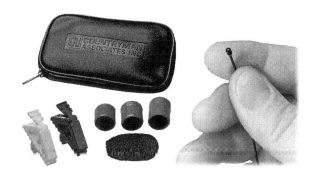

There are more lavalier choices available; research the ones available at the local sound equipment house and in your team's equipment package. The transmitters and receivers can vary, but most of the accessories are standard.

▸ **www.audio-technica.com**

▸ **https://countryman.com**

▸ **www.dpamicrophones.com**

▸ **www.lectrosonics.com**

▸ **www.sanken-mic.com/en/**

▸ **https://en-us.sennheiser.com**

Production will ask for a time estimate to wire the actors and give you updates on the actors' availability...and mood, if you ask. Check in with Costumes for any discussion necessary, such as any changes made or modification to the outfit, and check in with Props if necessary.

Rigging props: The Props Department has things that can make noise as well as great things that you can build microphones into.

We once hollowed out a "possum" croissant and put in a microphone. Vintage electronics can be a little tricky and require lead time—e.g., old projectors, tape recorders, television sets, computers, or radios that need to be made practical.

Hair: There may be a time when you need to use a hair rig. Borrowed from the live theater world, many accomplished hair people have experience with this and have the clips. Let the hair people take a first pass at placing the clip with your input.

Costumes

So far, you've been visiting the Costumes Department (also called Wardrobe) and chatting with those in charge of designing and building the costumes; now it's time to work closely with those running the show: the dressers, or on-set costumers.

You will work closely with this department because their choice of fabrics and clothing can greatly affect the quality of the sound, no matter whether radio-mic'd or boomed. You may have successfully influenced some clothing choices during pre-production and for the rest of the show will be mitigating any issues that could not be or were not alleviated. My first career in the arts was theatre costuming, but any experience you have in costumes or sewing will serve you well.

If you have no experience, consider this as a very rough primer. Fabrics such as cottons, cotton/polyester blends, and Rayon and Rayon blends will usually be quiet. Silks, synthetics, and metallics can be noisy. Wools and furry or thick fabrics *might* make the sound scratchy and muffled, as will plastic. Some materials make noise acoustically, and there is nothing we can do about it. Remember when your mom bought you corduroy pants (swoosh, swoosh)? The *drape* of a fabric refers to how easily it falls from a hanging point—think slinky dresses. A TX hidden along the waist of a Rayon dress will be more easily seen than one in a cotton dress—cotton being a thicker, stronger material.

Some of our wardrobe discussion centers around hiding transmitters and mics and potentially cutting holes in clothing to allow the passage of lavalier wires or antennae. Using any of these *italicized terms* may help foster goodwill with the Costumes Department.

Costume Construction

A few basics on how a garment is constructed: Shirts and dresses may have *collars*—a band and piece of cloth in the neck area that folds down over the garment. T-shirts and Henleys have a *band*—a knit piece that is sewn onto the body of the garment. *Serging* is a sewing stitch often used on knit fabrics (turn your T-shirt inside out to see it) to sew together and bind the edges in one operation. A *seam* is made when two pieces of fabric are sewn together. Opening a serged seam is more difficult than opening a straight-sewn seam.

Plackets are openings in the neck area (as in button-down shirts), sleeves (the slit that the cuff buttons to close), or pants (the flap that hides your jeans' zipper). On women's shirts, the placket is designed right over left, while men's shirts are left over right (so your right hand could easily pull out a sword and defend yourself!). You can start planning your shirt rig while you're on the move.

If you want to ask Costumes to sew a mic into a costume, it helps to be specific. *Tacking* it in means that only certain points will be sewn down, and the rest of the cable (or head) remains loose, and a *whipstitch* can quickly secure the entire length with quick, loose stitches that wrap it. A *chainstitch* is fast and will make loops that you can thread a lavalier cable through (make sure you specify how big you want the loop).

Ask to cut a hole in a costume as a last resort. On modest shows, it may be the actor's personal wardrobe, or it may have been promised as a perk after the shooting, or it may not be able to be repaired adequately after cutting it. Ask, instead, if the dresser can open the seam (if that works for you); it shows respect for the costume and the work needed to put it back together. In jeans, it will be easier to cut a hole in the pocket fabric rather than the *denim* (jeans material).

The best position for a rig is the one that sounds good, the actor allows, and doesn't make a cameo on screen. Higher up the chest does not necessarily make it better. If the voice quality is such that it's more natural, then yes. In general, try to place the microphone in the deepest part of the chest so that the fabric can fall naturally, and not be interrupted by the mic. Use the least amount of gak (accessories or tape) necessary to secure it. In my experience, most actors would rather have tape on their chest than a strap wrapped around them, holding the lavalier and cable. If mic'ing a hairy chest, use Skin Tac or Mepitac tape, which will hold down hair (make sure there's some skin to press it to or it will ride on top of the hair); these tapes will release without pulling hair. If an actor is skeptical, you can use a small piece on his forearm to prove the point.

Taping to an actor's skin: I get asked about this a lot. There is no hard-and-fast rule; do make sure you have that conversation with the actor *after* seeing the wardrobe, and if there's been a rehearsal so you can intelligently discuss action. If there's no rehearsal, read the scene and ask the actor about anything that might be an issue. I have used Transpore on many actors, and hypo-allergenic medical tapes are available. Know your options.

An old trick when removing tape: I had an actor insist on my using Transpore on his hairy chest (leave a tiny bit folded over onto itself to have a tab to hold for removal). When it came time to remove it, I asked him to turn his head and cough. Apparently, I was the first to do this, because he was surprised. When he coughed, I pulled, and he never felt a thing; the chest compression covered the feeling of pulling hairs.

Other non-chest options for mic placement include putting the mic in the collar, the placket, through a buttonhole, under a point of the collar, at the top of a pocket, on the apron instead of clothing, in the tie, under a uniform patch, in the brim of a hat, or using a pen mic (a lav is threaded through the shell of a pen).

Lately, I've had to wire very thin or see-through men's T-shirts; in this case, ask the dresser if he or she can sew a mic into the shirt, along the seam. Tape will be too stiff a material on such a lightweight fabric. If you get a negative response, try using Moleskin strips or Transpore to secure the cable and head.

Historically, Sound people put the TX pack in the small of an actor's back, and that's the obvious place to notice them while watching a movie. I was taught that way, too, but soon realized it is problematic. First, both genders of actors are obsessed with having a small waist. Women in

particular assess themselves from the side and
keep fussing with tucking in their tops. Less-
than-professional wardrobe people often point
out the pack and agree that it makes them
look "bulky."

A pen mic

For this type of rig, I put the pack on a waist belt on the side of a person
because the natural movements of an arm will hide the pack. Make sure to
place the pack against the body with the belt running *over* the pack; it will
help smooth the look and will feel more secure for the actor.

Men: Common rigs for men are in ties and dress shirts. Online videos are
available.

Women: Women have the advantage of almost always wearing bras, and
that gives you a (mostly) safe zone. Even without a bra, there's usually an
open spot for a microphone.

Medical personnel: For doctors, nurses, etc., you can also use a pen mic
in their pocket or possibly run a wire onto a stethoscope.

T-shirts: I have had great success using my own technique: Put a piece
of first-aid tape just larger than the head behind the mic and *very lightly* press the edges of the tape onto the inside of the band, placing the
mic against the band *or* just below the band and pointing out, sideways.
Lightly tape the mic cable down every 2 inches or so, placing the cable either on the band or just below it, *in the ditch* that the seam makes. Follow
the neckline around to the shoulder seam, tape or sew, thread the cable
down along the side seam, taping as you go—don't pull. At this point you
have to decide whether to put it in a pants pocket (cutting a small hole
down inside if necessary and with costume supervision) or attaching a
belt and pouch for the pack or continuing the cable down to a thigh or leg
or boot transmitter placement. The neck band acts as wind protection.

A-shirts: Also known as "Guido shirts" or "wife-beaters," these are
sleeveless undershirts. As with T-shirts, take extra care to tape securely
at the shoulder seams, or ask Costumes if it can be sewn in.

Military uniforms: These are usually made of wool and tightly fitted. I
had success with a COS-11 sideways, peeking out from under a chest-level
flap. Ask wardrobe for the jacket ahead of time to have a test listen and
work out a position.

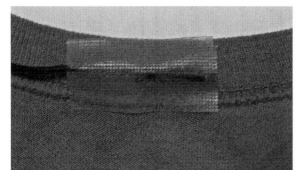

The author's T-shirt rig

Hats: Get hats ahead of time to run tests on placement. This works with felt hats as well as uniforms for first responders, pilots, boat captains, etc. Many uniform hats have black brims and a black mic head and black wind protection with discreet taping will pass a camera look. It may work for larger shots, with booming or an alternative plan for the closer work. If you place a pack in a hat, put Molefoam or something over it to buffer the actor's head.

I was hired for an Elayne Boosler special, and in one of the skits she turned into a cockroach; it wasn't boomable, so I had to explore options.

The author in a
cockroach uniform

Bathing suits: For a woman's bikini, use your best judgment as to the pack placement. If the DOP or Script or director says they will never see the actor's back, then use a pouch and slip it through the bra back and clasp. Secure the lav head between the breasts and as far down as necessary so that the camera won't see it. Secure with tape and then tape the mic cable to the top, going around the body as needed until you reach the pack.

For 360-degree views, secure the mic and tape as above, going to the less-seen-camera side (if there is one) and either placing the pack in the cup with the breast or taping it sideways to the side of the top, which will be mostly hidden by the upper arm. If there is no away side, ask the actor if she has a preference. Position the pack so it has the connectors to the back. Use a small transmitter like the Lectrosonics SSM. This might be a situation where the editors will need to "paint out the transmitter" using digital tools.

For women's one-piece suits, use the general procedure as above and consider a chest strap to hold the TX at the side, chest-level. Perhaps Costumes can sew in a pouch. A hair rig or bathing cap rig might be a solution as well.

For men, don't be so quick to write off the "Speedo rig"; use a small TX and hide it as you can and secure it, then place the head at the center top, with some wind protection. I used this rig with a DPA 4060, and it sounded amazing!

Scarves: Scarves can be blessings or curses depending on their fabric and positioning. Try to weave the head of the mic through a large-weave scarf and secure with a clip or tape if necessary. Use a windscreen as needed. Otherwise, tuck into and along one of the folds, keeping it hidden from camera.

Perspiration: Like red convertibles, movie clichés include joggers who sweat enough to drench themselves. If you're wiring a jogger or sports player character, coordinate with Costumes and/or Makeup to protect the lav from getting soaked with water from a spray bottle (by cupping a hand gently over the mic area). The water may not actually harm the mic but can clog the capsule with moisture and harm the take.

Very sweaty actors: Use Moleskin to dry the skin of the actor. Use Nexcare adhesive bandage tape to create a taped area, and then place the lav mount on it. This has worked in hot, humid areas with 80–100% humidity and has not failed due to sweat.

Ankle rigs: If you're using an ankle rig, consider whether placing the pack on the outside of the strap will make it too visible. If you place the transmitter against the ankle, inside the strap, it will lessen the visibility of the bulge. But you might want to use a bit of padding against an actor's anklebone. K-Tek makes heat shields to buffer against the heat buildup in transmitters, or you might use a piece of Moleskin, Molefoam, or a folded-up tissue. The heat won't be harmful or dangerous but can be distracting to the actor.

It's good to be fast, and often it's required. But never let yourself compromise your ability to do the job properly—you'll end up having to fix it anyway.

If the Mixer asks you to make an adjustment to the wire, it is expected that you fulfill the request right away, certainly before the scene is filming again.

Have your rig ready to be slapped on.

As much as we'd like to collaborate with Costumes, no matter what your skill or experience is, it's possible to be sabotaged by this department. On a day call, I was asked to put a radio mic on an actress who was getting ready for a close-up. The lens was a 60mm, and the frame was 8" above her head to a loose chest. Everything was fine until the wardrobe person made a comment to the actress about the *slight* fullness at the back of her waist from the radio mic (her tucked-in blouse was already making it look "normal"). The wardrobe person went on about it, and the actress got more and more concerned. I saw this, went over, and explained that the lens was a 60mm. After a blank stare from the wardrobe woman, she went to the head of her department, who called a meeting with the sound Mixer and AD. I didn't know anyone there, or the politics of the shoot, but it was clear that it became more important for this unknowledgeable person to save face than serve the shot: the radio mic was removed.

If you have an untenable situation with an actor, a costume, the Wardrobe Department, or even *time*, remember that the technology now exists to "paint out" visible rigs in post-production.

Actors

When actors arrive on set, they are putting themselves out there for everyone to see. They will be working through the director's needs for the character while a crew looks on. That can be a nerve-wracking experience at any budget. Will the director and the actors get along well? Will actors find a comfortable working relationship where there is trust? Will the director be able to earn the trust of the actors? What about those strong-willed actors who are cast in an ensemble? Clearly, actors may bring many unknowns to a project, and working them out in public can be daunting.

No matter the budget or size of the project, treat everyone with respect and professionalism; in the first days of *any* shoot, keep any excitement to yourself. This is not the time to become a fan over having the chance to work with someone you've admired.

Give everyone a chance to figure out the dynamics of this new group; the most important thing you can do is to *watch* and *learn*.

How much interaction you want to have with talent is really a matter of personal comfort—both of yours. In general, at the basic working-relationship level, you should introduce yourself at the moment you'll need to work with someone. I have tried humor since many people tell me I am funny, but my humor doesn't always seem to work well. I've seen others be successful and cross the hierarchy of the production. If you have the gift, God bless; use it wisely. For the rest of us, nothing except an introduction seems appropriate.

In pre-production, you will have discovered whether the actor has assistants. If the actor has no assistants, you'll talk with the actor directly on the day of shooting, unless there's a particularly tricky costume to discuss. To coordinate your timing with that of the Hair and Makeup Departments, keep in contact with the 2nd 2nd AD. On larger shows, there may be a specific PA assigned to coordinate at actors' trailers.

For actors without assistants, if the actor is in his or her trailer, knock and listen for an answer. I have learned to put my ear up almost onto the door because the noise of the trailers' generators makes it hard to hear. The more experienced actors tend to have realized that and have an open door and either let you in or ask you to wait x minutes. Expect to wait outside; sometimes you will be invited in to sit at the table while they are finishing up in the bedroom area.

If you are radio mic'ing an actor, introduce yourself and ask if he or she is ready to be wired. If you're not sure, just ask, "Have you ever worn a radio mic before?" Listen for how and where the wire was placed and the actor's tone: pleasant (everything went well the last time) or annoyed (something didn't go well). If you sense negativity, show your professionalism by not running scared. Ask one or two questions to understand what the problem was and make sure *not* to do it that way. Some things that might have gone wrong include:

▸ The pack or mic felt unsecure or was flopping about

▸ The UST needed multiple adjustments

▸ The pack got hot against the actor

It helps to have some phrases ready, so you are not caught off-guard if the actor has had a negative wiring experience. Without disparaging the Sound person, say something like, "How about if we [do x] instead?" Or "Would you prefer x?" This would also be the time to explain any procedure you would like followed: "I'll also be setting up in the next location, so if you are released and I don't come for your pack, please go to the Sound cart for help or [*Wardrobe person*] will de-rig you," or whatever procedure you would like. Make sure that everyone involved knows what you said the protocol would be!

Cold packs (transmitters): Most actors will not mention when the transmitter packs are cold because they expect that is a necessary part of the way things work. But it doesn't have to be. If you're on a cold weather shoot, you can leave the pack in the actor's trailer to keep it warm (if you will be wiring there). Ask if that would be OK.

For an extended cold shoot, carry a heating pad and place the transmitters on it if they'll end up next to the actor's body. I will then put the TX in my jeans pocket to keep warm until I reach the actor.

For packs that get hot and are against an actor's body, you can buy heat shields and place them toward the actor's body in the pouch or use a folded tissue or make your own heat shields. These pads can also be used to soften the pressure of a pack against an actor when needed.

I've put radios on kids as young as 2½ years old. Ask the AD staff for a short initial meet on set or at the child's trailer. Smile and introduce yourself and let them see how the rig works. For older kids, lend them your headphones or bring a pair of Comteks along so they can hear themselves (explain how to avoid feedback). I've used the secret agent analogy successfully with older children. Have a parent and teacher or other staff present to avoid legal issues.

Newbie actors of any age: I start off with a pleasantry and show them the equipment, explaining how it will be placed, and where and why, if it's within their comprehension. In case something changes that I'm not aware of, they are at least somewhat thinking with Sound's perspective in mind. I make sure to point out the delicate cables and that power will be turned off from the cart when they leave set (and do just that), so they don't need to pull everything off/apart to have their privacy. *This is an important personal concern of actors,* and their privacy should be respected.

A-list actors: While any budget show could have big-name talent, it's most likely that medium- to large-budget projects will have higher-paid actors who are main characters and will expect certain protocols.

If an actor has an entourage, they are there to buffer the actor from the rest of the world. Be considerate and learn the protocols desired: Does the actor have a personal dresser, voice coach, or assistant? Do you coordinate wiring with a particular person? Who do you talk to for wiring? Do you hand off the transmitter or wire together with someone? Is there a preferred rig? I worked with a leading man who brought his own black leather pouch and only allowed an ankle rig. (Make sure your lav wire is long enough.) Resist the urge to be conversational; speak only when necessary and be willing to wait as long as it takes for an actor to be comfortable with you. I worked with a mega-star for 7 months before I got a smile and "hello." The last time I worked with him I got a kiss in front of paparazzi.

If an actor has an assistant, that assistant might let you into the trailer or direct you to another location—e.g., the dressing area on set. If that's the case, let the 2nd 2nd know, and add a time estimate if you can, so the 2nd 2nd can factor in that step. If you think you can get something else done before the time you are to meet the actor, go for it. But be sure to always arrive a few minutes *before* that time because you never want to have them wait for you.

If an actor has assistants, go through them for communications. Build a relationship of trust with assistants. Offer them a Comtek, ask about any specific needs or pet peeves of the actor. Use the assistant for your prep work and save your face time with the A-list actor for necessary interaction. *Be brief!* Don't feel a need to talk; it is not a time for chatting or, heaven forbid, you commenting on their personal appearance or critiquing their work. *Not even to give them a compliment.* Give them the courtesy of letting them concentrate on their job. Have everything you need for the wire rig handy and prepped as much as possible in advance. Talk only if you need them to move an arm or to let them know you'll be under their shirt. Say it before you do it and wait a half beat. If you have established a procedure and what you're doing is the standard, you probably don't need any words *at all*. My "Thank you" says we're done. Understand the de-rigging procedure the actor prefers, and then leave. The less you interact or speak, the more the actor's appreciation may grow. Remember, you are the last person on their journey to the set, and they'll be concentrating on their work.

If ENG/EPK crews (behind-the-scenes crews) are present on the day, do remind them of that, short and sweet.

If you're able to see a rehearsal, you should have a good indication of the action, but *don't assume* each take will be the same. If there's a question about how secure your lav should be, ask the actor if they might run farther, jump, or scream louder than they have in rehearsal. In a short time, you'll be able to gauge what to expect from an actor.

On *Ad Astra,* the spacesuits took some time to get in and out of and weighed about 35 lbs. (almost 16 kg), so individual actor tents were set up in the warehouse, with individual air conditioners running, as makeshift dressing areas. The actors had cooling underwear—akin to thermal underwear but with water running through tubing to keep the actors cool. There were also fans built into the space suits as well as in the helmets for times when the DOP wanted to use their gold reflective visors and didn't want fog from their breath impairing visibility. Communicate with the 2nd AD and set up a system to streamline the delivery of actors to be wired. Actors go through Hair and Makeup (HMU) prior to wiring.

I found it's easier to wire on set unless there's a privacy issue; you don't take all the accessories away from the other people wiring, and you get instant audible feedback about the sound of your rig, in case you need an adjustment. Make sure you call the actors to your cart, not letting the ADs bring them straight to the set; once actors are on set, the director and 1st AD expect that they are ready to work.

On **A-list shows**, you need to step up your game by adding comfort and safety and neatness to everything you do. For rigging actors' clothing, we dress cables with Moleskin-backed adhesive tape; it's soft and black, and taping the entire run prevents an actor from accidentally pulling the wire loose. A-list shows *do not* usually use safety pins because of the possibility of one becoming undone. I have precut thin strips of Moleskin tape that can repair or replace any tape if an actor needs an adjustment on the set. I also carry safety pins, used to attach transmitter pouches or provide loops for lavaliers or cables to thread through to help them stay hidden. If you use a safety pin, cover it with a Moleskin strip so it can't open.

‣ **https://practicalshowtechcom.squarespace.com/show-archive/ rf-best-practices-with-lectrosonics-karl-winkler-pst-031?rq= lectrosonics**

‣ **www.professionalwireless.com/product/pws-2-way-high-power-splitter-combiner-bnc/**

Actors who don't want to wear wires: It's not your job to get into a battle. Go through production channels as they manage actors. Immediately inform the Mixer of the actor's refusal. She will need to take it to the director, who will have to decide how to proceed from there. This can be a little tricky, as the actor could potentially feel you have gone over their head. The higher responsibility, though, is that the director needs to know the dialogue is at risk.

Whether personal interaction is appropriate depends on the circumstances.

If a celebrity is a day player and is spending time on the set before needed, just to get a feel for how this particular show runs, it's possible that a very brief hello and welcome is all that would be appropriate. Actors will, by their demeanor and common body language, often telegraph their comfort with the level of interaction that they would like.

An actor who is very comfortable and conversational with crew is Martin Sheen. When he arrives on set, he has a smile and a hello for each person. And between takes he chats and tells stories, sometimes right up until the sticks are snapped, and then he's completely in character. Dustin Hoffman loves to tell stories and will re-enact his iconic characters from his previous movies. He loves chatting with the other actors and is inclusive of the crew.

At the other end of the spectrum are the method actors. Actors who use this approach completely "inhabit" the character; they "become" the character and stay in that frame of mind all day long. That can make it difficult when you must interact with that actor, and you must be prepared for whatever the tone of the character is. There may be specific requests by the actor communicated to the production that you need to be aware of—e.g., only address them by their character's name or avoid direct eye contact unless invited, etc.

As I was writing this book, I was asked multiple times to tell stories about my times on set. I started in the business as the Golden Age of Hollywood greats were getting ready to retire: Ray Milland, Sidney Guilaroff, Jason Robards, Jr., Ava Gardner, and Polly Bergen, to name a few. And, yes, I have stories. Really uplifting stories of good deeds, compassion, generosity, and even tips on the child-birthing process, going out to a restaurant after work, an actor calling the entire crew after an earthquake to check on each one, an actor who gave very generous gifts at Christmas. I have been witness to a famous couple learning that their toddler has a serious health condition, that someone was raped, that an underage girl was being propositioned by a heartthrob, and I have been invited to the most unusual Hollywood party.

Everyone's life is a story and deserves its dignity and privacy. That's one of the basic tenets of working on a film: everyone works closely and under great stresses, and the trust that is built is forever. And ever.

While it is not OK to fawn over actors while at work, sometimes someone comes along whom you can't help but feel excited about. I did an in-house commercial for McDonald's Hamburger University (yes, for real). They had just created their breakfast sandwich. I can't believe they got John Houseman to play the Professor, but they did. (John Houseman was an imposing, intimidating, authoritative figure, known for playing those kinds of roles later in life; he was Orson Welles's producer at the Mercury Theater and on *Citizen Kane*.) I knew him as the completely intimidating law professor of a very popular episodic show, *The Paper Chase*.

All the women on the set were buzzing about his arrival, and every one of us admitted to being nervous anticipating his arrival and having a crush on him. Of course, he wore a bow tie and wool vest and wool suit. I had trouble between that wardrobe and being nervous, and the Mixer wasn't happy with the sound, so I had to approach him several times. It was nerve-wracking, and I knew that part of the problem was *my* anxiety.

I made a bold decision: He was sitting in an office chair across the stage looking over his keynote speech for a convention that night. I stopped just in front of him, knelt, took a breath, and said, "Excuse me, have I told you yet that I'm in love with you?" and waited. He stopped reading, looked over his glasses, patted my knee and said, "Good! Keep going." I continued, "I just needed to get that off my chest because it's distracting me from my work."

We talked just a few minutes, and I walked back to all the women giving me The Look. They couldn't believe what I had just done. I couldn't either. For the rest of the day, it was a completely different relationship, and I am so touched to remember his grace and the astonished look on the director's face when I called Mr. Houseman "Johnny." (*I don't recommend that you imitate my behavior!*)

We're human, it happens, and not just to crewmembers. I remember a young heartthrob actor and a young actress played characters that become boyfriend and girlfriend. On Friday, the first day of shooting, they had a scene together that required radio mics. The boy's was fine, but the girl's had transmission issues. I changed the antenna position multiple times, replaced the battery, replaced the lavalier twice, and went through every transmitter we had, but it never was 100% static-free. We wondered over the weekend what else we could do.

On Monday I dreaded, yet needed, to radio mic them both again...no problem! When the scene was over and I was de-rigging the actress, I knew she was nervous about the show, so I tried to be friendly. I asked how her weekend was. She smiled wide and told me she had been asked out by the heartthrob actor. Being accepted and getting to know him a little was all it took for her to calm down. Yes, it really affected the transmission; her anxiety was *so high*. They dated and we had a clear signal for the rest of the show.

Be sensitive to events happening in actors' lives. I'm not a follower of *People* magazine gossip, but if I'm working with an actor, I'll check out an article while I'm in the checkout line at the grocery store. I'll ask Sound people and coworkers from the actor's last 3 years of work how the experience was, anything it would help me to know, anything that went badly or was a trigger for upset. When Hair and Makeup have spent some time with the actors, I'll ask the same.

Sometimes you're tasked with creating a solution for something unusual. On Ad Astra, I was tasked with creating a solution so that actors would be able to hear the director and each other as well as how we would record their voices.

To make the spacesuits look more interesting, pockets were added to the outside; some were decorative, with things hanging out of them, but a few were practical and used by Props and us. My solution was to place a Comtek receiver in one sleeve pocket and a wireless transmitter in another one. Extension cables for each of the devices were made and then threaded through the four layers of suit to the back; this allowed for easy access when connecting the actor-worn earpiece. The lavalier head was built into the suit itself. A piece of fur covered the lav to buffer it from the fan circulating air inside the helmet.

The last word on wiring: Your best doesn't always work in the time you are given. It will be frustrating, and the Mixer won't be happy. It happened to me recently because a key factor regarding a costume wasn't divulged to me and I ran out of time. Always have a plan for failing gracefully.

The author and Patrick Martens work out mic placement for *Ad Astra*

Embedding a practical earpiece in a costume earpiece

CHAPTER 16

Scene Elements

Rarely will you have scenes of two people talking at a table, and you can expect to find one or more of these elements throughout your career:

Aerial: Usually, aerial shots don't involve USTs. If the Mixer is involved, check to set up what he needs for his bag rig, pack extra expendables as well as doubles on specialized aircraft cables and connectors or equipment he might have requested. Scout the aircraft and be a liaison between the ADs, pilot, and Mixer. Be at the takeoff and landing points, waiting, before the Mixer arrives.

Airports: You'll have extra security protocols and processes, and most likely badges that designate the area to which you will have access. Background checks are becoming common as well. There may be clothing and PPE requirements. Pay very close attention to any instructions and follow them exactly. Check frequencies well in advance so that you can adjust if there are problems. Your follow cart may be farther away than usual, or you might need to take a reduced package.

Animals: Regarding booming: Work with the animal trainer, preferably before the shot. Have the microphone configured as it will be for the shot and show the trainer and animal. For most animals, bring the backed-off microphone in the space above the animal, let it hang there a bit, and then move it slowly in the general way you expect to work the shot. *Always defer to the trainer.*

Regarding your physical proximity: If you need to be near the animal, *follow the trainer's guidance.* More experienced trainers often have included presence of a boom as part of the training protocol for horses, dogs, and big cats. But *do not* assume that this is the case. Understand what actions may threaten or disturb the animal as well as what can help keep it calm. Ask for visible or audible signs that the animal is upset or about to relieve itself. Make sure that if you need to run out of harm's way, you have a clear path to do so. *Relieve itself?* you may ask. Yes, there's a story to go with that....

I was once booming in Kansas (cue *The Wizard of Oz* jokes now) in a barn with Michael Learned and Frederic Forrest. Michael was getting ready to milk the cow when Fred comes in, and they talk over the cow. Because of the stalls, I was near the back end of the cow. On Take 4, the cow's tail went up, and I was peed on. But I didn't break the setup. Thankfully, Costumes had a suitable change of clothes for me and I had a long shower back at the hotel.

When I worked on *Cujo*, the animal wrangler included a talk on the cantankerous nature of St. Bernards. When the scene came where Dee Wallace and Danny Pintauro were outside the barn with Cujo in their lap, the dog needed to be tranquilized. He was watched over by a medical doctor and representative from the Humane Society but was kept for several hours in a quasi-lucid state—neither too passed out nor too aware (even more dangerous). It added a level of anxiety because there was no predicting the actions of a 150- to 250-pound antisocial animal, nor was there an easy way to have controlled all those pounds of unmanageable beast. Use a long pole, place yourself out of the natural path of the animal, and have an escape plan.

Generally, be as inconspicuous as possible, and position yourself and pole as soon as possible before the animal is brought to set. Or slowly get into position if the animal is already there. Snakes are not opposed to raising up to reach a pole, chimpanzees will ignore them, dogs and cats are comfortable around them, but any animal will become distracted with a large enough movement. There is an exception: when the animal trainers ask for your inclusion.

When I did pickups for *Outbreak* (starring Dustin Hoffman, Rene Russo, Morgan Freeman, and Donald Sutherland), a movie about an epidemic caused by an Ebola-infected monkey, we shot the crucial scene when the audience discovers that the monkey is the carrier. The director wanted a close-up of the monkey's face, which was supposed to start friendly and innocent and change to surly and agitated. The animal trainer tried many ways to get a reaction from the monkey, but the monkey was comfortable with the trainer. At a standstill, I asked if I could offer a suggestion.

I got out my Sennheiser 816 Windshield, put on a Windjammer (the furriest windsock), placed one piece of white Gaffer's tape on either side of the end (nose), and poked at the monkey from just out of frame. Of course, the monkey had never seen an animal like this and was alarmed! Suddenly, he bared his teeth and shrieked...and that's how we got the shot. The moral of the story is: Don't underestimate how the Sound Department can contribute to your movie.

Babies: Babies will be fascinated by your microphone, and more so if you need to cue and/or you are using a contrasting foam. Try a colored foam close to the color of the ceiling or overhead elements. Try not to be interesting (it's hard, I know). And minimize noise and movement around them.

The newbies will be sleeping or crying. If they're crying, everyone will know it; if there's dialogue, try cuing away from the crying and catching the dialogue on the edge of the pattern. For older babies, their eyesight will be developed enough to follow the boom (remember, it's staring back at them). Try to limit your movements if possible or try a position forward of the actors so that the baby's look will not be too obvious.

Observation: The best takes from babies and animals are the rehearsals and possibly first takes. Most directors do not know this and rehearse.

Children: All children who need a radio mic need an accompanying adult—a parent, studio teacher, or AD. For liability reasons, *never* mic a child alone. Explain to the guardian every step before doing it. Ask whether the child has ever worn a mic before. Some type of explanation helps the child; for very young children, I have had success saying, "This is a special sticker you get to wear." For children, I'll say, "This is what spies wear! (Actor) and (Actor) have one, too." Use age-appropriate words and keep rules simple: "Only your mom and I can touch the mic. When you're wearing it, there's no shouting or playing." And to the parent: "If it starts to slip or bothers her, let me know. When the ADs break you, come to the cart so I can take it off safely, and let me know if you're taking a bathroom break."

Children are a little more difficult to wire because of their small size and the fact that their chests are smaller than their waists, the opposite of adults. The chest area tends to be particularly tight for getting a mic placed invisibly. Present this challenge to Costumes and find a workable solution. Consider a collar rig, placket rig, or running some lace in that area to hide the mic under, or a scarf or bandana. A smaller transmitter will help, such as the Lectrosonics SSM. Use the fullness of a boy's tucked-in shirt, or fullness of a girl's dress, to hide it or an ankle rig. Also consider putting the radio microphone in an accessory or using a placement next to the child.

Having done sound for *Cujo*, *Pet Sematary*, and *Once Upon a Time...in Hollywood*, I can tell you that experienced child actors are every bit as professional as their adult counterparts. Seven-year-old Danny Pintauro was in his character's bedroom with the DOP and director, blocking a scene. The DOP, Jan deBont, had an idea for camera placement, but Danny suggested that he drive a toy fire truck across the floor. That was a better idea for both the visual and the sound, and that is what we shot.

While doing a scene with Julia Butters, Quentin Tarantino asked her mother to give a wild line off camera. After wiring Julia, I asked if *she* would like to wire her mom. She said yes, took my direction very well (to my delight), and deftly related the story as a presenter at the 2019 Cinema Audio Society awards show:

https://vimeo.com/showcase/5776888
(See the second video listed on the page.)

It's common to give the guardian an IFB (and offer one to the studio teacher).

Elevated work areas: These can include apple boxes, ladders, scaffolding, or the greens area above a stage. Anytime you're working on an elevated surface, be aware of those boundaries. If you feel you need a spotter, don't be embarrassed to ask for one; grips spot Camera often. Keep your center of gravity as low as possible and balance your weight against any leaning you may have to do. Pay attention to any overhead hazards or electrical wires near you.

Extras: Extras, Forrest Gump might have said, are like a box of chocolates: You never know what you're going to get. Some are attorneys who fancy doing something completely different. Some are undiscovered actors or wannabes or...?

And they come to the production with varying levels of experience. The more professional shows have extras coordinators, who will have given instructions on certain clothing and accessories *not* to wear and will liaison when you need to give Sound notes. Still, it's important to try to anticipate special needs regarding extras and to communicate those in advance of the date of production to both the extras coordinator and the 2nd AD.

Unless it's urgent, go through proper channels. For heavy extras days, have a big supply of Molefoam and check their shoes and tableware before the scene. Also check their jewelry and whether they're wearing corduroy or rip-stop nylon—definite noisemakers. Experienced Costumes people will have taken care of this or will collaborate with you.

Extreme conditions: Films are shot in all conditions in all areas of our world or a fantasy world. Extreme conditions can be any natural weather elements or those manmade specifically to aid in the storytelling. If you find yourself working in one of these environments, make sure you understand any adverse health symptoms and safety measures being taken or safety concerns that you should be aware of.

When appropriate, a safety meeting is held at the beginning of each day or when beginning a potentially dangerous sequence, explaining the nature of unusual activities or circumstances. Pay attention and *ask questions* if you don't understand something or need more information. Don't be the person being interviewed on the 6:00 p.m. news saying, "I'm an artist; other people are supposed to protect me." You'll have to live that moment over and over for the rest of your life.

When working in extreme conditions, you have an added responsibility to make sure the Mixer and boom have extra support: water, clothing, sunscreen, or giving them breaks so they can get off the set.

Cold: One of the more common working conditions is cold weather. It may be cold and icy when you first arrive at work and then warm up later, so you'll have a temporary situation in which you need to exercise above-normal care in movement to lessen the risk of slipping on icy surfaces or carts tumbling off the tailgate (it happens more than you think)!

Pay attention to the temperature in that area. Will it warm up during the day, or is a storm coming? Dress in layers. Zippers are preferable on jackets, as sometimes it's inconvenient to pull clothing over your head. Outdoor sports stores have knowledgeable people and specialty clothing. Waterproof boots are a must. Consider hand warmers, tissues, lip balm, or electric socks. Special face cream will protect your skin in strong windy areas. Be aware that a long throw on your boom on a windy day could make you lose your balance. Stay further back from edges.

Or, like on the frigid set of *The Hateful Eight*, you may be in extreme weather for an extended time. For these kinds of climes, sufficient prep is necessary to secure a "cold room" where the equipment can be stored in consistent temperatures with the set to eliminate the possibility of condensation in the machines and subsequently failing. You'll need to have expedition-type clothing to keep you warm for the entire duration of shooting; pay particular attention to footwear, which can cause serious problems if your feet remain wet or in freezing temperatures. Listen to any safety instruction and alert the medic to any health condition you may have that could flare up.

In addition to the temperature of the Colorado Rockies was the element of that set's elevation. When working in high altitudes, your red blood cells need to increase to counteract the smaller levels of oxygen available in the air; it usually takes between one and two weeks to acclimate your lungs and as long as a month to acclimate your body fully. You may still need to make use of canned oxygen, and you will have difficulty performing at your usual level of activity. In addition, Gators, rather than flatbed trailers, will be the most common mode of travel, and the equipment should be configured appropriately. Pay attention to changing natural conditions—e.g., whiteouts, blizzards, avalanches, etc., and know the symptoms of hypothermia.

www.irunfar.com/2018/07/into-thin-air-the-science-of-altitude-acclimation.html

Heat—indoor: The AD Department will usually moderate the indoor heat to keep actors and their makeup fresh. Large air-conditioning units will have large tubes snaked through the set; you should have discussed the routing of these tubes with the HVAC installers to avoid blocking the ability of doors and windows to close (thereby allowing outside traffic and noises into the set). This often means establishing break points in the tubing to accommodate locking up the set for rolls and cuts. Continue to keep hydrated.

Temperatures can rise indoor as well as outdoors. For your safety, make sure that there are unblocked exits, people are limited to only those who are necessary, and that there is ventilation. If there is an indoor fire effect, insist there's a safety meeting and that the FX department has fire extinguishers (*plural*). Drink water and use cooling towels around your neck. For smoky interiors, use the right PPE (personal protective equipment) and review the industry smoke FX safety protocols. If wearing goggles and/or a facemask and headphones, your ability to be aware of your surroundings is severely limited—it's effectively having blinders on—so have someone keep an eye on you, and an eye out for you. If there is a danger of an uncontrollable element (fire, explosives), make sure you have a clear exit path and that someone is responsible for keeping it clear.

www.actsafe.ca/wp-content/uploads/2017/11/10-Artificial-Smoke-and-Fog-Motion-Picture-Bulletin.pdf

My unfortunate story: During the filming of a movie, one scene involved a fire in a hospital corridor. I was stationed behind the nurse's desk at the end of the hall. Wearing a full-charge respirator, goggles, headphones, and being cabled, I felt mobility-impacted. As we were doing final touches, I checked my exit once again; I had a clear path to an empty corridor just behind me.

As soon as we started rolling, the fire got out of control and a fireball came toward us. I felt my goggles start to cave in, softening from the heat. I turned to get away, but I was blocked by three producers who had come in at the last minute to watch the spectacle! Having nowhere to go, my goggles melted, and ash got in one of my eyes, scratching my cornea. After a trip to the hospital, I was sent home to wait and heal. I couldn't see out of that eye for 2 ½ days, for which the production decided they didn't have to compensate me, as it was a non-union show. I was also expected to cover my hospital bill. Thankfully, human eyes are one of the quickest body parts to recover; it's a survival mechanism.

Guns and gunfire: Guns require a very high standard of handling and safety. You must understand the cartridge load capacity: quarter-load, half-load, and full load. Full loads are necessary for the mechanical operation of automatic weapons and warfare equipment and cannot be modified to be less forceful. Ask whether any equipment will be using live ammunition. I worked on a show with WWII machine guns that only worked with live ammo! Don't assume (doing so makes an ass out of u and me). *Be aware!* Be prepared to record unusual sound pressure levels (SPLs). If you're working on the set during a setup with a gun, you have the right to ask the Props person handling it to show you its chamber, which should be empty at all times except for the take. Have there been accidents using guns on set that should have been empty? Yes. Has anyone died? Yes.

Heat—outdoor: Outdoor temperatures do not have to be extreme to take their toll on you—drink more water than you think you need, drink electrolytic beverages, consider salt tablets, and ask the medic for suggestions. Wear a wide-brimmed hat that still allows you to work, sunglasses with large lenses, and keep water, gum (if you're quiet), and lip balm. When applying sunscreen, don't forget the back of your neck, your shoulders if exposed, backs of legs, and ears if not covered. If the location is humid/hot and filled with biting bugs, try wearing a net suit to keep clothing light and spray-free. If you aren't wearing gloves, put some sunscreen on the tops of your hands. Using a good UV-blocking T-shirt will help keep you cool and protected from sunburn.

The saving grace with outdoor heat is that the temperature rises then falls throughout the day. That's not to say it doesn't get dangerous! Know the symptoms of heat exhaustion and heat stroke and watch for them in your department as well as in other crewmembers. PAs and cast members seem to be particularly susceptible or particularly unaware. See the Appendix for more information.

Make sure there are sufficient tents, tarps, umbrellas, and flags to cool the equipment as much as possible. Most Mixers will prefer to work on the truck and use the air conditioning it provides. The boom operator will need to spend a good portion of the time under the sun, so offer to trade off booming more often. Cooling scarves wrung out or dipped in Sea Breeze will help lower body temperatures. If using Sea Breeze, be sure to use your own private bucket and not a community one. Be sensible; keep hydrated, take salt tablets, and wear light clothing and a hat.

Noise: If unwanted sounds need to be addressed on set, talk to the department making the sound. If the noises are inherent in the location, get the Locations department on it. If noise is coming from the background actors, either talk to them directly or thru the extras coordinator or AD/PA.

Noisy floors: Any time you have noisy ground or a floor, try laying down carpet mats or runners, keeping them out of frame. Tape down the edges if there's any possibility of a trip (roll mats face out for that reason). If the surface is elevated (carpeting on platforms or apple boxes) tape all the edges and point out the surface to the actors *before* they rehearse. Sometimes booties will work if feet are out of frame (add these to your expendables order). It's better to *not* affect the lead actor's shoes, or elderly actors or those with any balance issues. If you do need to add something to the bottoms, ask Costumes to treat the heels in pre-production or use foot foam across the wide part of the sole and complete heel.

For noisy high heels: for a principal actor, ask the Costumes Department to have the shoes treated with anti-slip material (a pre-production discussion point) or use Molefoam or specialty products, such as Hush Heels. Baby bottle nipples in different sizes can work perfectly as a last-minute fix for heels; for large heels, rubber cane tips might work. Ask Costumes if there's another pair to exchange. If using these add-ons, make sure the cast is familiar with how they will impact their movement and safety, and ideally give talent an opportunity to try them out before arriving at the set.

Using mats to quiet footsteps

Rain: Moviemaking does not rely on actual rain; therefore, if you see a scene written as rain it will most likely be mechanical, and you'll need to have protective gear for yourself as well as having it for the equipment. Make sure you have a good rain hat with a brim (so that water is not dripping into your face), a rain jacket, pants that will not make noise as you move, and some kind of closure at your wrists. It is helpful to paper tape the wristbands of your jacket, or you'll have rain trickling down your armpit and chest. You don't want to wear a poncho because it doesn't give you the range of motion that you need, and I advise against hooded rain jackets because the hood blocks your vision as you turn your head. Mechanical rain is not the mild temperature of actual rain or the poetic patter of raindrops; it's more like a fire hydrant pouring cold water down your shirt.

Horsehair is a plastic open mesh material that absorbs water droplets to quiet the "plopping" sound. Make sure you've ordered some horsehair for the windshields (also called zeppelins) and make sure that FX has enough horsehair to put under areas of noisy dripping (windows or below gutters, for example). Horsehair can also be used with fountains or streams or small waterfalls where out of frame. Remote Audio and Cinela make rain products to cover windshields in wet weather.

‣ **www.trewaudio.com/product/cinela-pia-kelly/**

‣ **www.trewaudio.com/product/remote-audio-rainman/**

Special Effects (SFX): This can mean any made-to-look-real element: smoke, fire, steam, manufactured water, snow, and rain, to name a few. There is some overlap in oversight between Props, FX, and Costumes, so be sure to clarify which department you should address your questions to. Bullet strikes rigged to explode under costumes require coordination between Costumes, FX, and sometimes Sound (de-rigging an actor for the special effects shot). Many effects make noise, so be sure to get a thorough understanding of what will happen, including the levels and duration of noise exposure.

For fire or smoke: find out what is used for the effect and get the proper mask (air cartridge protection for fumes is different than for vapors, but both require time to get from a specialty store). Protective masks should be supplied by the production directly or through the FX department or Props. Do your own research, though, and have backup gear if there's a possibility of failure to prepare by the production company. *Be very wary of edicts from producers to not wear safety gear in the presence of actors for fear of alarming them!* This is prohibited on paper by all the major studios yet occurs with too much frequency in reality. Consider personal protective equipment an expendables item and order through the production if not provided.

Gas lines used to produce flame can be audible; in pre-production, discuss with the FX department their ability to add extension hoses and steel wool mufflers to distance their equipment from the dialogue area. E-fans must be in excellent working condition. When properly maintained, they should be mechanically silent, although at higher speeds the wind generated is noisy. In theory, Isotope should be a viable solution, but testing is highly recommended as proximity and angle of placement is very random. Ask how much equipment can be remoted from the set, or if it can be turned off and on to coordinate with the dialogue, or some other silencing method.

There should be a safety meeting to discuss the elements. Have questions ready to ask: What is the composition of the smoke? How long is it safe to breathe it? How often will the set be aired out? There are specific guidelines for ratio of exposure to breaks for smoke and flame. What are symptoms of overexposure? Who's the medic? Where will they be during the shooting?

www.actsafe.ca/wp-content/uploads/2017/11/10-Artificial-Smoke-and-Fog-Motion-Picture-Bulletin.pdf

Steam: Some microphones are more prone to humidity than others.

Special effects personnel will also bring many mechanical devices for wind, water, steam, fire, and smoke. These will need careful fine-tuning to avoid creating distraction from the actors' performances. These concerns go beyond the simple idea of turning things on and off. Sometimes off is not an option, and we need to navigate and negotiate a few things:

1. Achieve no more noise than is needed to have the effect succeed visually.

2. Pay close attention to consistency to minimize jarring leaps or changes in the noise from cut to cut. This can be problematic, as different placements needed for different camera angles within the same scene will alter the acoustic impact.

3. For SFX work, listen carefully to that department, and do your own research. I've had guys tell me a paper mask would be fine, only to have the safety equipment store staff look up the compounds in their book and then recommend full-charge respirators with specific canisters. Make sure you ask politely for the names of compounds being discharged, or the strength of explosions. The professional guys will issue a guidance bulletin to the crew and even make available the product packaging labels to confirm what's being used. Although I have had one experience where an unethical EFX person repacked forbidden oil-based fog liquid in containers for water-based stuff. His rationale? "It made better fog."

Stage work: When you're working on a studio in southern California, some things will be unique to studio work. The following will help you ease into the procedures.

Arriving: There are parking structures inside the studio compound as well as adjacent to or even a shuttle away. *Always* make sure you have a call sheet and the instructions for where to park; making a mistake by driving to the lot instead of a parking area off-lot could be a 25-minute loss in time. Sometimes a show will make badges that you must wear for the length of the production schedule. These will be necessary to get you into secured locations, parking areas, or though throngs of onlookers (also referred to as "non-coms").

You will need to show some type of picture ID at the gate unless the shuttle goes through the security line. Have a system for keeping your badge available. Productions usually supply lanyards; you may want to change that, as it's one more thing around your neck and could get tangled with your headphone cable.

The studio will have a "40" man (meaning the number of the union, IBEW Local **40,** the worker belongs to). The stage phone should have the phone number for several key departments including his. Call him for questions about the stage amenities and to bring the bell and light system to the stage. You may be moving to another stage later in the day or over the course of the show. When he arrives, confirm with him whether you are to leave the system or take it with you to the next stage. Have someone (PA or available person) watch the outside light to make sure it is operating correctly and that you can hear the bell (buzzer). Listen to make sure the air-conditioning unit also turns off. Go over the "quiet" protocols with the set PAs or whoever will be monitoring the doors to make sure the doors are closed when rolling and stay that way during the take, and make sure no one is moving unnecessarily during the take. The stage phone will automatically be silenced when the bell and lights are on. Ringing the bell one time and turning on the lights via the switch will signal everyone that you are rolling, called "being on a bell," and two short rings and turning off the light for going "off the bell." Interestingly, this protocol goes back to the earliest days of studio film production.

When shooting around southern California, productions erroneously refer to warehouses as "stages," but the warehouses can be sorely lacking in stage amenities or stage basics (like doors that close completely). As part of your prep, call Locations to ask if the space is completely insulated—for heat, light, and sound. Ask if there are double doors, if the elephant doors (large roll-up doors that allow trucks to dock) are also insulated and can close and *will be* closed during the shooting.

Ask if the Camera truck or Grip and Electric trucks will be left at the dock area. Make sure there is a remote light-and-bell system nearby for rolls and cuts. Make sure those trucks parked inside the space will not need air conditioning or heating units or if they do, ensure that they are silent when operating. The same goes if there will be changing tents for the actors.

For building-in your gold room, you'll need to collaborate with the Construction Department during pre-production to convey specific design needs. Measure your deepest, biggest case for shelf dimensions. Measure shallow cases, count them up, and give the info to the builders. Some of the items to consider for your gold room include a desk, lighting (with outlet/cable/power), electricity, room for x number of carts, two boom stands, x feet of counter space, space for x number of tool cabinet(s), two power strip bars in separate boxes (so you don't overload one), and a mat or rug corral.

Stunts: It's common these days to have stunt shots that include some dialogue or audible action. Often, the physical nature of the stunt prohibits use of radio mics for safety reasons, so expect to 2nd boom or to not work the shot. If you're not working the shot, *stay back*; not only to give everyone the space they need to work, but you also don't want to be an inadvertent victim if something goes wrong.

Understand *exactly* what is expected to happen and whether you have gear in the action zone. If you are booming the shot, confer with the stunt coordinator, and then make sure all performers know where you intend to be. For wirework (flying actors), confer with the stunt coordinator, stunt performers, and if needed, actor(s) directly to reach a solution.

Safety: Depending on the situation, wear PPE and possibly protection for the microphone (a zeppelin/blimp, windsock, horsehair). If grips are setting up safety shields, make sure they know if your department will need them as well. Try not to stand near Camera; they are involved in a high percentage of the accidents that affect crew people.

Stunts that went wrong: Early in my career, we did 2nd unit on what was our biggest movie to date: *The Sword and the Sorcerer*. I think it was the biggest stunt call in history at that time and there had been stories of problems. They were shooting in the San Bernardino area, and a stunt-man had been impaled on a spiked fence. And there we were, at the Bat Caves (Beachwood Canyon Park cave, so called because that's where the TV show *Batman* had been shot). The "C" camera operator brought us in, and there wasn't much to do that day but marvel at the production and its size.

We had hours while they set up for a stunt: a warrior jumps off the top of the hill of the cave, and then leaps into another time zone. The stunt coordinator directed the building of scaffolding against the slope, topped it with plywood sheathing, and then the largest airbag I've ever seen. Our position was perpendicular to the hill, and our camera was to catch the stuntman's jump across the entire slope, flailing through the air.

It was my first big stunt, and I watched closely. Twice I asked the camera operator about the angle; from our vantage point, it seemed the slope was too gradual to jump from the top to the air bag. He agreed and went to the stunt coordinator, who assured him that he knew what he was doing. The stuntman had done the same stunt before and there would be an Air Ram at the top (a hydraulic propulsion device). The third time we invited the coordinator to our position he refused and was so annoyed that he threw a baby crib mattress down in front of the scaffolding...we said nothing more.

When Jack Tyree did the stunt, we heard the Air Ram go off and saw Jack fly through the air. We know he hit the crib mattress with tremendous force as he bounced up into the plywood because we heard the splinter-ing; he had completely missed the air bag. He lay there about 8 minutes, it seemed—just enough time to give his stunt pals a final message to his wife and kids before he died. There was no ambulance standing by be-cause the stunt department thought it was bad luck to see it on location.

After a bit, the production called a wrap. All materials and film were impounded for subsequent investigation; and we all left quietly, alone, to consider whatever thoughts we had.

Traffic: When working in the street or very close to streets, there should be Intermittent Traffic Control (ITC) to direct traffic and make sure drivers are proceeding cautiously and carefully. Request a traffic safety vest from Production, and if you think a safety cone placed in the road before your position would be helpful, don't be shy about asking for it.

Vehicles—Driving/Tow Shots:

The definition of *picture car* or *hero car*: The vehicle that will be in the movie.

Drive-by: The camera and crew are stationary; the hero vehicle drives past the camera. Drive-by shots can be just boomed, boomed and with a radio mic in the car, or a recorder and mics (on actors or planted) in the car.

Camera mounted on the car: The camera is mounted on the hero car via a tray (called a *hostess tray*, as it is mounted on either the driver or passenger window like at a drive-in restaurant) or other means. If the driving distance is short, a plant or radio mic can be utilized, sometimes with a boom. Sometimes these shots are MOS (filmed without sound); sometimes you'll place a recorder and microphones in the vehicle and let it drive off.

www.bhphotovideo.com/c/product/33123-REG/Matthews _415167_Side_Mount_Kit.html/?ap=y&ap=y&smp=y&smp=y&lsft= BI%3A514&gclid=EAIaIQobChMIkYH74_LE6wIVlxatBh2ISgVs EAQYAiABEgK04vD_BwE

Camera car or *Insert car*: A specially designed truck with a series of platforms that is configured to allow key crew and gear to ride along with the towing of the hero vehicle. A likely scenario is that the Mixer rides in the cab with the driver. There is a tray table built in for the Mixer's equipment. Speedrail is a common component railing system used to contain equipment and personnel on the vehicle. Common Sound rigging runs include antenna (mast) bungeed to the vertical Speedrail above the cab, mic cable(s) run to the hero vehicle (tape is messy and gets pulled up by feet walking over the truck, so use bands or ties to hold the cable onto the Speedrail, following those horizontal rails). At the tow hitch, leave connectors allowing for the quick separation of the two vehicles if needed and a loop of cable so that the vehicles have slack to make turns. Scout the picture car, tow vehicle, and grip rig as soon as possible. Relay important notes on the configuration to the Mixer; sometimes pictures can help.

Camera car

Process trailer

Process trailer: A low-sided trailer with a base that the hero car rests atop.

Low Boy: A trailer for the front end of the car but the back tires are running on the road.

Shotmaker: A specialty vehicle with a camera crane mounted on it. Shotmaker is a specific company and brand of camera car. It is often applied as a generic name to these types of vehicles.

Biscuit: A self-driving vehicle with the hero car mounted directly on it, giving a strong impression that the actor is self-driving.

Side trailer: A type of process trailer mounted to the side of the camera car.

If there is a tow shot, I like to break away from the set and pre-rig the process trailer or camera tow vehicle. There's nothing more efficient than having the vehicle roughed in before the camera is mounted. The microphones can be easily adjusted once the frame is set.

Shotmaker

Biscuit

Crew vans/ follow vehicles: Sometimes you'll need to accompany the hero car in a follow vehicle with other crew (typically Hair, Makeup, Props, or stand-ins). A sample follow case/bag includes expendables, redundant cables or mics, a tape roll, and batteries (see also Chapter 8, "Equipment").

Be prepared to run out and make adjustments when the vehicles stop; carry a walkie-talkie so the Mixer can give you an alert about a situation. Sometimes the boom operator will bring a boom pole and will need to work when the hero car stops. If the boom operator doesn't bring one, think about packing one yourself.

Visual effects (VFX): Green screen and blue screen. These both refer to Chroma keying—layering two separate images to combine the elements of both. Learn what you can and cannot do regarding booming. Online tutorials are available.

Water: There are many variables with water: still, flowing, contained (pool or tank) or natural, beside the water, in the water, under the water, or in a boat.

Working on boats: Marine work with boats and ships of all sizes requires a set of questions and solutions to envision. As usual, it all begins with the script and quickly expands to a set of questions for the director, the Marine Department, Production, the medic, and others. From the UST's point of view, the range of potential logistical issues is enormous.

Here are some of the questions to think about as you analyze the information provided by the script and the production. This list is not fully comprehensive, as each production will have its unique elements. It's important to understand the wide range of possibilities involved in water work and the importance of meticulous prep since once the work begins, it's usually impossible to return to the staging area.

These questions will help you form an understanding of the upcoming work:

▸ Will we be filming day or night?

▸ What is the location: ocean, lake, river, tank, or combinations?

▸ What is the anticipated size and mode of propulsion of the craft/crafts?

▸ Who is the Marine coordinator and team and what is their contact info? Are any marine planning meetings scheduled?

▸ Is there an intended shot design or approach to the boat scenes? What about any pre-vis (pre-visualization) storyboards or animation?

▸ How many actors are expected at one time?

▸ How many cameras?

▸ What's the expected weather?

▸ Will there be real elements or FX? CGI? Rain or rough weather?

▸ Is waterproof sound gear needed?

▸ What is the nature of the support craft? Is there access and space reserved for the Sound Department? Will the work be above and/or below decks? (Try very hard *not* to ask, "Will Sound be needed...?" Do not give a non-Sound person the decision-making power; that's the Sound Department's job.)

▸ Is staging space available? Will it be above or below decks? Will there be a green room—someplace on land or a houseboat?

▸ Are there limits on how many crew can be present?

▸ Is there dock work? Open sea?

▸ How long do we expect to be on the water? Per day? The whole shoot?

▸ Any specific safety concerns not already thought of?

▸ How about provisions to mitigate seasickness? Scopolamine, Dramamine? Research getting one's sea legs.
www.goodrx.com/blog/best-medication-motion-sickness-patches-pills/

▸ Will there be ITC of adjacent marine traffic?

▸ What is the wardrobe for the cast? Any special clothing underneath their costumes (wetsuits or drysuits)?

▸ Is special weather gear or clothing needed for crew?

Physical space is confined no matter what the craft (hatches, no room for carts), so expect that it will be bag work. There might be reasonable wireless reception above deck but not so much below. Prepare for the use of wider lenses and everyone backed in corners—and there aren't that many corners. Try to get the Mixer in a central position and run a video feed. Count on all the departments jockeying for space. Have at least one weather app and monitor it, if possible.

When you're below deck and in rough water, you're at risk for motion sickness. Be preemptive about medications and side effects and the duration of use. I knew I was motion sensitive and used Scopolamine for a boat show but reached a point where I had to call the helpline: no one had used it as long as I had. I ended up needing to take 2 days off to recover and get it out of my system. Coordinate with a doctor if you have sensitivities or call the helpline for specific questions.

In cases of working in extreme wet: the condition might be ongoing. You might not be allowed *on* the boat but be responsible for prepping and restoring the gear package after.

Most times, the accessibility of actors after wiring is limited. Be sure to secure wires properly the first time and, when placing, consider ease of access. Think about waterproof lavaliers and waterproof cases for transmitters and securing them, along with wind and rain protection for booms, and bring along some horsehair.

Kayaks, small boats, canoes, rafts—what's the game plan for support vessels? Make sure there's space for Sound.

Who's in charge of your vessel? Communications are extremely important. Will you have private contact with your department or be on walkie-talkies (WTs)? If you'll be on a WT, get an in-ear monitor. What type of access will you have to actors and the set once filming is underway? Review the shot list and get as clear an idea as possible but be prepared and expect last-minute inspiration. For military vessels—destroyers, aircraft carriers, and the like—there's a strong probability you'll need additional security clearance and specific documentation.

Beach: When you're working on or close to the beach, you can imagine that the sound of the waves will be an issue. For that reason, radio-mic'ing the actors is a good bet; and if they're wearing bathing suits, be sure to go to the wiring section to learn some good practices for placement.

Awaiting department boats at the landing site

We take our fun as seriously as our work.

Is the shoot on the actual beach? How will you move the cart or what kind of cart rig does the Mixer have? Think about towels and compressed air, wind and sand protection, sun protection for you and the Mixer, and pop-up tents or sunshields for the gear. Where will the generator be placed? Has the Mixer decided to set up his cart on the sand or on the boardwalk? Will there be crowd control? Are shops operating nearby? Do they have music blaring? Camera usually requests an air tank for the truck for every show, but do not assume—have the conversation; you may need to provide a nozzle for it. Based on the information you gather, think about whether you should change the cart tires to balloon tires. When shooting at the beach, the shift in microphone position greatly changes the sound level of the tide. Moving water is difficult for Izotope or Post people to clean up.

If your shoot is in or around water, you'll also want to think about some kind of in-the-water outfit. Some shows will provide wetsuits or drysuits or hip waders when needed; you'll need to request them from Costumes (part of your prep)! On the film *Blue Crush*, boom operator John Reynolds adapted a float tube designed for fishing in which to boom from.

Arriving at the houseboat for the first time

On a production shot almost entirely on the Louisiana bayou, our day went like this: Leave the hotel in a shuttle van that dropped us at a landing at the edge of the water. There we picked up our cooler from Craft Services and took a skiff to our department's off-season crawfish boat. From there, we traveled without visible landmarks to a barge that carried the Camera-Sound and Grip-Electric trucks. There was a 4-foot (1.22 meter) difference between the height of the barge and skiff decks, so we lifted the carts and cases by hand. Our captain took us to another ambiguous spot where two houseboats waited—one for crew and one for shooting (the picture boat).

When it was time for lunch, a skiff picked us up and dropped us at a different landing for catering. Then it was back to the skiff to the houseboat to the department boat to the barge to the skiff to the landing to the crew van, and finally, to the hotel.

One memorable day, we were chasing the light (hurrying to beat sunset) at a remote shack on an island. I was booming with a long throw on a 10-step ladder chained to a floating platform, being maneuvered by a grip with an egg-beater-like tiny motor-propeller gig they had. The sun was going down fast as the 1st AD called wrap, and by the time I got down and off that platform onto the crawfish boat it was dusk; all the production staff were gone, and we headed deeper into the bayou, leaving the grips still working.

That's when we learned from our captain that the barge had to be in a different location in the morning, so it had started moving hours ago. Crawfish boats don't need lights because they only work during the day, so we had none. In the darkness, we had to creep slowly so as not to get tangled in the metal mesh fishing nets. I thought of the alligators earlier in the day rising out of the water like enemy periscopes to watch us film and took keen note of any shadows. Mark Ulano remembered he had a mini-Maglite in his bag, and that helped us move a bit faster.

Our captain couldn't find the barge in the darkness, so he had no choice but to take us to a drop point, where a crew van would be waiting. After about 20 more minutes, we saw a lone overhead light, casting a yellow glow over a boardwalk and headed for it. There were neither vehicles nor people. The captain had no qualms about leaving us; he had a dangerous trip back.

Isolated shack in the bayou

It was so noir! But I couldn't enjoy it fully because we were concerned that there was no world to speak of—at the end of the boardwalk was a dirt road, with either direction leading into dark nothingness. No streetlights, no houses. After walking a bit, we came upon a closed diner and headed for it; there was a pay phone that didn't work. We thought our safest bet was to walk along the levee, eventually finding someone or some bit of civilization.

There weren't cell phones back in the 1980s, but there were trunking phones—high-powered walkie-talkie-like communications that could latch onto phone wires and complete calls on a shared exchange. Mr. Smarty Pants Mixer had gotten one of those for the show (smart thinking!), and we eventually had service and connected with the hotel. The production manager sent a van, even though we couldn't tell him where we were. Almost three hours after wrap, we arrived in the lobby—and we weren't the last people back.

CHAPTER 17

Special Tools

There are some tools that, though not normally part of a sound package, do require periodic inclusion. The following items may need to be rented for your production, so make sure you reserve all the components of a system for the time frame proposed.

Voice of God

The *Voice of God*, or VOG, as it's often written on the call sheet, is *not* a biblical event but an idiom for a public address system (or PA, not to be confused with a Production Assistant). It is primarily used as a communications tool for the director and assistant director and can take many forms, from the smallest self-powered speaker in an intimate setting to a stadium-sized setup that cues and controls thousands of extras. There may be other situations, such as music, dance, stunts, special effects, or distance that may be aided by having a VOG available.

Basically, it involves the use of amplified microphones and speaker placement for giving verbal direction spontaneously. Most often, these systems are routed through the production Mixer's mixer so that she can control its use and levels as needed.

The Mixer and the 1st assistant director usually discuss whether it will be used and to what extent during pre-production. Certain directors or assistant directors make use of this rig every day and expect it as part of their daily setup, while others will request it only for particular situations. Additionally, the Mixer may suggest a PA on occasion, or it may become an unexpected request during the day.

The UST becomes the essential link in the logistics of the VOG and is the liaison between the various parties involved: the 1st AD, the director, the Production office, the rental house, Transpo, the choreographer, and others. During its run of use, expect that the speaker(s) will need repositioning as the shots change and, depending on the microphone user, you'll need to monitor the use and care of the microphone. Make sure in advance that power will always be available (with power from Electric or with sufficient batteries) and that cabling will not present any problems.

On *Ad Astra*, the VOG was used to provide a practical communication system between the director and the actors, who wore Apollo spacesuits with helmets on and visors down. Most of the time, you'll be able to set up, run, and wrap the system in the course of your day. If the needed system is moderately elaborate or required for a director/actor rehearsal exactly at the announced call time, the UST may need a pre-call so that the principals are not kept waiting to begin their work.

If the requirements are more complex, the UST may be asked to monitor and control the VOG system, or an additional Sound person may be needed to attend to it fulltime. There also might be times when a request is made for a walkie-talkie or music to be patched in.

Although having the right tools available often depends on good communications in advance, many production Mixers have begun to carry the essentials for a VOG system every day in their package as a means of protecting the production and themselves from not having what is needed on the filming day.

Induction Earpieces

Cue-Aids, Earwigs, and Phonak Invisity are wireless earpieces that are important communication tools provided by the production Sound team. The simplest description of these tiny, ultra-expensive devices is that they are sub-miniature,

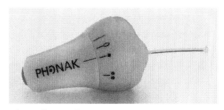

Phonak earpiece

battery-powered hearing aid-like receivers that fit in the ear of the performer(s) for a variety of possible reasons. Originally, they became a way of supplying pitch, tempo, and place-in-song information for invisible and silent-to-the-set music playback. This might be for the musicians in a band or orchestra who are performing visually but in silent mime to avoid damaging simultaneous live dialogue being recorded. They can be used for tempo reference for dancers, or cueing or direction for the performers' timing in relation to other action in the scene or the ability for the director to speak to the actor without ruining the take.

Then there's the oft-referenced "Marlon Brando" use of live cueing of lines during takes if the actor needs support for line reading—a growing preference among certain actors seeking the security of not forgetting their lines or if the lines were just supplied and insufficient time to learn them had been given. It's kind of a "teleprompter" with sound. These tools can also be employed to simulate a phone conversation in real time for the actors. There's an actor who prefers to listen to music all day long and hired a personal sound Mixer full-time to accompany him on every shoot and every movie, around the world.

There are basically two types of technology applied: The old and substantially less reliable method uses a tiny flesh-colored induction receiver in the ear that is activated by surrounding the performers with an unshielded magnetic wire loop, either embedded in the set and powered by an amplifier or a loop worn hidden around the neck plugged into a small body-pack receiver. The main vulnerability of this system is that if the receiver should stray, even slightly, from proximity to the loop, signal can be lost.

This method has been almost universally replaced by a much more sophisticated and expensive way to get the signal to the performer by wireless transmission. This has become the norm and is a much more reliable method, allowing for multiple frequencies to avoid interference and much greater freedom of motion for the actors. These are not sonically superior devices and shouldn't be confused with in-ear monitors or IFB receivers.

The UST is the major link to the cast with this technology. She must know how to set up the whole system, including a separate and acoustically isolated workstation for the transmitter and microphone/mixer required to feed signal if someone is reading to the actor or to interface the system with the various possible music playback methods being applied. Also, frequency coordination is necessary for the transmission channel or channels if more than one "send" is required. Further, there may be interaction with the Make-Up Department if the receivers need to be color-matched to the skin tone of the user.

Your job is to be the guardian of these delicate devices, ever vigilant to make sure the batteries are sufficiently viable, that performers are receiving signal without incident, and to ensure the performer's comfort with volume and usability. This includes always sanitizing before and after use and keeping track of the location and status of each unit. On a larger production, these duties can easily migrate into requiring full-time attention and additional UST or even Mixer personnel to fully focus on the specific requirements.

To begin, always assemble and test the system within your department first! Once a moderate level is set, clean and disinfect the receiver (there's a special tool that is inserted into the receiver to push out earwax). If the actor has a support team, ask the assistant if the actor has any known hearing issues or loss and adjust the level to start. If the subject is a musician, start with the gain higher.

Make sure the ADs know a bit of time will be needed to explain and test the system with the actor and have him or her brought to the workstation. If the Mixer will be supplying music playback, it will be easier to set levels and answer questions if everyone is in the same space. Offer a cotton swab (Q-tip) to the talent to clean out the ear of their choice *or* the away-from-camera ear if the action and shot angle is known. Then have him or her insert the receiver and test the level with either the microphone and person who will be reading lines or with the music. Make sure the actor knows to return the earpiece to you once released from set and, of course, monitor the set and be ready to grab it yourself. Because they can be fickle devices, be sure to have a backup ready to go.

EZ-UPs, Pelsue Tents, and Other Shelter

While camping is not a regular part of the production process, spontaneous quick shelter for the Sound Department is another logistical responsibility involving the UST. The issue of protecting the gear and the department from the elements is a very important concern that can happen in many different ways, but it usually starts with an assessment of the location geography and the shooting schedule.

One hopes that sufficient pre-production has taken place informing the departments of where they can position themselves around the set or work area to achieve the closest proximity to the work without obstructing any other department from access. Without a proper location scout involving the key heads of departments, a mini land-grab often occurs as the departments work out where they can stage their carts and equipment. Depending on the style of the production

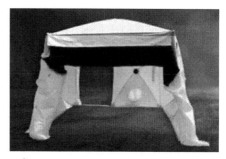

Pelsue tents

Mixer and the protocol established with the project, the UST is usually the "advance troop" for the Sound Department's placement at the location. Sun, rain, and cold are the most common reasons for needing shelter if exterior work is planned or if there is no available interior space for setting up. Two products frequently used for quick cover are Pelsue tents (**https://pelsue.com/product-category/tents/**) and EZ-UP folding shelters (**www.ezup.com**).

The usual size EZ-UP used is the 10-foot unit. Side panels are available, and there are many configurations and accessories. Side panels are a must for active weather conditions. Pelsue tents come in 8-foot and 6-foot versions and are used as individual shelter for the Sound cart and satellite carts if needed. Pelsue tents can also be linked if needed. Neither of the tent options have floors, so consider wind and prepare for some type of staking.

Many Mixers include one or the other or even both in their equipment packages.

Also, most narrative productions keep a supply of EZ-UP shelters available for staging at location. These may be managed by one of several different sources on production, e.g., Craft Services, Transportation, or PAs. It is a good idea for the UST to determine whether the production includes the Sound department in their planning for instant shelters or if they expect the department to store and travel shelter equipment themselves. Sometimes sharing with another department can make sense, but that's usually not the case. Also, weatherproof Visqueen cart covering bags, although not actually shelter, are also an essential expendable to have in the kit to protect the equipment.

www.filmtools.com/instantsearchplus/result/?q=bag%20it

Assistive Devices for Boom Operators

With the introduction of digital moviemaking, directors want to shoot continuously; some takes have gone on for 25 minutes or more! This puts an unhealthy strain on boom operators (not to mention camera operators and others working the shot) and eliminates opportunities to make corrections. The labor and management Safety Committee recommends communication between affected parties at all stages of production and that options be considered.

Fortunately, several companies make products for the construction industries and are being modified for film work. Exoskeletons are devices that take some of the weight and strain off holding loaded boom poles. There are multiple manufacturers producing the Ekso Vest, Shoulder X, Comau Mate, Paexo Shoulder, and Airframe by Levitate.

Shoulder X v.3

CHAPTER 18

Cleaning the Gear

An important task is to keep the equipment and accessories clean and in good working order. There never seems to be enough time to concentrate on a "cleaning day," but you can find small blocks of time if you stay mindful. This is one task that benefits from regular, consistent bits of attention.

Your location will dictate how often the carts and equipment on them will need cleaning. Pay attention to the areas that your department touches often: sliders on the mixing panel, drawer pulls, cart handles, etc. Run a baby wipe and/or disinfectant over them regularly.

Wipe down the fronts of racked equipment and carts. Battery blocks and whatever is on the cart bottoms get dustier faster and need wiping or brushing.

Microphones

Manufacturers have their own methods for cleaning specific microphones, and one method *does not* fit all. Check the manufacturers' websites. Below are procedures for some commonly used microphones. Compressed air is fine for all equipment as long as you are careful not to drive dirt further into the item.

Neumann: Microphone housings may be cleaned with either ethyl alcohol (ethanol) or isopropyl alcohol (isopropanol), commonly a 70% solution, applied *to the outside* with a soft cloth, soft brush, or paper tissue. Some models have removable head baskets for cleaning but do not touch the capsule! Inner assemblies/amplifiers should not be cleaned with alcohol, but a soft brush for dust is safe. Only a service technician should clean a capsule.

https://en-de.neumann.com/mic-cleaning

Schoeps: Always ensure that the capsules are not used in a dusty environment and that they are kept in a closed container (e.g., in the case provided) after use, as the ingress of dust may impair their function. In conjunction with high humidity, this can lead to condensation and thus cracking noises. If the microphone capsule has become wet, it should dry for about half an hour at room temperature, and then it will usually work properly again.

If the microphone makes clicks, it is likely that the capsule inside is dusty. At this point, it is necessary to send it for cleaning. The manufacturers strongly advise against opening and cleaning by the customer, partly because this invalidates all warranty claims. Also, the contact rings of the capsules must not be cleaned with liquids.

If use in a dirty or dusty environment is unavoidable, a windshield should be used to avoid the problems described above. A dirty capsule, microphone amplifier, or active accessory can be cleaned by blowing out the contact plate with oil-free compressed air. If this does not help, a new toothbrush soaked with isopropyl alcohol (isopropanol) can be used to clean the contact plate while the amplifier or active accessory is held down. Then shake off excess liquid. It must not get inside the amplifier or active accessory! Ensure adequate drying.

https://schoeps.de/en/knowledge/knowledge-base/microphone-use-covid-19.html

Sennheiser: Clean all products only with a soft, dry cloth. Unscrew the sound inlet basket. Remove the foam insert from the sound inlet basket. Use a slightly damp cloth to clean the sound inlet basket from the inside and outside.

https://en-us.sennheiser.com/microphone-hygiene

Windscreens

Windscreens should be cleaned in a mild solution of warm water and dish soap. Windscreens made from plastic and other solid materials can be cleaned with cleaning agents or disinfectants (e.g., 70% isopropyl alcohol) without problems. Foam can be carefully washed with warm water and mild detergent and dried at up to 70° F.

Information from Rycote for windjammers: "We recommend only hand washing with either lukewarm or cold water in a mild detergent. Then allow the fur to air dry (NEVER tumble dry your Windjammer), and then brush out to avoid the fur becoming matted."

Boom Poles

K-Tek offers a product called Boomshine to keep boom poles cleaned and polished throughout their long life on set. Boomshine is ideal for K-Tek Klassic and Avalon **Aluminum** and **Graphite** poles, as well as **Carbon Fiber** boom poles and other brands.

https://ktekpro.com/product/kbos-boomshine-kit/

Cables

Canare Cable recommends a simple wipe down with a damp cloth. If it requires something more, use a bucket of soapy water and some drying rags. Some people use Armor All or olive oil to renew their cables.

Cases

Pelican Commercial Support (**csrcomm@pelican.com**) recommends removing adhesive from their cases by using Goo Gone (**https://googone.com/**). Be careful if you choose to use a stronger product, as it can dull the case surface and not necessarily remove the adhesive.

Label your cases rather than letting the shippers do so.

Radio Microphones

Lectrosonics: Battery doors and the 5-pin jacks are particularly suscepti-ble to wear and tear. These tips from Lectrosonics can help:

If the battery door and mating surface on your SM series transmitters are starting to become difficult to open, don't scrub them with an abra-sive! Units can be damaged by steel wool, sandpaper, and other materials. Multiple problems can be created as a result, such as getting particulate (tiny pieces that break off) into the unit, damaging the battery contacts on the door, and removing the conductive coating from this area and even the entire housing.

To clean, use Wright's Silver Cream (available in Wal-Mart and Home Depot; a small container will last you a year or more) to clean the door and housing. Using a small amount of cream, allow drying and then *gently* clean the transmitter the door and housing. If excessive force is used when removing the dried cream, the conductive finish can be removed along with it. Removing the thumbscrew from the door can make cleaning easier, though it should be done in a specific manner. Instructions on how to properly do that follow.

Please keep an eye on the e-clip and washer that, if lost, damaged, or replaced incorrectly, can cause the thumbscrew to not seat properly in the case and cause wear to both the door and mating surface. In general, alcohol is a safe solution. Bleach or Lysol solutions are not recommended, as they can be corrosive. The solution made at Lectrosonics consists of 16 ounces of 91% isopropyl alcohol plus 4 ounces of water (which makes a 70% alcohol solution), mixed in a 32-ounce spray bottle. Look for a spray bottle with a fine mist that will disperse the solution without soaking what you are spraying. You can also use 70% alcohol packaged wipes, as they are lint-free and save you from the worry of accidentally spray-ing or dripping solution into the equipment. Depending on the surface to be cleaned, it can be lightly sprayed, wiped, or dabbed with Q-tips. Lectrosonics provides these general guidelines:

▸ Remove any batteries and disconnect power cords prior to cleaning.

▸ Wear rubber gloves when cleaning equipment and discard the gloves after use. Do not reuse the gloves, as the [corona]virus can survive for a time on many surfaces.

- Use disposable lint-free cloths/wipes/Q-tips and do not be tempted to reuse them.

- Clean in an open area with good ventilation, alone or around minimal people, observing the 6-foot social distancing protocols.

- Once equipment is disinfected and is dry, you can keep it in Ziploc bags to ensure that it remains disinfected until you are ready to use it. Ensure that the unit is fully dry, and then put it into the bag and squeeze out all the air before closing.

The 5-pin opening and contacts for microphones on SMs can also collect grease and dirt.

Use canned air first to blow out any dust or lint-like particles inside. If more is needed, clean it using alcohol and an acid brush (used to apply paste flux for soldering) *while holding the unit upside down* to keep the contaminants out of the transmitter.

Removing the battery door assembly:

1. Remove the battery door assembly from the transmitter by unscrewing the knob (hereafter referred to as the thumbscrew) on the battery door.

2. Using isopropyl alcohol and a Q-Tip, carefully clean the threads on the housing of the transmitter.

3. Use a small slotted screwdriver to remove the e-clip from the thumbscrew. Insert the tip of the screwdriver in notches of the e-clip to pop it off the screw.

4. Remove the thumbscrew from the door.

5. Put the new washer onto the new thumbscrew and then place them on the door.

6. Add any vinyl tape to the door to prevent scratching when applying the e-clip. Install the e-clip onto the thumbscrew using pliers. Remove the tape after installing the e-clip.

7. Apply silver conductive paste to the thumbscrew threads to improve electrical connection from the battery compartment through the housing on the transmitter.

8. Open the vial and transfer a pinhead speck of silver conductive paste to the second thread from the end of the thumbscrew. An easy way to pick up a speck of paste is to partially unfold a paper clip and use

the end of the wire to acquire a tiny bit of paste. A toothpick will also work. An amount that covers the end of the wire is sufficient.

9. Replace the battery door on the transmitter.

Lavalier mics: Wipe down the cord and head with the alcohol and a clean cloth. If the lav has a foam head (head basket), remove it, lightly spray it with the alcohol, and let it dry. You can then clean the head with a Q-tip.

- ▸ www.dpamicrophones.com/mic-university/5-simple-steps-to-wash-your-dpa-microphone
- ▸ www.youtube.com/watch?v=N3xsWvGHhig&vl=en

Bubblebee windbubble:

www.youtube.com/watch?v=WX4O8P3eINc&feature=emb_rel_end

Cleaning a Bubblebee concealer:

www.bubblebeeindustries.com/blogs/guides/cleaning-the-lav-concealer

"Invisible" face-contacting mics: As these contact the skin and body and are in the breathing trajectory, wipe the surfaces with alcohol and a clean cloth.

Cords/antennas/power supplies: Wipe down with alcohol and a clean cloth.

Transmitters and receivers: Wipe down with the alcohol and a clean cloth. You may also carefully clean the terminals and switch areas with a Q-tip lightly moistened with the alcohol. Take care not to drip liquid into any of the openings.

Carry bags: As these are a fabric-like woven material, lightly spray with the alcohol and allow to dry thoroughly. Do not shake bags, as this can cause any viral particles to disperse into the air.

Many technicians in broadcast work in environments such as medical news, crime scenes, war zones, or documentaries, where maintaining cleanliness and safety are challenging. If you have any questions about proper disinfection of your equipment, email the manufacturers or reach out on their Facebook groups.

CHAPTER 19

COVID-19 Protocols

While the Alliance of Motion Picture and Television Producers (AMPTP) and IATSE have agreed to Covid-19 work protocols to address health concerns in returning to work, individual companies have leeway to institute some procedures of their own. Therefore, read your company's rules carefully and check them against current health department information. The CDC guidelines are official government health guidelines and take precedence over any advice that I am sharing.

> Washing your hands often with soap and water and wearing masks are established, effective actions. Keeping at least 6 feet (US guidelines) from others will lessen the chance of becoming exposed to the virus. Areas outside the US advocate one meter or two meters distance from other people, depending on the country.

The following information is the most up to date as of this writing and reflects information gathered from the Internet, crewmember experiences, and a major Hollywood studio's collaboration with an otolaryngologist (ear, nose, and throat doctor).

Testing

Some projects are directing crewmembers to a specific facility for screening, some are asking you to go to a facility of your own choosing and submit the results to the production company and receive a stipend, and some are asking you to get a test at your expense. Even though the (US) IRS guidelines state that stipends are not tax-deductible, some payroll companies are nonetheless withholding tax on the amounts. You will most likely have a questionnaire to fill out about your activities in the recent past. Nasal swabs are not Food and Drug Administration (FDA) approved for screening, as there are a lot of false positives. Once the virus is in the air, it can lie in ventilation systems for months. Frequent testing allows the production company to identify Covid-19 carriers *before* they shed viral load.

Again, individual shows are creating their own procedures. Options include the honor system of each person stating they have practiced conscientious safety procedures by signing a form, self-quarantining an arbitrary number of days before principal photography, or a mandatory 2-week lockdown in a hotel.

The Set

Many of the locations have a one-way entrance and exit. Most sets now have the producers and other video village residents work remotely. Sometimes a Covid-19 Compliance Officer is present to oversee operations, but there are also stories of glorified PAs handling this responsibility.

Pods

Pods are individual workstations (a 4' x 6' space for a chair and gear, spaced 6 feet apart) or areas that are essentially department spaces. Some people will have a "bubble buddy"—someone who the work dictates is closely related with your work. There are hand sanitizer stations throughout the set and at many carts. Signage will inform you of the company's directives.

Zones/Colors

These are actually people designations, based on proximity to the actors. While there are variations from project to project, the following description is a mainstream studio breakdown:

▸ "Zone A" consists of (A) all performers and background actors working on set; and (B) all employees who are present in a workspace with a performer or background actor while the performer or background actor is not wearing PPE (personal protective equipment).

▸ "Zone B" consists of those employees who work on a "hot" set, but who are not present in a workspace with a performer or background actor while the performer or background actor is not wearing PPE, all Zone B employees while they work during prep, and employees who work in any other area where the production has a footprint that is not an area where "Zone C" or "Zone D" employees work.

▸ "Zone C" consists of those employees who:

(A) are able to wear PPE at all times while working;

(B) only work with other employees who are also able to wear PPE at all times while working;

(C) are not required to be within six (6) feet of other individuals for longer than fifteen (15) minutes while working (provided that if the local governmental authority has issued guidelines with a more stringent time/distance standard for determining when individuals come into "close contact" with other individuals for purposes of Covid-19 contact tracing, the standard in such guidelines shall apply instead); and

(D) do not come into contact with "Zone A" or "Zone B" employees in the course of their work, unless both the Zone "A" or "Zone B" employee and the "Zone C" employee are wearing PPE at all times and do not come within six (6) feet of each other for longer than fifteen (15) minutes; provided, however, "Zone C" employees may not enter "Zone A" or "Zone B" when "Zone A" or "Zone B" employees are present unless they have tested negative.

At another studio, for example, *orange* is wherever the actors are present—on set or their holding area. The set changes to *yellow* when they are not present. The majority of grips/set lighting are designated *yellow* with a couple from each department being designated *orange* for when changes need to be made while actors are on set. The boom operator is *orange*, as is the UST. *Yellow*-designated people are not allowed to be around the actors. *Orange*-designated crew are allowed to be around them for immediate need only and must wear eye protection in conjunction with masks.

Quarantining

If someone in a pod tests positive, the pod members should isolate for 10 days, and anyone contact-traced should quarantine for 14 days. As of this writing, there are still no standard parameters or criteria for returning to work. Some crewmembers have reported having the company send everyone home immediately but then return the next day, someone reported staying home the next day after someone tested positive, and others have said there was no change in work.

The Bubble

An option preferred by some productions is to house the company in a hotel, sequestering everyone for a two-week period before work commences and then following pre-Covid-19 workflow. This ensures everyone's safety and negates the need for extra measures, sanitizing, testing expenses, time spent disinfecting and the inevitable shutdown when someone tests positive.

Face Shields

Mixers have commented that cheap face shields work well, and more expensive ones are not necessary. As with most topics in the sound world, equipment and procedures are constantly changing; the latest discussions, reviews, and recommendations can be found online, through your union or in local professional groups.

Gloves

The risk of the job should be considered when deciding between latex, vinyl, and nitrile exam gloves. Doctors, nurses, caregivers, dentists and other healthcare workers typically use examination gloves. Latex and nitrile gloves are commonly used when dealing with high-risk situations involving blood, bodily fluids, or patients with infectious diseases. Both latex and vinyl gloves can be used for low-risk, general procedures. Surgical gloves are higher quality and are designed specifically for the accuracy and sensitivity required by surgeons. Consider whether surgical gloves would be the best choice for wiring actors.

Comments from Sound People

Following are some comments from Sound people who have worked during the Covid-19 pandemic:

> *"Well, anyone helping the boom operator, pulling cable, planting microphones, placing rugs, or working second boom has to be Zone A. So you need a Zone B person to assist the Mixer, help with the extra load at video assist, and pass cables halfway in, plus get stuff from the truck. If you want gender-matching wiring, you'd need both genders in Zone A."*

> *"This is how I pitched an additional person to Company X:*
>
> *As for the UST, responsibilities include but are not limited to: Sanitization of all sound gear, including radio mic transmitters, lavaliers, pouches, and belts, boom mic windscreens, Comteks, and headsets. She will also handle distribution and collection of Comteks and headsets as needed. This person shall act as the Sound Department's sole connection between outside-zone personnel as well as video village, DIT, and Transpo. This will help insulate the boom guys who will be in direct contact with the cast most often. On high cast count days, she will assist with wiring and additional boom. She checks off diversity boxes and helps us get onboard with IATSE's diversity training program. For the cost of one background person, we get a lot of bang for our buck!"*

> *"When it comes to mic'ing the actor, I give the lavalier to him to put in place, keeping a relatively safe distance, helping with guidance on adjustments in positioning for him to do. After that, I put the transmitter on his belt at the back and make sure the cable is hidden. After finishing, I immediately put alcohol gel on my hands, and go straight to the bathroom to wash hands, arms, and face with soap and water, put alcohol gel back on my hands, and change the mask.*
>
> *This is my daily hard work, as well as that of so many other audio professionals, videographers, reporters, and technicians who are risking their health so that the population can have information in their homes."*

ClearCom hosted a webinar to discuss communication systems during Covid-19 protocols:

www.assets.clearcom.com/web/10644023aefc427d/2020-webinar-comms-for-socially-distanced-media-production/?mediaId=C3BFB0D7-81B3-416C-993FD9A9C7B1CBC1

NOTES

CHAPTER 20

Safety

I t is prudent to *ALWAYS keep your wits about you.* No shot is worth a life.

> *FILMMAKING IS DANGEROUS. FILM SETS ARE INDUSTRIAL WORKSITES, AND ULTIMATELY EACH PERSON IS RESPONSIBLE FOR HIS OR HER OWN SAFETY.*

Nothing you do on a set is more professional, or more personal, than maintaining safety. Film sets are dangerous, and you are the best person to keep yourself out of harm's way. You should not run on a set even if the Mixer or some authority figure pressures you to do so—*unless you are running to safety.*

Filmmaking is not only dangerous, but can be deadly, and every setup and take is different. Understand that everyone can be fresh and aware on Take One but may be tired, distracted, or lax on Take Seventeen. While safety meetings are usually provided in filmmaking environments, it's always appropriate for you to inquire whenever you feel concerned. Don't put yourself in a situation that just feels wrong. It's one of the "perks" that Sound may call a shot MOS (a shot filmed without recording sound).

MOS

MOS is usually the designation called when a shot is being filmed without sound and may occur for a variety of reasons—e.g., filming a shot at a speed other than "normal" (24 frames per second in film or 30 or 29.97 frames per second for video), when there is no possible usable sound or guide track desired, or when the situation is dangerous. A *guide track* is a temporary track used for editorial purposes as a "guide" for when the replacement sounds/dialogue are synced with the picture. However, recording sound anyway can sometimes give Postproduction staff inter-esting material to work with. At times, while recording a guide track, you will need to boom the slate and then assume a backed-off position. Use caution in making your way quickly off the set after the slate and be mindful of where you end up; boom operators have had flaming gas cans land where they were standing just a minute before.

I've been on a set where the DOP had a tantrum, picked up a baling hook, and threw it across the barn, landing just beside me! I've had actors step on me or decide to scream during a quiet scene, sending me to the hospital to test for hearing damage.

Do not create hazards. Make sure cable runs are laid flat (mats are faster, cleaner, and cover a wider area than tape; when you must use tape, use paper tape, never gaffer's tape), stabilize the carts, speakers, and antennae masts. Lift heavy cases using your legs more than your arms. Ask for help if you must lift heavy cases or music speakers. Never lose control of your cart; never let it tip over.

Remember: *Use the production report to note any little thing that happens to you that might affect your health or safety.* It's impossible to predict what may develop from what seems to be a minor injury. It's important to document these events for your own protection or that of your department. Case in point: A boom operator pushed a case on the top shelf of the Sound truck and felt a "ping!" in his wrist. It resulted in carpal tunnel surgery that ended up affecting both hands, a very painful recovery (the body part with the most nerves in it, the physical therapist said), and after 18 months, a determination that he should be trained for another career. If he hadn't listed that little "ping" feeling on the production report, he would have had to pay all those costs himself.

Or the UST who was hit on the nose by an XLR connector when the boom operator threw a cable at her instead of *to* her; she was off the set for 25 minutes while icing it, needed a CAT scan, and 2 years later still has loose cartilage.

Or the stunt guy who wanted to promote himself to stunt coordinator and perform his own stunt. When it went wrong and the stunt action slammed him into the side of a garage, he convulsed and became unconscious. The producer yelled to pick up the stuntman and put him in the back of the producer's Mercedes to drive him to the hospital. Thankfully, enough crew yelled, *"Don't move someone with a potential spine injury!"* It took 35 minutes for an ambulance to arrive because it was a busy Friday night, and the producers had decided to save money by not having an ambulance stand by. I heard he was in the hospital for six or seven months, and in physical therapy for a year.

And—I hope this hits closer to home for film school students: a 20' x 20' grifflon (tarp) hanging from a crane lost some tie-down straps in a big wind. The key grip yelled for everyone to help grab a rope. The experienced crew let go when the wind pulled hard; a 19-year-old girl PA grabbed tighter. The wind picked her up, slammed her against a building, and she dropped to the ground.

The next day I went to the hospital with flowers from the department. Her family told me she was being kept in a coma because, when awake, the pain was unbearable. She was completely covered in bandages except for part of her face. After a time, they transported her to a bigger-city hospital where she would undergo multiple surgeries for an indefinite period.

The MOS myth: Some of the early Hollywood directors came from Europe during the first half of the 20th century. Their first language was German, and they had trouble pronouncing the word "with." Instead of saying, "We are recording this scene without sound," they allegedly said, "Mit out sound," or MOS.

MOS may stand for:

▸ Minus optical signal (This is the most likely origin, as surviving studio logs from the 1930s show this column on the camera reports.)

▸ Minus optical sound

▸ Minus optical stripe

▸ Muted on screen

▸ Mute on sound

▸ Mic off stage

▸ Music on side

▸ Motor only shot

▸ Motor only sync

Learn the value of the Sound Department calling the shot MOS: for example, when there are dangerous or uncontrollable elements, when there wouldn't be any value to recording the sound (such as for a pastoral scene that has a freeway just out of frame, and therefore a guide track would be worthless), or when there's somewhere more important that the Sound Department should be.

When there are dangerous elements and you want to roll, consider using a locked-off boom, a wire, or a plant mic. Conversely, don't be too quick to call a shot MOS; you could get some lovely sounds that the postproduction Sound teams will appreciate. And don't be too quick to leave the set and go off to lunch lest you be treated to an exceptional moment, like when George Harrison autographed Daniels's guitar on the set of *Checking Out* and then decided to play for the crew.

Mark Ulano,
George Harrison, and
Patrushkha Mierzwa

The job of a UST requires nearly constant movement; it's common to walk 14,000 or more steps in a workday. Make sure you stay hydrated and eat when you can. Wash your hands often and wear work gloves when handling cables and carts. Always be aware of your surroundings and safety guidelines. If you're working in an unsavory location, ask for someone to accompany you.

I recommend some personal products to keep on the truck: aspirin, Advil (for muscle strain), a muscle strain ointment, ice packs, Salonpas medicated pads, Kinesio tape, and elastic bandages, in case you pull a muscle. I have felt energized after taking Berocca (a fizzy tablet to put in water, which contains B vitamins and caffeine), which I first received from a medic but now carry with me.

Midnight Rider

Midnight Rider is the name of a non-union biopic shot in Georgia that has been so publicized that I think it's important to take a moment and reflect on the circumstances of how the events unfolded. It's not the first movie to have someone die during production, and it's not the most surprising, but it *has* gotten a lot of publicity and therefore should be mentioned as a cautionary tale.

Train trestle

I remember that at the time Georgia was known on the West Coast as a "wild west" location, where productions could escape the rules and procedures in Hollywood and allegedly shoot smaller, faster, and cheaper. There were a couple of shows prior to *Midnight Rider*, and the stories from those sets supported that notion.

Here's a distillation from a published article, "A Train, a Narrow Trestle and 60 Seconds to Escape: How *Midnight Rider* Victim Sarah Jones Lost Her Life" by Scott Johnson (*The Hollywood Reporter*, March 4, 2014), of the event:

> *As the day wore on, director* **Randall Miller** *moved the shoot from the land beside the river onto the narrow grid work of the trestle itself, which extends over the edge of the Altamaha (river). The trestle's wood and metal bottom [were] covered with pebbles and had gaping holes in some places. The blustery wind rang through the girders, making it hard to stay steady, said a crewperson.*

> *From shore, several dozen yards away, a voice shouted to the crew that in the event a train appeared, everyone would have 60 seconds to clear the tracks. "Everybody on the crew was tripping over that. A minute? Are you serious?" Several crewmembers were nervous enough that before shooting they gathered in an informal prayer circle. "Lord, please protect us on these tracks. Surround us with your angels and help us, Lord."*

While they prayed, a camera assistant helped load film, monitor the cameras' and transport gear. She wasn't really the type to fret much. The crew was filming a dream sequence, and they had placed a twin-size metal-framed bed and mattress in the middle of the tracks. Someone looked up and saw a light in the distance, followed by the immense howl of a locomotive. It was a train hurtling toward them.

Two stories high, screaming with the sound of a blast horn and possibly brakes, the train was nearly as wide as the trestle. Miller yelled at everyone to run. The camera assistant had several bags slung over each shoulder and wondered what to do with the expensive camera equipment.

With no intention of commenting on religion or people's personal coping mechanisms, everyone on that shoot had the option to say they were uncomfortable. Everyone had the option to speak quietly among the crew and cast and consider a united front to speak up about safety concerns.

Your best defense is your instinct and the instincts of your fellow crewmembers.

It makes for good copy to portray the tragedy as "an accident" or that the blame and a lawsuit should be placed on someone else, such as a deep-pocket company that did not approve the shoot in no uncertain terms. I read many accounts of the incident, as well as hearing firsthand from a crewmember when he got back to the hotel that night. Here are some bits to consider:

The actor said he didn't think the situation was safe, but no one backed him up, so they all continued. A crewmember was quoted as saying that he himself was an artist and someone else was responsible for protecting him. The experienced 2nd assistant cameraperson understood that getting off the track was a critical mission, loaded herself with equipment, and wondered what to do.

YOU ARE YOUR OWN FIRST DEFENSE FOR SAFETY AT WORK

The bottom line is: Regardless of who was right or wrong, someone is dead, and others are traumatized for life. **You can debate both sides of this situation, but in the end:** *Do you want to be "a team player" or stay alive?*

CHAPTER 21

Wasted Time and Energy

I can't tell you how many hours of my life were wasted on sets while a committee of producers discussed all the different ideas that they wanted the director to take into consideration—while the crew waited. All the waiting would honestly add up to months.

Or the silliness of having split calls on Fridays on a stage because the director could never complete his day's work in the time that he was tasked. Somewhere along the way, it became OK for directors to learn during work hours, at the expense of the film crew, rather than at a film school; it became OK to have people who had paid their dues and learned their craft be shrugged off.

I remember a belly-dancing scene in a fairly famous movie of the week I worked on in the '90s. Based on the established characters from the long-lived series, none of the squeaky-clean male characters would ever be placed in this type of plot situation. It didn't make sense to any of the filming crew.

Alas, 60 crewmembers found themselves at 1:00 A.M. on a Saturday morning being the *last* crew working on the Warner Brothers lot because of that scene.

The director was delighted, as were the producers and some of the cast. You can imagine the looks on the faces of the crew. Very little shooting was done, but we did indeed take at least four hours to shoot the scene with coverage. The lead actor smiling? Of course. Dad and a brother? Duh. Grandpa, too? Yes, the Grandpa character leered.

When we wrapped, even the gate guard couldn't resist a condolence; he was dumbfounded when I told him what we had shot. Did it make its way into the show? No way in hell. Who approved it all the way down the line says a lot about waste and how a production thinks about crew welfare.

If only I could tell this story when ridiculousness raises its ugly head on the set.

If you're new to this business, know that you will be kept away from your family, sleep, and regular meals, tearing your hair out to create good work for shots that will never be in the movie. And you'll do it over and over and over.

Directors

The less the director knows what they need to accomplish in a day, the more difficult your job becomes. It has become more common these days to need to guess at shots. This takes away from the time you have available to do the work and/or interferes with your ability to consider best-case options; you are scrambling just to have *one* option.

In the past, directors had answers to your questions; they had done their prep. Over the years, directors have not come up through the ranks of ADs or DOPs; instead, they're often writers or editors or producers or actors who don't know how movies are really made. When productions had financial consequences for shooting more than 12 hours, you better believe that directors came prepared, or suffered the wrath of the money people—yes, even the non-union Roger Corman shoots!

In fact, when I worked at *old* New World— there was a *new* New World— there was a policy: if the work wasn't done in 12 hours, everything stopped and the crew was gathered. The production manager explained the desire of the director to continue and why, and then management left while the crew deliberated. If we stayed, it was for a specific time only, and we were all given cash bumps (bonuses) at wrap. If we voted no, there was no discussion or retaliation. And we *always* wrapped by midnight Friday (no "Fraturdays" or worse—a *Fraturday* meaning a shooting day that begins with a Friday evening call time and ends with a Saturday morning wrap—also known as the blown weekend and sleep-deprivation sickness).

> *Remember this: The Roger Corman movies came in on time and on budget.*

CHAPTER 22

Building Your Career

It's easy: Be perfect—every take, every interaction.

—Patrushkha Mierzwa

Discipline is choosing between what you want now and what you want most.

—(possibly) Abraham Lincoln

We are what we repeatedly do. Excellence, then, is not an act, but a habit.

—Will Durant

Try not to become a person of success, but rather a person of value.

—Albert Einstein

Luck is what happens when preparation meets opportunity.

—Seneca

Opportunity is missed by most people because it is dressed in overalls and looks like work.

—Anonymous

I received this example for the book from a colleague: "My Utility does a really good job of making sure we have all the supplies we need, from alcohol to zeppelins. If it's an expendable or a permanent piece of kit, he knows what we have, how many we have, and if it needs maintenance or replacing.... On my team, he has assumed those duties and manages them well. It certainly makes him a valuable team member."

Make an Impression: Memorize Names

Learn the names of the people you'll deal with the most and use each of their names before lunch. On a one-day shoot, do that before the first shot. It really makes a difference! After your contacts with the Sound

Department, start with Camera crew, Script, grip and electric best boys, keys (heads of departments), and the dolly grip, but memorize as many crew names as fast as you can.

Continuing Education

To stay current with your education, there are Sound and Sound-related apps that you can find with a search engine or an app store. Do your due diligence and check out reviews first. Visit manufacturers' websites, equipment house websites, and industry Facebook groups. Sound is an ever-evolving craft, as is moviemaking, and you are ever evolving yourself. If you're not continuing to grow and learn, you're becoming obsolete.

When you're new to the set, you'll see a lot of specialized tools and equipment, and you should be familiar with other departments' tools. Read through grip equipment and still camera catalogs; keep an eye out for tools from other industries that could work for Sound (it will be far less expensive as well!).

If You're Just Starting Out

There are programs in which you shadow or intern on productions. The Academy of Motion Picture Arts and Sciences (AMPAS) has their Gold program.

> *The Academy Gold Program is a multi-tiered educational and experiential initiative designed to enhance and extend an industry-wide diversity internship enhancement program under the Academy brand. The initiative affords top film entertainment, technology, production services, and digital media companies an all-inclusive pass to recruit and educate a nationwide pool of diverse talent. The program offers interns exclusive access to Academy members, industry professionals, screenings, and educational workshops offering an inclusive industry networking experience.*

www.oscars.org/learn/academy-gold-program

In the United Kingdom (UK), ScreenSkills offers its program:

> Screenskills is the industry-led skills body for the screen industries. We work across the UK to ensure that film, television (including children's and high-end drama), VFX (visual effects), animation, and games have the skills and talent they need. We provide insight, career development and other opportunities to help grow and sustain the skilled and inclusive workforce, which is the foundation stone of the UK's global screen success.

www.screenskills.com

Individual learning institutions may have their own programs and ties to the local film community and are worth looking into.

Some production Mixers ask for and receive permission to bring on individuals who are already in a higher-education program; one approach if you don't know anyone is to write a fan letter to a specific Mixer and inquire.

Size Matters!

The biggest deficiencies I experience when working on smaller projects are the *lack of interaction the Sound Department has with the other departments and the lack of respect given to the Sound Department.* And the biggest difference I see on working the big A-list shows is *the amount of collaboration and preparation and that "extra" that each person gives to the project.*

That extra step of care and concern and effort: For example, we all use essentially the same or a similar palette of microphones and accessories, as there are only a few manufacturers of our specialty equipment. And everyone has access (Internet) to the same classes, resources, manufacturer webinars, and YouTube videos. So what is the difference between working on smaller shows and big tent-pole movies?

If a small show gives a Mixer one day of prep, a large-scale project gives her two to three weeks. If there's a locations scout, Mixers probably won't be invited to the scout on a small shoot—nay, won't even be *allowed* (Production won't want to spend the money for the Mixer's contribution). On a major production, however, Mixers will scout *wherever* the location is (sometimes around the globe). During that time, they'll learn about the working relationship between the director and DOP and producers and their respective points of view. They'll have an opportunity to learn about potential future problems (generator placement, construction, public works projects and street closures, school class bells, and AC systems that can't be turned off—or maybe they can be turned off but need 15 minutes between shut down and turn on). In short, they'll be included in the process of helping extract the maximum production value for the money.

> *People think that because it's a big-budget movie you get all the money in the world and all the time you need to do your work. NO! We work harder and make it look like it's a normal experience.*

Quentin Tarantino movies are notable for their writing, craft value (production, cinematography, sound, makeup, hair, costumes, and acting), and really for every contribution. They're all made on modest budgets. Here's a link to a video in which he explains how; I love this talk about realizing a director's vision, from Quentin himself:

www.youtube.com/watch?v-nQkZO3YkXXU&list-PLo8g-WtWiVLAi7rQMg5Yo-N9zeCR8fyqZk&index=2&t=0s&app=desktop

Getting Established

Some people are concerned about putting their personal information on a crew list; that's understandable but do think about phone numbers (not addresses) and websites.

A private company that compiles detailed information about motion picture and television projects creates the Internet Movie Database (IMDb). Projects and the people associated with it are listed automatically, based on available information. If you worked on something but aren't listed, you can request an addition. Once information is uploaded about you—whether you want it posted or not—it will only be taken down if it is incorrect. There is no charge to be listed. Be sure to put contact information on your IMDb listing; twice I didn't have time to track down numbers while on *Once Upon a Time…in Hollywood,* so I logged onto the website—two people missed out on working that show because their phone numbers weren't listed. IMDbPro is a subscription service that will give you vastly more information about people, projects, and shows in development.

Business Training

My opinion is that the UST is more than a best boy or a 1st assistant. It is someone who, in general business terms, is the front office, receptionist, Accounting Department, Payroll Department, substitute work force, and air traffic controller of expendables, special equipment, and temporary personnel. The UST assumes incredible responsibilities and duties with little room for error. Any classes or seminars/webinars that you can attend to get better at those standard job descriptions will help. Organizational skills are a must.

Branding

As much as we are part of a team, part of a department, part of a production company—we really are our own individual companies. Think like a business owner. Give some thought to what your values are and how you'll set yourself apart from others. If you're only doing your job, it's not enough to rise above the masses.

My best advice is to be very clear about your goals, your attitude, and your branding—what you want the professional world to understand about you. What are you offering? Write down those three to five key points and do everything to present them consistently—the colors of your business cards, the color of your work shirts, and your company logo on paperwork. Pay attention to the business side of your business.

Here are some suggestions for attributes: Reliable. Funny. Detail oriented. Business savvy. Social director (knows the best restaurants, bars, and live events). You're bulletproof (perhaps a lavalier bullet logo?). Resourceful. Great at organizing. Experienced boom operator. Repair technician.

Public relations and marketing coach Diane Foy offers a focused approach to getting at the heart of your goal and defining your values:

http://singdanceactthrive.com/podcast/finding-your-why-bio-personal-branding/

Write your business name (optional) below and what you want to be known for: _____

1. _____

2. _____

3. _____

4. _____

5. _____

Set aside some time to think about how to make these ideals part of your brand. My friend JuliAnn Stitick built a career around teaching branding and offers some good information on her site. Check out *Step into Your Power*, a step-by-step strategy guide:

www.GetYourPowerBook.com

My Branding

I love baking and gardening and celebrating holidays, and when I began to integrate my life with my work, I began to pay attention to people and moods on the set. I brought food goodies and organized a Halloween trick-or-treat event at work so those of us in film could finally have those memories with our kids. I celebrated people's personal accomplishments, noticed someone who was having a hard day, and made it a point to add some fun or humor.

Part of my personal prep is to make sure I keep an assortment of greet-ings cards in the paperwork drawer on the truck, and when it's someone's birthday or they need a kind word from a friend, I tuck a card onto their cart. And I keep some props, too: a couple of hats and a tiara can always come in handy. And a magic wand to give to producers when they're frus-trated that things are running behind? Priceless.

When you don't have a job booked, look for opportunities to offer some service to your intended clients, or you might want to branch out when film work is slow. Maybe people participating in Zoom meetings now have technical questions about microphones and headphones. Answer those questions and maybe suggest some framing tips. Or maybe they're doing a charity event; you can offer your services or non-Sound services. If they're not looking for you, try emailing them—e.g., "Tips for Your Company Zoom Meetings." Offer free consultations over the phone to suggest headphones or microphones or how to use virtual backgrounds. Don't forget your business logo or a bit about your company and contact information. If you think it doesn't work, look up the Internet article about the Seattle architect who advertised that he would answer a professional question for $5; he ended up getting a lot of media coverage and then serious work offers.

The bottom line is that *media is a people business*, and there are some people that no one wants to work with regardless of their years of knowledge—the business just isn't a factory line and *people aren't interchangeable* (no matter what the corporate holding companies that control studios might imagine). So be the kind of person you want to work with and be willing to try an experiment: Mark your calendar for 4 months from today. Think very specifically about how you want to present your business and pull it all together. Then spend an hour or two brainstorming how to meet the clients that you want and make *them* the focus of your work: *How can you help them?* Think from a service standpoint. What can you offer that's different from others? Remember that not every person hiring chooses the lower price.

And there's marketing involved. You may find that you're doing some one-man-band jobs in the beginning. And if a PM's budget is off, find a diplomatic way to say so. Use the opportunity as a teaching moment without talking down to people. Think of the business from *their* side and think about how you can have their back.

Mixers comment that they need a UST, but the production won't budget for them. But others have been successful by having an honest conversation—for example, "We understand that you haven't budgeted for the UST, but there are three days with crowd scenes *or* four company moves. Let's agree that we'll bring on someone just for those days." And remember the example of hiring a UST to save money from the first chapter? Speaking the language of production managers works.

Timing Your Career

Whatever time you are living in, there are opportunities to innovate, think, and create.

Don't be fearful. You must be fearless. Here's a link to a video of Oliver Stone on fear:

www.youtube.com/watch?v=WqvyOx_qZAI

When I Started in the Business

It was the 1980s and a time of innovation. Here are some examples of some of those innovations:

I remember that the grips would periodically leave the set to go to the parking lot of New World (a previous lumberyard) and spray paint aluminum foil by the roll. They would roll out the foil, paint it, and when it was dry, it was rolled up again. Pieces were cut, and it was used over and over until you saw the paint flake on set. Then it was repainted or thrown away. Why? Because Black Wrap, which they had created an early version of, hadn't been invented yet.

Someone had a friend who made a crispy Fritos-like snack and left it at Craft Services for us to try. It was too salty for my taste; I think now it's called Sun Chips.

And my friend Mike Schmidt, a video assist operator, realized that he had to cut up showcard (posterboard) to make monitor shades, and in different sizes, over and over for each time we shot outside. In between jobs, he created several versions and then started his own company, Hoodman, LLC (**www.hoodmanusa.com**).

A few companies produced radio microphones. We bought Microns, and they came with black leather pouches. Classy! The lavaliers we used were Trams, and there were a few accessories: a tie tack, a leather-backed holder for shirt buttons, and a Vampire clip. There were no accessories for heavy coats or bulky clothing. Things were invented on the set based on what someone needed for the shot. There was no Internet, and most people didn't list phone numbers in the White Pages of phone books for privacy reasons, so word of mouth was the main form of communication.

One day, I learned about a new trick using champagne cages (the wire cap that holds down the cork). If you crush it vertically, but not so hard that you break the welds, it will give just enough lift to let a lavalier breathe under heavy coats or bulky clothing. To attach the mic, tape the leather-backed clip across the welds. Voilà! So we bought some Veuve Cliquot as a business expense.

In the early 1980s, there was a belief among union members (and perhaps their business agents, or BAs) that job security would be theirs through preventing people from being able to join their respective craft Locals. For a few years, film professionals beginning their careers were prohibited from becoming members; it was a "closed shop." The non-union workers honed their skills through independent film companies like Roger Corman's New World (old New World and new New World iterations) and Cannon Films. (The independent production sound Mixers mustered the courage to share their concerns and rates with each other and soon formed a collective called "The Alliance," which grew and matured into "Sound United" because they came to understand that production managers were pitting them against each other to drive down rates.)

I believe I experienced the seed of the decline of unionism in Hollywood when I worked on the first television show to be "non-union." First, a bit of explanation of the nomenclature: The movies and television shows of the 1980s and 1990s were made under contracts between the Screen Actors Guild (SAG), Directors Guild of America (DGA), Teamsters (drivers), and International Alliance of Theatrical Stage Employees (IATSE) for editors, but non-IATSE for the production crew. The productions were referred to as "non-union" anyway.

In 1982, studio executives from L.A. flew to a production location as the first non-union crew was about to shoot a movie of the week. This was a huge gamble for the networks and one in which the landscape of the production work would forever change. By the third day (when two sets of dailies had been processed and screened), there was a marked shift in the body language and demeanor of the executives; they were satisfied that they had a viable option besides working under an IATSE union contract, and they flew back to L.A. confident. That began a consistent decline in IATSE union work and a proliferation of movies of the week (MOWs) using television stars during their hiatus from their episodic work. During the 1980s, movies of the week had become a staple for television; most began as non-union work, but many shifted to having a union contract, as most crewmembers were union members taking the jobs. (My guess is that the production managers knew union crewmembers rather than non-union crewmembers but simply told them the show would not be under a contract. By the end of the first week, crews asked for union representation and the companies, in my experience, took it in stride.) By the end of the decade, however, as the non-union labor pool became experienced, MOWs remained non-IATSE for production crews throughout their production shoot, and under an IATSE contract for their postproduction work.

Negotiating

Boom operators and USTs think that Mixers are very powerful and could get everything that they request approved in negotiations, including boom rate increases, generous kit rentals, and more. Having lived with a sound Mixer for 40 years, I'm telling you that they can't get everything they want. Mixers are not your agents, and negotiating is yet another skill you will need to learn. It doesn't come easily to most people. Thankfully, however, non-movie people need to learn negotiating as well, and there are plenty of sources for help. Mixers do sincerely try to do what they can to better your deal, as it helps their work situation, too.

Workplace Problems

The workplace is full of problems; learn to thrive in that realm. I did so by seeing things differently. Understand that wording is often more important than technique. For example:

Is it a Sound problem? Or a location/Production problem?

Try saying *noise* problem, instead of *sound* problem.

And consider: Is it a sound *problem*? Or is it an *opportunity* for a creative solution? A *Sound problem* or a moment to shine? Think about how you want to convey a situation to the person whose attention you need to bring it to. How you describe it, defines it.

Being a UST is like being an air traffic controller: You see the big picture of moving elements, things changing constantly in real time, and you must not let elements collide.

Keep a clear head. Remember that fear and anger or frustration can block clear thinking and spontaneous problem solving.

When you need to address an issue, go first to the person in the lowest position in that department and work your way up. It's usually possible to resolve issues at the lower levels, and therefore everyone gets to save face within their department *and* within the company. Saving face is a very important, unspoken consideration on a film set.

Someone who saw dailies might comment, "I saw the boom/boom shadow in the shot." During the takes, help the operator by watching for those issues and ask for clarification on the frame boundaries if needed (within the department first, with the use of monitors). If you think you may have created a shadow or dipped into frame, speak up right after the take; point out the action. It's your responsibility to address the situation before the company moves on.

NOTE: There really isn't a need for a boom operator to go to dailies, but it can be a good feeling to hear your work before it goes down the line to be processed. It also shows a sense of camaraderie with the core filmmakers and can illuminate more about the relationships and politics of the show. Attending dailies can include you in a circle of key filmmakers. Dailies are likely to happen on location if moviemaking, unlike for TV shows.

One possible scenario is that during dailies there was a microphone/pole/you/sound equipment/shadow visible in the shot. The next day, you hear about it from multiple sources. *Do not accept the responsibility for that.* The operator is the person charged with protecting the frame, and many times there are monitors for Script, the director, and all the video villages, wherein countless people crowd around to watch.

For any core filmmakers who mention the problem, I'll let them know that I heard about it and will speak, or have already spoken, with the camera operator. I do not blame the operator publicly and will not "throw him under the bus." I'll always go over quietly to the operator and open a dialogue about the specifics and figure out if there is anything either of us can do differently to minimize another occurrence. Hopefully, you've already worked out the signals of communication between Camera and UST during the first day. You may have even seen the problem at the time and brought it to the attention of the operator for checking, in which case this dailies scenario wouldn't even occur. You would have earned credibility with the operator for protecting *both* of you. It may be a simple oversight of the operator or the director didn't want another take.

If appropriate, make sure to tell the DOP the outcome of your conversation, so that he, too, can appreciate the professionalism of the Sound Department working things out.

Think about it; you don't hear anyone say, "There was a light stand leg in the frame, blame the electrician." Of course, if the operator is a big jerk, then I say, "How embarrassing for you." Well, at least I think it.

Technical

Don't confuse something technical with tools or techniques, as everything in film is technical—from hitting your marks and knowing your lines, to matching eye lines and setting an F-stop to timing background crosses and matching the blood on a scar. Don't let the word "technical" somehow be derogatory to your department; speak up in a calm, educational way (and remember to let the person save face).

Group Dynamics

On-set communications take place through bits of conversation and interruptions. *Listen to everything.* Most of the information necessary for understanding the immediate situation is not announced out loud, so every little bit of knowledge is a valuable piece of the puzzle. Have a departmental communication system in place, just like the other departments. They use walkie-talkies or their own internal system, and it's a good idea to monitor those systems if they allow it.

You must already understand the filmmaking process and put energy into trying to understand what the director and Production want out of *their* workflow and *their* vision. It doesn't matter the size of the project or the big names involved; when you're in Sound, there's always the potential to need to navigate negative (biased) opinions from those who misunderstand your craft.

Anticipation is a key factor in keeping up with workflow. Petr Janata, a cognitive neuroscientist at the University of California, Davis, explains one basic human survival skill: "Our brains are all about predicting what's going to happen next."

This inherent human instinct will serve you well in film as well as life. It's OK to go into a situation not knowing how you'll meet someone's expectations. Or how you'll successfully capture dialogue in a difficult scene.

Make sure you have all the tools you'll need for multiple scenarios and run them at the same time until there's a reason to discontinue. While it makes for a bit of busywork, it's value is in giving you some time to consider the merits of each option and giving you a head start on taking action once the way is clear. You may conclude that the best approach is to combine elements from different scenarios.

When you give advance thought, discussion, or treatment to a situation, you are (somewhat) able to control the speed of some of the actions, and you have also given yourself the time to consider many factors and come to an objective conclusion on the subject, rather than a reactionary one. Having the ability to think through something before it's at hand is a luxury not often afforded on a set. If called upon, you'll be able to confidently discuss options and their consequences. There's a kind of power in having a clearheaded, thoughtful approach to something that seems to have come up at the last minute.

Social Dynamics

No part of a film education would be complete without discussing social dynamics. After all, if success were only about knowing the equipment, every gearhead would be successful beyond their dreams.

No matter how large a crew, how important a celebrity, how spectacular a project intends to be, it will be made by flawed human beings—creative people who will be there because of the integrity of their work or their social relationships with a key participant. Always think the best of a person until they prove you wrong, and then try to keep a compassionate mind. Try to learn their individual story that brought them to the project. Act as if they're competent, and many times they can rise to the occasion to some degree.

Try to separate a person's work ethic from the person. There are many people I would never want to go to lunch with, although I do enjoy working with them primarily because we share a work ethic based on information and proper set protocols. We follow common conventions for being able to provide our best work (even some nasty people).

The key concept to remember is that *you need to work with them to do your job and get your next one.* If the production sound Mixer (PSM) you're working with is having issues with someone, it's a good signal for you to make an extra effort to establish a decent relationship with that individual—for the sake of the department and to show you're an asset to the PSM.

Political Dynamics

It's a good use of your time to find out what the interpersonal relationships are and how people came to be involved in the project. It's simple preservation politics. There is a hierarchy on every set, and you need to learn it. Practice mindful awareness. Sometimes a star may have far more power than is reflected by their role as an actor. I have experienced directors who acted like hired help toward the production, and others who are the center of the production universe.

From how you say "Good morning" to where you sit in the crew van...it's all political. The Sound Department interacts with nearly all other departments and receives the more sensitive threads of information that do not travel by walkie-talkie.

Sexual Dynamics

When I started out, there was only one woman boom operator I had heard of, and it was 11 years until I saw another one on a set. It was a novelty for crews to see me on the hard crew, and I'll pause now to thank the scores of men who were so kind to me throughout my career. Most of the people I have met on the set have been dedicated, quirky, funny, creative, brilliant, and above all, professional. But, as a caveat to my sisters and a wakeup call to my brothers, there were men who felt the power of their position and, perhaps because it takes so many years to work one's way to that position, they were older and of a different generation.

Early on, with filmmaking being a collaborative effort, I set about meeting people on a show, having been acquainted only with the Mixer and production manager. The DOP was also the operator (not unusual), and I made a point to chat him up and joke around. By the second day, I found myself wondering whether I had said or done something to mislead him about my friendly banter. I made sure to say something directly to him after lunch. But I noticed him finding opportunities to press against the chests of many of the female members and taking other sexual liberties. I went to the production manager and made a complaint.

I must add that in the production sound craft, 99.999% of people are respectful, generous, talented, and supportive people; I sincerely am blessed to have gotten to know so many of them around the globe.

But I bring this up because I was invited to the first women-in-Sound get-together only a few years ago and found that there were so many women who had negative stories of their own. Even though the older, conventionally minded men have mostly passed away, not everyone works in a progressive city, and chauvinistic attitudes pervade all crafts and communities. The first step is to understand that it isn't anything you're doing wrong. Seek guidance.

Insecurity

Insecurity is one trait that each of us has come to the set with. It is a quality easily seen by everyone except the person feeling it. It manifests itself in many ways, not the least of which is by perceived self-preservation. When someone feels their job or credibility is threatened, it's a human survival instinct to blame another person. If you're on the receiving end, it can feel quite uncomfortable, and you may be tempted to overreact. Instead, this is a moment to shine. In this moment, you have the ability for everyone to appreciate your integrity and compassion.

Try to keep things dispassionate and informational. Do not be quick to draw conclusions. Investigate and ask questions and concentrate on the issue. Sidestepping blame will allow the parties to feel that it's safe to work on the problem instead of trying to save their jobs.

Of course, if something *is* your fault, do your best to stay calm. Don't shrug it off or make it bigger than it is or grovel. Apologize, and try to fix the problem. When it's done, it's done. Don't ruminate or joke about it later. Don't belittle anyone who acted poorly, as we've all had our off moments.

Confidence

The Confidence Code, a book about confidence and gender, by Katty Kay and Claire Shipman, should be required reading for everyone.

I recommend taking the quiz and having a working knowledge of their findings.

▸ **https://theconfidencecode.com**

▸ **www.confidencecodegirls.com/quiz/**

Overachieving

Some crew people want to "give it their all" and mistakenly believe they need to put themselves or other people in danger to achieve their best. I have seen a cameraman design shot after shot that was so intricate with moves that he himself could not successfully maneuver and fell off the dolly—time after time, day after day.

A boom operator was injured on the set during a rehearsal. The action was that the actor would say a few lines and get in a car. During the filming, the actor said his lines, got in a car, and drove away. For some unknown reason, the boom operator had tied his boom cable to the bumper! When the car drove away, he was dragged down the road!

I had a successful side business for many years being the first call to replace him because he kept getting hurt. He huffed and puffed and complained all day long to the crew about how heavy his boom was, yet he stood behind the entire crew, necessitating an additional 10 feet of pole! He cared deeply about his job, and he is a gem of a man, and I have him to thank for the substantial part of my career apart from my work with my regular Mixer.

Micromanaging

It seems important for some personalities to want to impose their process of organizing (sometimes chaos) onto others. Having found a successful system and sharing it is different from making someone do their job the way *you* say, even if the process doesn't affect the outcome. A case in point: I worked Utility on a TV series. Each episode was 5 days on a stage, 3 days out, and the walkie-talkie package was 11 WTs for stage days and 19 WTs for location days. I was in charge of checking them in and out from the studio, distribution to the company, and managing broken WTs and their accessories.

My organizing principle was to establish the base package and assign regulars the same walkie-talkie each day. The additional WTs would be distributed to the additional crew brought on for away days: traffic control, stunts, FX, etc.

The Mixer, who I had never worked with before, came into the truck on a location day, admonishing me for not having the WTs distributed in ascending numerical order, with the 1st AD getting the lowest number. I explained that they were, in fact, in numerical order by base package and then by additional package. He took great pains to explain in child-like terms how to correctly organize them, and I was to hurry and redistribute them (exchanging them during shooting) before the setup was ready.

During the run of the show, the 1st AD had a problem and was annoyed that I couldn't track his headset. I couldn't wrap my head around memorizing each person's WT for the day, and it added layers of stress for no reason. My advice: let the person in charge of it make sense of it.

Pregnancy

Pregnancy is something that never came up during my generation because we were the first. Before a pregnancy, you should have a serious discussion with your partner wherein you both decide at what point you'll stop working. Booming is hard on a pregnant body, and I suffered many miscarriages during that education. I moved from boom operator into Utility work, but that did not guarantee success.

I have worked while pregnant and offer these tips: the first trimester is such a delicate time: 1. Don't fall, don't lift even medium-heavy cases, and sit down a lot. 2. Don't ride in the back of pickup trucks or any such similar activity. 3. Tell only the people you're comfortable with at work and let them help. As with any health situation, the situation varies with the individual. Seek medical information and guidance.

Related Skills

These skills may come in handy: psychology, a bit of acting experience, an understanding of music, a foreign language, soldering competency, massage, magic, any performing talent to amuse the company, and all manner of repair work.

The exciting thing about filmmaking is that any life experience you've had can potentially lead to a contribution. A case in point: I day-played on a TV series, knowing only the Mixer. There was a scene with Russian spies, and suddenly the director called out on set: "Patrushkha, what's a Russian name? This doesn't sound right," and everyone looked at me. Well, first off, I'm Polish, and if you think that isn't a difference, it's like being a New Yorker versus a Los Angeleno.

I don't speak Russian, and I know only a few words in Polish (my parents wanting to be American). I knew one name that I thought sounded very Eastern European "Grzegorcz." Too hard, he decided. "Leshik," I offered. "That's the one!" the director announced, and we shot the scene...no one paid attention to me the rest of the night.

Was it Russian? No...well, in fact, *I don't know*. The point is that the director needed something. I kept the set moving and scored points for the Sound Department, and by association, the Mixer. In the end, what we do is tell stories; if there's an important fact to check, there's someone to do that.

Another point: Listen carefully to questions like these and answer *that*, not what jumped into your head. Did the director ask if I was Russian or if I even knew any Russian? No. That gives you an indication of the degree of specificity with which you need to reply.

The most technically proficient people in our industry are not necessarily the most in-demand.

The number one challenge for Utilities (in my opinion) is day playing. Each Mixer has an equally different method and workflow, and it is difficult indeed for a Utility to make the near-instant transition from one team to the next. As a broad stroke, having a Utility who knows the "to-do" list every day without being told is the foundation for success.

Regarding USTs, a Mixer recently confided in me, "I don't care that they don't know what drawer my lavs are kept in, but I definitely don't want to be telling them to jam the slates and sync boxes every day."

The number one lesson for Utilities is to *be 1000% proactive*. Think ahead of the shot, ask questions, or pose a plan of action. Don't wait to be told something; the Mixer and boom operator have enough to do.

The natural place for people to connect is at work, but it's inappropriate to consider the workplace as a dating environment. Distant locations can be a temptation for behavior you wouldn't usually consider. I've seen and heard enough stories to share that it can negatively affect your career if things sour. And work contacts have soured for whole departments.

It's common sense to keep professional. Don't assume that everyone has the set of same values, and respect personal space, physicality, gender, and non-gender. You're part of a department and represent a work unit.

Freelance Financial Planning

Because most work in the film and television industry is freelance, it's not enough to know film production and your craft; you also need to be able to take care of yourself in life.

This primer on financial planning is to help you understand the nature of freelance work and some actions to take in moderating the all-or-nothing lifestyle. The first thing to understand is the work hours. During production, your work can start at any hour of the day or night and continue for as long as the company says; rarely do two consecutive days have the same call and wrap times. Along with widely shifting call times will be the location of your work; some days you may be at the beach at 5 A.M., other times you may be at a power plant on the other side of town at 9 P.M. A job may last one day, one week, or six or more months in multiple countries. Because you have so little control of your life during the work time, you need to pay extra attention to its management during the other times.

If you haven't heard it before, life goes by very quickly when you're working, and the more successful you are, the more of your life you will have spent. I'm a big believer in goal setting, and it's the way I have been able to have a notable career, a family, and accomplished 90% of my New Years' resolutions. My friends call me a force of nature, a tsunami, a monster— but it's really just knowing what I want. The financial part is important but above that is having a good life, so I'm sharing my approach.

I love New Year's Day as a beginning but *today* is also a very good day. Sit down in a comfy chair when it's quiet, and the time is your own. Put on some music, have a beverage, and be with your thoughts. Write down every dream, every adventure a friend has had that you marveled at, something that you want people to remember you for, something you do that makes the world better for you having been here, etc.

You need a Master Plan. I recommend getting a full-size notepad and writing *everything* down on different pages. Start with these titles: Financial (income sources and bills), Personal (medical checkups, flu shots, haircuts, vacations, buying new jeans, reading that book, etc.), Social (birthdays, get-togethers, hosting the annual Halloween party, etc.), Goals (learning a language, tap dancing, seeing the northern lights), and any other categories that are meaningful to you. Keep the pad with you for the week as items pop into your head. If you have any old New Year's resolutions lists (good for you!) add them, as well as any due dates.

I use a file folder to store all the notes and old plans and notes on places to visit, cooking classes, manufacturer's tours, baby names, a dream house, whatever strikes me in any way. My categories vary a bit year to year, but the regulars are: Financial, Investment, Career, Home, Lifestyle, Personal, Kids & Pets, Creativity, and Future. And the ones I focus on during a given year might be: Organization, Health, Education, Community, Spiritual, Estate Planning, School, Summer/Vacation, Home Business, Old Business, or Debts. When I began, I didn't need separate financial and investment categories; that grew as the business grew. Start small so you can get success under your belt.

Take that dream list and star the ones that are most doable in your current lifestyle; break each of those dreams into steps, guesstimating a time frame to fulfill each one.

I make my own "Goals for 20_ _" from a standard sheet of paper since it's easy to store in a file folder (save them every year, and you can reflect on your life and how far you've come). Fill in your category headings, starting with Financial and Career, and then other categories in rough order of importance to you. Start listing the first steps under the category that applies. If you need to start simpler, make a Goal plan for this month and only include things that really need to be accomplished.

You need one (*only one*) Master Calendar. Get a large January to December calendar and start penciling in items with dates, leaving Fridays open. Add the other items in rough order of importance. If you have solid show dates, pencil those in and don't schedule anything major the week before the show starts or the two weeks after; transfer those activities to a corresponding personal calendar you carry with you and concentrate just on the current day and tomorrow. Use Friday as a catchup day for anything that couldn't be completed that week.

Financial	Career	Family
Make a budget	Rework résumé	May- Stevie's canoe trip
Regular savings ($35/week)	Meet 3 USTs	Record bedtime stories before
Get a copy of Mom's will	Join a Facebook group	show
		Host Carrie's 29th birthday party
Home	**Art**	**Personal**
Marie Kondo my work T-shirts	Work on the first draft of "Wicked,	Learn about Buddhism
Clean the refrigerator coils	Wicked Cowgirls" with Dwayne	Pick an exercise program
Buy bookcases for the family room	Print Emmi's recital pics	Get the prostate exam!
Next year		
Vacation in Italy (swim on the Amalfi coast)	Plant a Saturn peach tree	

If you use a personal calendar, fill in goal tasks for the time period of your open page (week or month), scheduling no more than two or three items per day.

For day-to-day success, a good place to start is to consider your daily and weekly activities and find ways to streamline and/or minimize them.

For money matters, set up online banking services and use Auto Pay every chance you can. Request e-bills so you won't have to be home to pick up your important mail and because they won't get lost. Use an accounting software program that coordinates with your bank and accountant so you can download transactions rather than having to input them manually. Request digital receipts and subscriptions rather than paperwork that could be lost or damaged. To prevent excessive expenses, barter with roommates for things you'll need to have handled while on a show. Schedule into the master calendar sending files to your accountant in November (for year-end tax planning) or quarterly if you have a business entity (so they can file your payroll tax info if you don't do that yourself).

Leave enough petty cash in your house so that someone can handle unexpected expenses if you're away. Consider pre-paying regular bills at the beginning of a long show if you have the money, and then review the accounting months down the line when you have time. I usually pre-pay phone and utilities 3—4 months in advance and any property tax deadlines during production or the two weeks after.

If you don't have work lined up, schedule any medical appointments as soon as possible and get them out of the way in case you get a work call. Automate your personal life as much as possible: subscribe to a greeting card service that remembers birthdays every year and schedule x months of delivery for staples, so you don't spend your day off running routine errands (think pet food, office supplies, etc.). Or decide to have a shopping day and buy routine items in bulk. Set up regular maintenance people such as a housekeeper, gardener, bookkeeper, or masseuse, and then add them to your calendar.

For pets, get an automatic dog water fountain and an automatic feeder if you're the only caregiver, install a pet door, stock up on chews and toys, or build a cat tunnel. If you have a significant other and you have a long-term job, consider scheduling flowers for a future date or a gift certificate and marking the calendar for the date to present it. On shopping day, buy some music or gift cards or small gifts for the kids and keep in a box in the closet until they're needed. If you're going on location, record some of the kids' bedtime stories so you can read them to sleep even when you're gone.

Fitting in longer-term goals requires a bit more thought. Break down each long-term goal into manageable pieces. For instance, if you want to learn a language, start with lessons you can listen to while driving to and from work. Set a goal for learning 10 basic phrases in a month. Find someone on the cast or crew to speak the new language with. Take each step of a goal, think about the completion dates that you think are realistic, and then add a week and pencil that in. Don't schedule more than two items on any one workday, and don't use every day to complete your goals.

If you don't have a family, it's a great time in your life to save as much money as you can and put the funds into a savings, investment, or retirement account since your expenses may be quite low.

A Financial Plan (According to Me)

I consider these necessary beginning steps when you're starting out: Write down where every penny goes for a month to begin creating your realistic budget; this is one thing that no one can do for you, and every person's financial situation is different. To make it manageable, just get a receipt for *everything*, write down its category, and put it in a Ziploc bag you take with you. At the end of the month, total all the collected receipts by category, review them, and decide on any changes you want to make to the amount you spend on that category and create your first budget. List any regular money you have coming in. Hopefully, you are bringing in more money than is going out. Look at your notepad or master calendar and note any dates that have finances attached to them: tax deadlines, Christmas presents, or an anniversary trip, for example. Consider whether you will have the money needed by the deadlines or whether you need to add a budget item that starts saving for them in advance (the amount needed divided by the number of months you have until the deadline—*or*, for short-term work, divide by the number of paychecks).

When you set up your online banking, create both checking and savings accounts—or start a money market account at a brokerage—and set up an automatic payment to it. Always pay yourself first, or you'll find that you're not saving enough money. Start by saving 10% of any income. Consider this your emergency fund, and once you meet your goal (6–12 months reserve), the overage becomes your discretionary money. I strongly recommend using the money toward a retirement fund first; it'll grow much faster if you start it early in life and it will continue to grow even when you do get to spend your discretionary income.

If you have any debts that carry interest (except for real estate), work at paying those down first. Shop for credit cards that don't offer airline miles, as freelance schedules are too uncertain to book anything in advance or with airline blackout periods. I have a credit card that offers a variety of options, and I chose to get money back, which I can use for anything. Any time you have a debt, make sure to pay the installments on time; that builds your credit rating.

Part of financial planning is mental, and I want to point out that knowing you have that emergency fund if needed (and it always seems to be needed) goes a *very* long way to giving you a sense of relief, knowing that you can survive or hold out for the start of a show you really want to work on.

Financial-Library.com offers a variety of suggestions for each step of your financial growth:

www.financial-library.com/budgetingbasics.html

There are industry and world events that we may not have anything to do with personally but that affect our livelihoods:

Labor strikes: Historically, labor strikes occur every 8—13 years:

https://en.wikipedia.org/wiki/List_of_Hollywood_strikes

When a strike occurs, expect a pause in your monthly cash flow for at least 6 months.

Pandemics/regional conflict: The year 2020 is a great example of what can happen to all industries when there is a health crisis (a pandemic) or a regional conflict that is controlled by the government. The pandemic was affecting all production worldwide; however, local governments all had different strategies for handling the problem. For example, in Sweden the government decided not to impose a quarantine. In the United States, the country was in various stages of quarantine depending on which state you were physically present in. Florida lifted all quarantine restrictions, and New York and California had strict quarantine regulations. As a result, you may have had a surprise in your cash flow due to a local problem that was controlled by the local government.

Seasonality: Entertainment projects have start dates and end dates that are different for each project. Some freelancers have the relationships to jump from one project to the next without much gap in time regarding cash flow. Others may have a much bigger gap in cash flow that is 3—4 months long in between projects. As a freelancer, you need to be prepared for a 4-month income drought if you do not find your next project after your current project ends.

World Events: The Financial Crisis of 2008 impacted the film world for 18 months because the funding vehicles that financed film projects dried up. As a result, there were fewer projects shooting, and the budgets were smaller since the funders did not want to take additional risk in film projects.

As you grow your business, questions will arise: For example, should I buy or lease a car? Because you may be travelling for months or working overseas, buying a used car outright will probably make more sense. Don't forget to suspend motor vehicles licenses and, if appropriate, liability insurance if you'll be away from home for an extended period; some states allow you to submit a non-operational declaration, and you can save on license fees. (Don't forget to reinstate your license and insurance when your job is over and you return home!)

Should I buy or rent a piece of gear I need? The answer most often expressed on Internet forums is to weigh the cost of the item against the length of the rental. At a 30—50% return, most people will buy the item. Sometimes a show will buy the item, and it's possible to purchase it at a discount at wrap (typically 50% of the original cost).

Some shows sell their Art and Costumes Department items once they are sure there won't be any reshoots. I've bought Stickley tables, Calphalon pots, and antiques at very reasonable prices.

Health and Insurance

After fulfilling your immediate needs, look into insurance: medical coverage is a must and the possibility of your becoming disabled is more likely than your death. (If you're in an industrial country other than the US, you probably have reasonable coverage already.) According to Affordable Insurance Protection, you are three and a half times more likely to be injured and therefore need disability coverage than your probability of death and therefore needing life insurance. Deaths due to cancer, heart attack, and stroke have reduced dramatically, but things that used to kill us may now disable us. A 35-year-old has a *50 percent* chance of becoming disabled for a 90-day period or longer before age 65. About *30 percent* of *Americans* ages 35—65 will suffer a disability lasting at least 90 days during their working careers. About *one in seven* people ages 35—65 can expect to become disabled for 5 years or longer.

The Social Security Administration currently states that for an insured worker born in 2000, the probability of becoming disabled between age

20 and normal retirement age is 25 percent, and the probability of dying between age 20 and normal retirement age is 13 percent.

Be sure to specify your actual job position when you get disability insurance because the rates vary by job and be sure to specify that you can leave the set for dangerous situations. If you have people who depend on you and your income, get life insurance. Term insurance is the least expensive option because you are paying just for insurance; other options offer cash accounts combined with insurance.

Film work is exciting because every day is a new adventure, and the same goes for life. I could never have imagined the things that have happened to me, and I have a very good imagination. *Drama isn't just in movies; it will make a guest appearance in your life.* Expect it, prepare for it, and you'll come through it as well as possible. I'll conclude this chapter with a couple real-life scenarios to impress upon you the value of paying attention to your health.

IMPORTANT: No movie is worth your life.

Here's a story I am sad to tell: A prominent Mixer knew in early spring that he needed a surgery but had two big feature films lined up, so he scheduled it for December 23. When the doctors opened him up, they found the problem had grown so big that there was nothing they could do to save him. They closed him up, gave him 3 weeks to 6 months to live, and 5 weeks later he died, leaving a wife and two boys.

Another time, we had a one-day gig doing camera tests for an upcoming TV series. Our UST mentioned at lunch that he had been having some pain in his groin the last few days and asked the Mixer if that was something he also had ever experienced. The Mixer told him no, and both of us encouraged him all afternoon to go right after work to have it looked at.

It turned out to be early-stage cancer, for which he promptly scheduled surgery. He thanked us later for saving his life; he thought that being in his late 20s, it wasn't something that could happen to him.

CHAPTER 23

Maintaining Your Career

A key to success is finding a way to reconcile your career with your personal life. Your career encompasses not only your actual work, but also how you want to interact with your professional community.

Freelance Work

The life of a freelancer is inherently unbalanced, and it's a constant pull between work/art and life/ family. For years, I used to keep life on hold while I was on a job, but then I was just as unbalanced and frenetic "catching up" in my personal life. Over the course of about a year, I realized that we were stringing one show after another because, well, you never know when someone will go on strike or there'll be an earthquake or who knows what. I finally saw that trying to balance personal life with professional life could never happen—they are both 600-pound chickens in my life. You know the reference? A 600-pound chicken cannot be ignored.

My workdays are now easy to look forward to, even if it's a grueling show, because the other crewmembers who relate at the level of communication that I do tend to find each other.

It's nice to have a support network and another way of communicating on the set. Everyone must find their own way of making life and work make sense for them; the sooner you find it, the quicker you'll put your energy to a higher purpose.

Maintaining your career is really building your career. Always be engaged in learning, sharing, and mentoring; make yourself valuable to the community—it's the key to staying relevant. That, and a bit of luck.

How does a person keep working in Sound? *We talk!* We talk by text, by phone calls, by meeting for lunch, within Facebook groups, or Zoom panels and chats. We're a *very* welcoming and social group.

Power

There are different kinds of power: knowledge is a kind of power, as is being right. Everything that happens on a set is a potential power moment. Use this information wisely; your actions speak louder than words. *Accept your power* by acting like a filmmaker, not a factory worker.

Knowledge is power: Who will likely know if an actor is delayed? Transpo, Hair & Makeup, on-set Costumes. Who will likely know if the actor is in a bad mood? The 2nd AD, 2nd 2nd, their driver, Hair, Makeup, Costumes, or personal Caterer. Knowing these things is the difference between maneuvering around a potentially volatile situation or getting caught in the crosshairs. Real power on a set is knowing how to survive come what may.

Conflict

If you must choose between fighting for your point of view or maintaining a work relationship, pick the political one. Sometimes you may be on a show where there are multiple conflicts, differing philosophical groups who will be in near-constant disagreement about how to cover a scene or when to break for lunch or even what the shot should be. These are usually above-the-line groups that have come together to create the project. You may not know what the nature of the conflict is, because it's an issue that came up in the office. They may have had the best of intentions starting out, but basic differences are straining the relationship by the time production starts. It's tricky to nurture all the relationships without alienating anyone, but it can be done.

Be sympathetic if you are confided in, but remain neutral. Don't feel a need to take sides and don't say anything that will be hard to stand by later on. Attempt to satisfy any request, and if it butts up against something already decided, bring it to the attention of the Mixer. Even if it means doing something two different ways, I recommend making it happen. Remember, you're there to support the director and producers, to give them knowledge of the sound issue; the choice of what to do with that information is theirs. Don't make it a personal battle; listen to your client.

Maintaining your perspective and sanity lends a certain credibility and, in turn, power to your actions and words.

Résumés

You should have a résumé available and up to date. In the film arts, formats are not as strictly followed as in other industries, but there are common conventions. Your name and contact information should be at the top and clearly identified. If you have any filmography, add the IMDb link. If you have union and professional affiliations, add them here.

One difference is the "Objective" heading: You're applying for a job in the Sound Department; if you ultimately want to direct or produce, no one cares. In fact, it could hurt you by implying that you aren't serious about Sound. If you're seeking only a particular kind of work, such as television or jobs in your area, then say so; otherwise, decide at the time a project comes to you.

List your work experience with most recent first, unless you worked on an outstanding project (award-nominated, high-visibility, etc.), which would then be your lead. Keep items succinct: date, project name, sound Mixer, important director or actor names, awards won. Don't list descriptions of duties unless you did something unusual for your job category.

If you don't have work experience, list any Sound-related activities such as high-school drama productions, community theatre, or arts activities.

After experience, it's very valuable to list skills. Because film can reflect anything in this world, you just don't know which skill becomes the deciding factor in choosing you over someone else. List any languages you speak, skills you have, sports you participate in (e.g., several situations require booming in water).

When *The Hateful Eight* production went to Telluride, Colorado, to shoot, we started a search for an intern. The Production office was inundated with résumés of aspiring crewmembers. I think there were over 600 applications for 30 jobs. I called the one person I knew who lived there but hadn't worked with in 34 years; not only was he still there, but I didn't even get out my last name without him remembering me! (Be kind to everyone.) He gave me the name of someone to interview, and I called her. She was working for a film festival and stressed her student directing. I said, "You have no idea what you're in for, so don't even tell me about your directing." We talked more. I needed to know what kind of person she was, and could she handle the stresses of major moviemaking?

Why was she the one hired over everyone else? She had been on the 10th and 11th grade ski team. Think about it. Does a Sound team need a student director on a Quentin Tarantino movie? Or do they need someone who could run to the truck ¼ mile away through snow to get a windshield? I knew the trucks would be parked down the hill and imagined that someone acclimated to high altitudes and who owned snowshoes would be invaluable. She did a great job and was hired again for *Ad Astra*.

Don't forget any volunteer activities; they help tell someone about you and your values. Use action words when describing your activity.

Professional Affiliations

Membership with professional unions, societies, and other institutions introduces you to other spheres of engaged Sound people and broadens your education through their websites, magazines, and events/panel discussions.

Unions in the U.S. include:

▸ IATSE, also called "The IA," is the predominant entertainment industry union in the U.S. and Canada. It is one of the remaining industrial unions with legitimate power.

▸ IATSE Local 52 (New York)

▸ IATSE Local 695 (West Coast)

▸ IATSE mixed Locals. Branches in regional areas include all the crafts in the same group, called a "mixed" Local.

The Cinema Audio Society

The Cinema Audio Society (CAS) fosters community among Mixers, educating and informing the public and the motion picture and television industry about good and effective sound usage, and works to achieve deserved recognition for sound Mixers as major contributors to the field of entertainment. They have six categories of membership: Active (Full), Associate, Career Achievement, Honorary, Student, and Retired.

It is the one unique professional organization that joins together the production and postproduction community in the creative world of sound for film and television. It is the cinema sound world's analog to the ASC, or American Society of Cinematographers. The CAS is a clearinghouse for new technology and processes and produces the most prestigious awards event in the international world of cinema sound, surpassing the Academy Awards in peer recognition for excellence in the cinema sound arts.

Pay It Forward: Mentoring

Mentoring is a satisfying way to stay connected to the knowledge, and it also reminds us of why we love what we do.

It is heartening to be appreciated; recently two workshop attendees told me: "I think the biggest thing I struggled with in the beginning of my career was not having an experienced boom operator to reach out to. I think what you and some of the experienced members are doing— trying to get newer members a better jumping-off point—is huge." "The first time I met you, you and four other girls were teaching us how to lav at a workshop, so when I saw all those women there, I felt really good. It's important to see women doing what you do, and at the level you are working in. That makes everyone proud!"

CHAPTER 24

But I Want to Direct!

That's understandable; you're in the arts, and you have stories you want to tell—nothing wrong with that. In fact, it happens on sets everywhere: you meet 60—150 creative people with their own amazing lives and stories to tell. You may have to dig a bit to learn about them; good filmmakers know how to support other projects and not expound on their own wonderfulness. By getting to know people, you will find dedicated, passionate artists, and you can't help but be sucked into their passion projects (and they yours). I would sooner volunteer for a friend's project than a new director, and I have.

I spent a weekend on a sweet short film directed and produced by two grips with whom I've worked. I admire their dedication and their continued delivery under pressure. They are as honest and honorable as the summer day is long. And that's why a famous television star also agreed to work for free.

Being a UST allows you more freedom on a set and more interaction with other departments. On a television pilot, the executive producer and I began a chat in which I told him I wanted to learn producing. We had time to talk because the crew needed several hours for the last shot of the show, in which the family dog takes a bite of a birthday cake on a table in the den. The camera pulls back to reveal the entire room, the living room, and then moves through the mullioned picture window to the front yard and ends in a pan down the street.

The executive producer, Michael, invited me to produce that shot. With the Mixer's OK (only the boom operator worked the shot), I stayed by Michael's side for 3 hours. When the 1st AD and director came to ask a question, Michael told them they had to ask me. And they did. (I learned that directors who don't understand how long shots take to set up, and how changes affect the time, can really drag down a production and cost more money than any crewmember's salary. And I also learned that, as executive producer, I couldn't force my will on the director.) What a gift that experience was! And Michael called me to be his assistant for the entire run of the series.

I have personally co-directed and produced more than a dozen educational projects: one was picked up by the BBC, one for the United States Department of Education (for all US public school systems), and 15 projects that went straight to direct sales (all made a profit). I shamelessly admit that walking up the steps of New York City's mid-town library, past the stone lions, and seeing my name in the card catalogue, is as big a thrill as going to the Oscars. Believe me; I've done both.

Working on a crew is a great way to meet that network of professionals who have integrity and commitment and enjoy the work. The path to producing a memorable project is rarely a straight line, and no one makes a movie alone (not even Robert Rodriquez, regardless of the title of his book). I met a sound Mixer on the set of a television project, and he was so interesting at lunch that I found myself at his apartment looking at footage of his documentary. I found it fascinating and agreed to help finish it. I thought a few more interviews and some rehearsals of the actress's latest production would wrap it up, but during the second interview came to learn that she had a famous friend, also an actress. Because there was a logical connection to the documentary between the two, I contacted the actress, and she agreed to do an introduction to the movie! We flew to New York, and when I called to confirm the day and time (the next Thursday), she told me we'd better move up the schedule to Monday, because she might not be around that long.

Holy cow! We were shooting Katharine Hepburn's last movie! All weekend we worried and prayed for her good health. On Monday, we arrived at the non-descript door of her brownstone on 49th Street and rang the bell. Mark Ulano, the director, had the brilliant insight to tell me to start recording sound *now*. Her assistant showed us into the foyer, and we waited. It wasn't long before Ms. Hepburn came bouncing down the stairs in a navy jogging suit with white stripes and a brand-new pair of sneakers! OK, I thought—her health seems fine (I wondered if she was amused by setting us up with angst all weekend).

The upstairs landing opened to something of a sitting room, with a fireplace and a marble mantel filled with souvenirs from her iconic movies.

There were large leaded-glass French doors that opened over her stunning courtyard garden.

We were inside a study, where she sat in a comfortable Windsor chair, with Mark on the couch perpendicular to her, and I sat by her feet.

She and Mark discussed the subject of our documentary and Mark's perspective of the subject, and after a bit she informed us that she would only do a voice interview, not on camera, because of her eye infection (which began during production of the film *Summertime* in 1955, when she fell into one of the Venetian canals and contracted an eye infection, with recurring issues).

The first take went fine, but after the second take, she wasn't happy and said, "That stunk, didn't it?" Mark found kinder words, and I was struck with how trusting she was of her director, how collaborative and "in the artistic moment" they both were. I found myself longing for directors I could work with who can exude passion, and actors who can rise above their own infatuation with themselves.

When we were all satisfied, we wrapped up and were down again in the foyer, ready to leave. Apparently, she had an appointment, too. "Can I take you somewhere?" she asked. Our truck was parked half a block away, so we said, "No, thank you." I wish we would have had the sense to say, "Yes, please" and picked any place on the other side of town. We said goodbye, and we went left, as she went right to a car waiting, double-parked, one building down. Two days later, I saw a small news report that said she had had an altercation with a parking meter maid! She was scheduled for a future court appearance. Oh, the stories that get away....

NOTES

CHAPTER 25

Frequently Asked Questions

When I'm working, contributing on Facebook, on panels or lecturing around the world, people starting out ask many of the same questions. You might have these questions, too, so I put them together in a Q&A format for quick reference.

How Do I Get into the Industry?

Every way imaginable! I answered an ad on a fashion school bulletin board. I know a nuclear physicist who started producing films, a drug dealer who gripped, and an emergency room nurse who worked as a boom operator. One person met a director at a weight-loss camp, expressed an interest, and became a PA on the biggest movie of the year; someone who used to run a film school equipment department moved into production. I received an actual fan letter in the mail and brought a high school student on as an intern. There are as many stories as there are people. It's not that hard to find a way in; the trick is to show the crew that you belong there.

What Role Do Most Utilities/2nd ASs Perform Before Getting Their First Utility Job?

The 2nd AS/UST position is becoming more common, but there is a long history of small project Sound Departments consisting of two people, so most were boom operators first. When someone works as a PA (production assistant), she has an opportunity to learn about all the departments and see how each contributes. Many times, sound crews will need additional, occasional help and utilize PAs, so let your Sound Department know that you'd like a chance.

How Do You Find Work as a Utility? How Do I Market Myself as a 2nd Assistant Sound?

The same way as a boom operator: Let everyone you meet know that you are a UST/2nd AS. Attend trade meetings, use social media to contribute, offer help, or ask questions. Find a mentor. Get to know people in the rental departments of equipment houses and film schools. Most film schools don't teach production sound; however, there is often a directory or place to post your card. Take those jobs, knowing that you can make a quick call to your mentor from the set when you get stuck. Let your instructors know you have chosen sound as a career. So few people want to work in sound that your name will get around. Join a camera group. Watch for news of productions that will shoot in your area and contact the production company to send your résumé to the Sound Department. Many cities and countries have film commissions to promote their area and publish information on upcoming projects. Go to film festivals and approach people who you feel you connect with. If you post on Facebook, saying, "Hey, I'm looking for work. Thanks"...well, that's not enough for professional people to consider. Tell me your skills and talents. Why do we need *you*?

How Does Someone Get an Apprenticeship?

Check with your local film groups; some offer types of apprenticeship, and the same goes for many film schools. Or just post on their bulletin board/jobs listing sites. The Academy of Motion Picture Arts and Sciences (AMPAS) offers their Gold program; check their website for details.

IATSE Local 695 (the Los Angeles sound union) offers an introductory job classification: Y-16A (Y-1s are Mixers). This apprenticeship allows you to work on a union production with experienced people, learning the ins and outs of established work protocols in Hollywood. You will gain hours toward medical insurance and getting onto the Roster (the official list of accepted personnel for West Coast union productions) as well as a working wage. There are restrictions, so contact IATSE Local 695 for details. Local 695 does *not* keep a directory of interested apprentices; Mixers request someone after a discussion with their production manager. Get the word out to boom ops and USTs, consider a well thought-out posting on Facebook, and a grammatically correct, concise résumé.

Are Career Silos Still a Thing: How Often Do IATSE 695 Members Have to Work Their Way Up Through the Ranks as Opposed to Staying in Their Preferred Classification?

There used to be a tier system in which you could move up classifications after a certain time, but that system no longer exists. You can change your classification (subject to the Local's guidelines) at will. Understand that

Mixers work less than boom operators, and boom operators work less than USTs. Some boom operators and Mixers have downgraded their classification, realizing that they need more experience working on bigger-budget productions and gaining experience from working with other crews. It's a personal decision to make based on your own experiences.

How Does One Break into the Union?

Don't break anything! Seriously, union membership is available by contacting the IATSE Local and paying your initiation and dues. Working on a union production is an entirely different beast, and in Los Angeles, requires being on the Industry Experience Roster (IER), a separate process not administered by the Union (see Contract Services at: **www.csatf.org**).

How Does One Find UST Opportunities for Mixers Who May Already Have Established Regular Teams?

The most common ways of working with established teams are by being recommended by other USTs or boom operators; they naturally work in more circles more often than Mixers. Word of mouth can be helpful; not every referral comes from a Sound person. Remember, we all have friendships with people in other departments; grips and electricians and dressers know Sound people who are professional and pleasant to work with. You can make an introduction to the Sound team directly, as there are always times when one of them may need to find someone to fill in.

Chain of Command on Set: Who Addresses an Issue First, the Utility or Mixer?

It depends; this is one of the questions to ask during prep or when you are first working with a Mixer, *before* you have a situation. That aside, when the issue is within your job duties, you should try to resolve it with the person directly. Go to the person lowest in the hierarchy of that department and then work your way up.

For example, a question or request for a power drop: that's your job. Ask the best boy electrician who is responsible for coordinating a power drop with you. And use words like "coordinate with" rather than "I need" or "Can you help me?"; the former implies working together equally, whereas the others connote a tone of aloofness or granting a favor or helplessness.

For the timing of wiring actors, that's also your job unless the Mixer insists on wiring or the boom operator shares the responsibility. Coordinate with the 2nd 2nd AD or set PA in charge of the trailers or the crewmember who readies the actor just before you. Props people usually get the actor *after* you, so they may ask to be kept in the loop, especially if they need to explain weapons and safety information to the actor. If any special props are in use that may have an interactive aspect with sound, it's wise to be present when the prop is being given to the actor and to request a demonstration of the prop by the actor.

If you have a problem with wardrobe, it depends; if the issue is an individual costume or person, try to resolve it directly. If a Costumes Department policy applies to the situation, and it is affecting you, try speaking to the person who set the policy directly. Then, if needed, take it to the Mixer with a detailed account of with whom and when you tried to resolve it, what was said, *and the attitude* of the person. Be as specific as possible, using the exact words spoken. (Use your notebook.)

If an actor refuses to wear a wire: if it's an A-list talent, walk away and inform the 1st AD and Mixer, who may then either confer with the director or ask that you have that discussion. When talking with a director, keep your words succinct and unemotional; this is not the time for attitude. Remember that it is the director's movie, not yours! Don't make the acquisition of sound a petty tug-of-war with other departments; it's not us against them.

If the actor is someone you think would accept your brief explanation, state what you plan to achieve by wiring the actor, in actor terms. For example, "This scene is about your inner conflict, and those quiet murmurs or sighs will add to the audience feeling your pain." Speak like a filmmaker.

If an actor is obstinate, ask a Wardrobe person to accompany you; most people won't make a scene with more people around.

What's in Your Toolbox as a Utility Tech?

I have a truck bag (for raingear, winter clothing, boots, etc.), a cart bag (for personal items, schedule/notebook, a current crew list, a set of black clothing that fits over my outfit, and my short pole. If a phone is allowed on set, I have mine with many Sound people's contact info. If it's a no-phone set, I carry a printed list, a fanny pack, and belt). In my belt pouch, I used to carry a Swiss army knife, but with professional Costumes people available to work out minor adjustments to costumes, I just carry scissors, Moleskin, Transpore, Super Stick strips, additional cut foam if we're using it a lot, Moleskin strips, a voltage tester, safety pins, gloves, pens, a Sharpie, a small notebook, the Lectrosonics tool, spare wireless batteries and Comtek batteries, a couple of cable ties, a mini-Maglite, and lip balm. If we're using fur on the lavs, I carry a spare.

How to Best Adapt to Different Mixers When Day Playing?

Try to have a conversation with the Utility or with the boom op who is working with her. Or try to ask someone who has worked with her in the past. If that's not an option, arrange a conversation when the Mixer can spend 15 minutes telling you how she likes to work. Keep a notebook and jot down cart setups and preferences. Memorize them as best you can the night before. Learn their set persona and fall in line—mostly. Understand the personality of the person you're filling in for and whether that's complementary or contrasting. Try to present a consistent face of the department to the rest of the crew and production. Ask the person you're replacing for the little details she does that you can copy to make the transition smoother. It can be OK for you to show a bit of your personality; make your best assessment.

What Information Should I Ask for When Day Playing as a UST, Especially in the Middle of a Show?

Did you have a walk-away wrap? What's the location, and do you have any production notes about it? How long does it take generally until the first shot? Do you get enough time to wire actors? Do you wire alone, or who wires actors? What's the procedure for each actor? Is anyone difficult? How's the DOP? Does she operate as well? What are the names of the best boys? Who gives you a power drop? Who do you talk to for a flag or cutter (for booming)? What things do the Mixers want or dislike? *Read* the call sheet, look for names you recognize, and call them up. Check to see who has pre-calls (especially Camera), and then request the same. Usually, the boom operator will come in a bit early to ease the transition.

Call the UST for notes on IFB distribution and morning and wrap procedures. Ask what things the Mixer typically forgets, and make sure you remind him or her.

It can be a little more stressful coming onto a show where relationships have been worked out and there is a particular groove. But it can also offer the weary crew a change of pace to see someone new; it's a great time to be a fresh face! If it's been a long, grueling show, think about how you can be the bit of sunshine, be the breath of fresh air everyone needs. Bring news from home if you're on location (better yet, bring a local food that is shareable). Update them with news from the union meeting or latest gear you've seen demonstrated. Offer to work a day so the boom op can take a medical day *or* fill in a couple of hours so someone can attend his or her child's sports or school event. Offer to make an equipment run before or after work. Wash the wire accessories overnight. Offer alternative ways of doing things. Lastly, check out my Day Playing Checklist in the Appendix.

What Are a Few Things That a Utility Should Always Keep an Eye and Ear Out for on Set?

Any changes that aren't announced or information you overhear. Anything you hear from Costumes or the 2nd 2nds or the Camera Department that could affect work. Dangerous things. Director's and actors' moods.

What Are the Small Things That Sometimes Get Overlooked?

A lot of things aren't addressed in *pre-production* if you aren't on the payroll. Honestly, Sound people work unpaid during some part of the prep period, even on the biggest movies. And most keep track of their actual days and then have a conversation with the PM once trust has been established. Many have agreed on a number of previously unscheduled days to add to a timecard. It's a function of production not understanding what we do, and it requires everyone to make it an educational moment, and eventually it will become a known necessity.

Distributing a prelim is not always part of the production's process and means that you'll have to pull out your script and one-liner and compare them to the advance section on the call sheet, and then check it again when actual call sheets come out. You may have to call an equipment house for gear or find additional help after wrap.

USTs can be nervous about getting lavs placed correctly and forget other things, like telling actors the de-wiring protocols you'd like and how you want them to let you know when they need an adjustment. Or asking them to let you know if they will change their voice level significantly. On the film *Outbreak*, Dustin Hoffman had been saying his lines at a certain level. During one take he did just that but, without cutting, said, "Sound! Sound! I'm going to be shouting this time." That gave us just the warning we needed to adjust my boom's distance and give a heads-up to the Mixer—and save the take. That's being professional.

When you have actors on radio mics, don't forget to periodically check the battery level (remotely). On *Ad Astra*, we were frantically changing batteries on our *one* actor (Brad Pitt, in a space suit in a tight ship corridor!) sometimes as often as every 20 minutes! And in between takes and setups, checking and changing out every possible contributing piece of gear. It turned out that we had a shipment of several boxes of defective batteries. You can't always control what's happening in the moment, but you can act professionally and calmly; that's ultimately why you get hired: how you perform under pressure.

When you're just starting out, you can be UST-centric, forgetting other departments. Remember: no one makes a movie alone. Remember to appreciate the people around you. When you're starting out, it's easy to miss the little ways you are being helped by others...and trust me, you are. Smile and tell them you appreciate them.

Until you have some experience, your brain will be filled with trying to remember everything you should be doing *now*. It's easy to overlook *thinking ahead*, but that's the goal.

Voltage testing can be overlooked with horrible consequences (don't ask how many veterans have a story about blowing up their power supplies!). Always check with your voltage meter and ground tester before plugging in. *And set the brakes on the sound cart before lowering the gate!* (There are far too many stories of carts going over the edge!)

You might think that you don't need to scout the next location, but the time you don't is likely to be the one that will bite you in the behind. If you absolutely can't get to the location ahead of time, ask either the Locations person about the particulars or a grip or electrician what plans they have and if there are any rigging crews that were hired—and what work they are doing.

Don't forget washing TX packs and straps or belts! With Covid-19 protocols in place, this shouldn't be an issue anymore, but do think about the little items that can be cleaned but aren't because the department is shorthanded. Put them in a box for those times when you have some free moments or enough turnaround time to take them home and wash them.

What Are the Miscellaneous Tasks That a UST Performs?

Goodwill, taking care of the Mixer and boom op, food/beverage runs (it's never beneath me to take care of my department members who cannot leave the set), make phone calls, deep cleaning the gear or truck (the yucky jobs), soldering, organizing, inventorying. Before starting *Once Upon a Time...in Hollywood*, I shook *a lot* of snow out of the multi-track mixer from *The Hateful Eight* (from 3 years before!). USTs may want to dress up or participate in creative set antics or decorate the cart(s) for the holidays. Find out if dailies are being shown at lunchtime. If the Mixer is attending, order a meal for him. Occasionally checking with the video village to make sure IFBs are working...and maybe offering to get a coffee for producers. Making sure that the cart's tires have the correct amount of air; if doing a beach shoot, know how to change the cart tires to balloon tires (check with the Mixer before doing the work). Check manufacturers' websites for updates for gear or software programs. Obtaining the production's Wi-Fi information so Mixers can send electronic reports or talk to Production. Researching good restaurants nearby and/or a local coffeehouse. Because there are so many variables in every film project and every scene, the only way to stay on top of things is to be thinking and analyzing constantly. Don't be surprised to find yourself returning home from work physically and mentally exhausted.

Where Does the Line Between Boom Operator and Utility Start to Differ?

The line changes when you get a UST on your show: until then, it's just the boom op and the Mixer—and the division of labor is defined by what is comfortable for the Mixer.

What Are the Crossover Responsibilities for the UST When There Is Playback or Second-Unit Work?

For playback: help them set up the gear if possible, advising on show protocols and procedures, and names and personalities they'll be dealing with—particularly the 1st AD and director and actors. The operator should have made contact with the editors and music people during her pre-production time, but have a crew list handy just in case. Help set up the Cue-aid system if it was deemed necessary. If it's a simple playback situation, the UST may handle that directly.

For 2nd units: there is an opportunity for you to "bump up" to that position and be paid accordingly (check your local regulations). The additional work of the UST will be to fill out the 2nd unit crew timecards. Unless they offer and/or have start and wrap times you will not be aware of, you should add them to the daily timesheet (unless, again, they are going off on the unit's own schedule—then ask them to hand in their paperwork directly), possibly acquire their start paperwork, schedule and manage additional equipment, offer insights into the personalities on the production, and offer some help if possible.

In Case of a Last-Minute Second Boom, How Do I Quickly Set Up the Communication System Between the Sound Mixer, Boom Op, and Sound Utility?

I recommend always having that communication system in use from the beginning of the day, every day. You will want a system that allows you to go to another department for a conversation that the Mixer can hear and possibly participate in. You may need to give information to your department from the trailer or caterer.

What Cart Gadgets or Items Will Help with Workflow?

Anything that keeps you from having to run to the truck. Think about small cases or bags that can wrap small equipment before moving the cart. Keep a battery tester, extra cable ties, and spare cables. The farther the set is from your truck, the more gear you should have in an additional cart or cases. Make sure things are strapped down so they don't fall off during a move! Try to keep like-use items in one bag so that you make one trip and have everything you need (e.g., a small playback case or Cue-aid bag). Have doubles of some often-used tapes and a few basic tools like screwdrivers and scissors. If you're doing an outdoor show with a lot of extras, or crowd control, you can carry a bullhorn on the follow cart. *Think* about the particular reoccurring elements of your show and how you can incorporate them into your other job duties without being interrupted for any length of time.

What Is the Workflow in a Larger Sound Department?

Sometimes there are large Sound Departments because of the nature of the work—think *Cats* or *1917*. Most other shows are three-person production crews—Mixer, Boom Operator, and UST—with occasional additions of a music playback operator or video playback operator. The most important difference is in delegation; with additional hands, the tasks of the UST can be divided and can also involve multiple units to record sound or sound effects or simultaneous work on different aspects.

On Quentin Tarantino productions, I'm responsible for managing Quentin's headsets. During tow shots, I run cables and a speaker to the car. I run out the director's headphones and communication system, manage our feed from the DOP's comm system, set up the Mixer's bag package for car work, pack and grab the follow car case, ride in the follow van, wire the actors, prep the next set or car, order and help set up the Fisher boom, set up speakers VOG, and boom full-time. We used multiple Y-16As to supplement or workload on very busy days.

On *Ad Astra*, I assisted actors with their communications within the space suits, figured out how to wire all the versions of space and flight suits, dealt with difficult clothing, liaised with the Costumes Department, managed the director's VOG system and video assist feed, and occasionally 2nd boomed.

How Often Do You Experiment with Mics on Your Own to Test?

When I have time. If you're just starting out, you'll have a lot of time, so go to the equipment houses and check them out. If you have access to school equipment, schedule a few sessions just to experiment with everything they have available. Bringing a friend will help in practicing booming and testing different voices—e.g., male, female, and children.

What Inventory Must USTs Perform?

Your show may differ, but generally USTs fill out all paperwork for the Sound Department, review invoices from equipment houses, manage tracking and repair items and their paperwork, fill out and track Transportation run slips or PA run slips (if it's a small shoot, PAs may make runs. *Always* give them a run slip with *exactly* what you need and when you need it written on it and two contact phone numbers). USTs fill out timecards and make sure department signatures are on them. USTs track the inventory of expendables items and make sure there are enough for whatever the locations or shooting calls for.

How Much Production Sound Is Used in the Final Film?

It depends. First, there are two kinds of dialogue replacement (ADR): the creative and the technical. Sometimes dialogue is changed for creative reasons—e.g., a character's name or town name is changed, or the director wants a different reading of the lines. Sometimes there's a technical issue—e.g., there wasn't time to wait for the train to go by, etc.

With postproduction schedules getting shorter and shorter, and technology allowing for fewer editors, there isn't time to add to the workload. When in production, you should assume that the work you are doing *will* be in the movie. Don't believe it when you read that post-people say that everything is replaced, and we're just providing a guide track; that might be the case for a movie here and there, but not as a standard process in filmmaking. We capture the performances and all the relevant sounds that are created on the day. This lays the foundation for the other creative sound work to follow.

On *Once Upon a Time...in Hollywood*, well, you know Quentin (Tarantino); he doesn't want to replace dialogue. He's known for great soundtracks, and people always rave about them. Mark Ulano has been the production sound Mixer on his last seven films. Quentin says, "What happens on the day is it, guys, and I'm trusting you to bring it all." Everybody brings everything they have to every take, every time; that's the magic he captures.

How Do You Gauge the Distance of a Long Throw? Sometimes I Find That I'm Off of the Sweet Spot and Not Sure How to Find It Again.

VDB poles have ruler markings on their sections, and that allows for easy measuring if you have to collapse the pole to go wire or something, and then come back and quickly be ready to boom. You can make your own temporary mark if using another brand of pole. Or you can "spot" something (triangulate) on the back wall or on the same plane as where you want the boom. Sometimes you'll need a stand-in or body right there to spot your position by looking up at the mic and confirming that it is aimed correctly. There's nothing wrong with that, as long as it isn't a constant need.

How Do You Treat Spaces That Are Not Good for Sound?

So many problems that arise are because the Mixer is not included during the location scout. Compounding that problem is that many location people are not trained to think of sound as part of filmmaking and insist on showing directors visually interesting but terribly problematic sound locations. During pre-production, questions to the Grip and Electric Departments can add information and perhaps head off some of the negative elements. Ask where the generator will be. Will there be other motors, generators, or compressors in use? Can the Art Department baffle the noisemaker? In which direction will the action take place (use a microphone with a polar pattern that can help avoid some of that ambient

noise)? Try using carpets, mats, or furniture-pad baffles to break up standing waves. Talk to departments who may have an influence on the specific negative sound elements. If no on-site solution can be made effective, the Mixer may apply Cedar (audio software) for noise mitigation and will probably give the editor and/or the Post sound team a notification and suggest testing solutions with Izotope. This may be especially important if the location will be used extensively.

▸ www.cedar-audio.com/products/products.shtml

▸ www.izotope.com/en/products/rx.html?utm_medium=
cpc&utm_source=google&utm_campaign=SU_SE_BR_UU_US_
RX&utm_content=RX7_BM_KW&utm_term=%2Bizotope%20
%2Brx%20%2B7%7Cb%7Cg%7Cc%7C%7C433699172777&gclid=EAIaIQo
bChMIwqm-nf7B6wIVJBvnCh3VIA4GEAAYASAAEgLSnvD_BwE

What Is the Best Way to Handle Your Staging Area on Set or on Location?

Have as small a footprint as possible but give yourself room to access all the sides of the cart(s). Try to minimize how many cart moves you'll need to make. Talk in advance with the best boys and Props to stake a space. Make sure the bell and light system reaches you on a studio stage.

On location: pick cart and staging locations that get you out at wrap without getting stuck behind Grip and Electric and Craft Services carts. Make sure there is active security, and lock things up if you're in a sketchy area and ensure that Production or Locations signs off on leaving the equipment in place for insurance reasons. If not, you may be required to wrap all the gear back to the truck. Also confirm that there is power for carts and a light after dark.

What Are Different Types of Lavalier Mounts and What Materials Does Each Work Best For?

This could be the subject of an entire book and is just too much to cover. The Facebook group "**Lavalier mic hiding techniques**" constantly includes postings of successful mounts and tapes and questions members need help with. In general, know what the clothing is, and it's very helpful to know the actor's movements before deciding on a placement. Most actors will understand that if they are speaking loudly, you'll want them to give you a level while you are setting the TX level.

Think about matching colors or using black lavaliers, which most often if seen will look like a shadow. Keep a low profile, and don't press fabric down over the mic; doing so ends up making a 3D impression rather than smoothing bulges. Do some research online.

When planting lavaliers, make sure any tapes or sticky products you use will not damage the item.

What About Lavalier Techniques?

VideoMantis.com has a good e-book, *Down to the Wire*, which shows actual mainstream techniques for a variety of costumes. Some YouTube videos give current narrative techniques, but some are outdated or never used on mainstream productions. Try to meet Costume people in pre-production and schedule time to test a rig if there's an unusual costume. Ask about building in a pouch or an easy-access area for a transmitter and for battery changes. Work out your collaboration before shooting; the more professional Costume people already consider sound in pre-production.

Introduce yourself to the 2nd 2nd AD. Explain how you want the process to go, how much time you need to wire the actors, which ones you'll wire first (if there's a reason), where you'll wire, and the procedure you want for de-rigging. Ask if the 2nd 2nd has any contrary information. Give them a heads-up if there are any particularly challenging rigs due to costumes or personalities that should be factored into their timing.

Invite the dresser to accompany you. Introduce yourself to the actor's assistant or to the actor directly, giving yourself a bit more time initially. If there hasn't been a rehearsal, ask the actor if he or she anticipates making active movements with the clothing (putting on a scarf or removing a garment) or large movements (practicing basketball, picking up a child, etc.). Suggest a plan, wait briefly for a response, and proceed. Explain minimally but show that you are attentive to the actor. If there is a big movement, ask for a test—and be sure the Mixer has been notified, and the pot on the actor is up. Make any adjustments. Explain your de-rigging protocol. If it's the first time an actor has been on the show, I repeat my name again and request that if something falls or doesn't feel right, to ask for me; I'll be on set. I also watch them to look for signs that something has changed or needs adjusting before they need to call my name. Lastly, I let them know that we'll have them potted down between shots, and I'll advise them if we have BTS (Behind The Scenes or EPK crews—e.g., shooting *The Making of...*) crews working. This lets them know you are thinking of and protecting their privacy.

Some actors have a game they play to make sure they are private between takes, and it's a test of trust. During the first couple of weeks of a shoot, a [*big-name actor*] will ask for Sound, not through an AD, but over his lavalier. If anyone responds, he will give you a hard time for the rest of the show. *Do not* turn your head, look at him, or acknowledge him in any way. Of course, it's best to truly give an actor his or her privacy, but you also want to make sure nothing has shifted. Do what you need, then pot it down until ready for shooting.

How Do I Avoid Lavalier Cable Noise?

Try securing the first few inches of the cable near the head and make sure there isn't any pulling. Clear the microphone head of any unnecessary clothing contact.

How to Get Rid of Rustling Sound for Lavs?

Distinguish between acoustic noise and transmitting noise. Acoustic rustling might just be the actual sound of the costume materials rubbing together, and a boom mic would pick it up it as well. If you hear clothing rustle because of your placement of the lavalier, try adding a small piece of fur in between the mic head and fabric or add a concealer a bit higher up than the mic head to separate the fabric from the mic.

Have You Compared the Lightweight Transmitters, and Which Do You Use?

Weight isn't the only factor when considering transmitters: With smaller sizes, you'll be sacrificing battery longevity; a smaller transmitter means a smaller-capacity battery. Consider where the transmitter will be hidden, how long it will need to be worn, how fast rigging and de-rigging might be, the level of comfort for the actor, and how easy accessing the battery compartment or making adjustments will be.

What Are Some Lav Hiding Techniques for Handling Stressful Situations with Actors Who Don't Like Being Touched?

If the actor has an assistant, include that person. Be efficient, be quiet, enlist the help of Wardrobe people and/or assistants, and try to wire outerwear. Explain exactly what you will need to do and try not to directly touch the actor (I worked with a lead actor who felt this way; I pre-wired his jackets, hats, and objects that would be near him). Decide with the Mixer whether it's necessary to have a discussion with the 1st AD and/or director about the sensitivity of the actor. Understand the resulting parameters.

Also know that things might change; after 6 months of being told to never let the actor even see me wiring his wardrobe, he then allowed me to apply rigs to his skin. Trust built; issue gone!

When Can You Say That Lavs Are Not an Option?

When the actor says no. When Production *and* the director say no. When wiring the actor might harm or interfere with some type of movement or action or stunt. When the actor is submerged for a length of time (e.g., wireless mics were always used together with the boom on *Titanic*). Or when you've run out of ideas.

How Are Professional Sports Games Handled?

Before Covid-19, players were wired with waist/chest/shoulder straps and lavs. There wasn't much clothing noise, as the volume (gain) was set low due to the screaming crowds. Players are not currently mic'd; the umpires have TX and RX, and FX mics are on cameras and the sidelines. You can only hear the players during this time because there aren't any crowds. If you're hearing the players more clearly, it's the umpires and possibly the boundary and goal mics that are contributing. Engineers can pump the volume since there is little crowd noise to compete against or filter out.

What Is a Professional Cableman?

The correct term is either a 2nd AS or a Utility Sound Technician; using the outdated "cableman" title implies a ridiculous understating of what you now know the job entails. To be professional means you carry yourself with dignity, you respect the artists you collaborate with and are discreet, you leave your ego at home, and that you take your job seriously; you understand set etiquette and the show politics. Make sure you're always learning.

How Can I Become the Best Utility Sound Technician?

Be a constant student! Learn about filmmaking, acting, related skills, and psychology. Be adaptable, develop stellar people skills, be known as bulletproof (nothing can sidetrack you). Stay in good shape and have a great attitude.

Go out and live your passion!

Why Do Sound People Answer Questions with the Words "It Depends" So Often?

We say that so often because nearly all the questions are too general! There are a staggering number of complex parameters to assess in our work, and to get a precise answer (which we *could* provide) means that you will need to give us *all* the information: the lighting, camera placement, time of day, temperament of the key players, etc. for us to assess the best options from our perspectives. This work is far more art than science.

Appendix

Movies That Use Sound Well

Here's a list of movies that I feel use sound to its best advantage in storytelling:

- *Inglourious Basterds*
- *Kill Bill: Vol. 1 and Vol. 2*
- *Once Upon a Time...in Hollywood*
- *Wait Until Dark*
- *The Fugitive*
- *Song of the Sea*
- *Titanic*
- *Baby Driver*
- *Skyfall*
- *The Fog of War*
- *The Conversation*
- *Isle of Dogs*
- *Citizen Kane*
- *Apocalypse Now*

Script and Schedule Color Progressions

The progression of colors varies from one production to the next, but a typical sequence would be: white, blue, pink, yellow, green, goldenrod, buff, salmon, cherry, tan, ivory, white (this time known as "double white"), and back to blue ("double blue").

Resources

Physical Health

▸ https://centr.com/join-us
▸ www.nike.com/ntc-app

An In-Depth, *Accurate* History of Film Sound

▸ http://filmsound.org/ulano/

DPA Microphone Dictionary with Audio Terminology

▸ www.dpamicrophones.com/mic-dictionary

Facebook Groups

▸ Utility Sound Technicians
▸ BOOM Operator
▸ Microphone Boom Operators
▸ Lavalier mic hiding techniques
▸ The Plant Mic Page
▸ LASoundMixers (worldwide contributions, but focus is on the Los Angeles area)
▸ LA Sound Mixers Underground (strictly Los Angeles-based)
▸ LA Sound Sisters
▸ **Soundgirls.org** (Primarily focused on FOH—front of house-live mixing for music bands—and sound reinforcement, and not just for girls.

Manufacturers' Websites

BOOM POLES

▸ https://ambient.de

▸ https://ktekpro.com

▸ www.panamic.net

▸ vdbboompoles.com

MICROPHONES

▸ https://en-us.sennheiser.com

▸ https://schoeps.de

▸ www.rode.com

▸ https://en-de.neumann.com/?

▸ https://countryman.com

▸ www.sankenmicrophones.com

▸ www.dpamicrophones.com

WIRELESS MICROPHONES

▸ www.audioltd.com

▸ www.audio-technica.com/world_map/

▸ www.deitymic.com

▸ www.dpamicrophones.com

▸ www.lectrosonics.com

▸ www.rode.com

▸ https://en-us.sennheiser.com

▸ www.shure.eu

▸ https://pro.sony/en_SI/products/wireless-audio

▸ https://wisycom.com/products

▸ https://zaxcom.com

WIRELESS ACCESSORIES

▸ www.hideamic.com

▸ https://lmcsound.com

▸ https://remoteaudio.com

▸ https://rycote.com

▸ www.sound-guys.com

▸ https://www.bubblebeeindustries.com

▸ https://ursastraps.com

▸ www.vivianastraps.com

Reliable Training Sources

Here are just a few reliable training sources; there are other sources as well.

▸ Videomantis.com

▸ Soundfish Academy: www.soundfish.it/academy/

▸ Sound Speeds: www.youtube.com/SoundSpeeds

IMDb.com

IMDb, or Internet Movie Database, offers a plethora of film and TV information, including data on actors, directors, producers, movie ratings, and much more.

IATSE Paragraph 106 of the Basic Agreement

Composition of Sound Crew

The basic production sound crew shall consist of three (3) people: Mixer (Y-1), Microphone Boom Operator (Y-8) and Utility Sound Technician (Y-7a). The Utility Sound Technician (Y-7a) shall be paid at the rate of a Microphone Boom Operator (Y-8) and the duties of the Utility Sound Technician shall be performed by a Microphone Boom Operator (Y-8) or a Service Recorder (Y-7). The Utility Sound Technician (Y-7a) assigned to the basic production sound crew may be required to perform any sound functions other than those of the Audio Mixer without any adjustment of compensation.

The Producer is not required to utilize a three-person sound crew on promos, tests, location looping, second units, documentaries, industrials, educational films, and when recording wild effects.

It is recognized that there are other types of production that do not require a three-person sound crew. If Producer believes that any specific production, or portion thereof, does not require a three-person sound crew, it may request from the Union a waiver of this requirement. The Union will promptly consider the facts concerning the sound recording requirements for the production and, as soon as practicable thereafter, advise the Producer of its response to the Producer's request. In such consideration, the Union agrees to act in good faith and will not unreasonably withhold its waiver. If the Union agrees that a sound crew of less than three (3) persons would be appropriate, it will grant a waiver for a lesser-sized crew.

If the Union refuses to grant its waiver, the Producer shall use a three-person sound crew and may file a grievance against the Union and proceed directly to arbitration without a Step One or Step Two proceeding. If the arbitrator rules that the Union did not act in good faith or unreasonably withheld its waiver, the Union shall be liable to the Producer for the labor costs of the third person for the period of time that the Producer used the third person on the specific production or portion thereof.

Goal Worksheet

SMART Goal Setting Worksheet

Name: _ _ _ _ _ _ _ _ _ _

1. What is the goal? _ _ _ _ _ _ _ _ _ _ _ _ _ _
_ _
_ _
_ _

2. Why is the goal important? _ _ _ _ _ _ _
_ _
_ _
_ _
_ _
_ _

3. SMART goal checklist

Specific — Is the goal clearly written, with no ambivalence? Is it clear who needs to accomplish the goal, and any support they might expect?

Measurable — Does the goal answer the questions of how many, how much and/or how often?

Achievable — Can you get the support needed to achieve the goal by the target date? Do you have all the resources needed to achieve the goal? Are the results expected realistic?

Relevant — I want this goal make a difference in your career? Is it going to make an improvement in your personal life? Is it going to significantly make a difference to your business?

Time-bound — Does the goal state a clear and specific completion date?

4. List potential problems that might keep you from completing your goal
....
....
....
....
....
....
....
....
....
....
....

5. Goal Completion date _ _ _ _ _ _ _ _ _ _ _ _ _

Action Item	Who	When
Action Item	Who	When
Action Item	Who	When
Action Item	Who	When
Action Item	Who	When
Action Item	Who	When
Action Item	Who	When

DevelopGoodHabits.com

www.developgoodhabits.com/wp-content/uploads/2017/04/
SMART-Goal-Setting-Worksheet-819x1024.jpg

First Aid

BLEEDING

Before providing care, put on protective gloves or use a barrier between you and the victim, to reduce the chance of disease transmission while assisting the injured person. Cleanse your hands thoroughly with soap and water when finished.

Basic first aid treatment:

- CALL 911 for medical assistance.
- Keep victim lying down.
- Apply direct pressure using a clean cloth or sterile dressing directly on the wound.
- DO NOT take out any object that is lodged in a wound; see a doctor for help in removal.
- If there are no signs of a fracture in the injured area, carefully elevate the wound above the victim's heart.
- Once bleeding is controlled, keep victim warm by covering with a blanket, continuing to monitor for shock.

CLEANING & BANDAGING WOUNDS

- Wash your hands and cleanse the injured area with clean soap and water, then blot dry.
- Apply antibiotic ointment to minor wound and cover with a sterile gauze dressing or bandage that is slightly larger than the actual wound.

EYE INJURIES

- If an object is impaled in the eye, CALL 911 and DO NOT remove the object.
- Cover both eyes with sterile dressings or eye cups to immobilize.
- Covering both eyes will minimize the movement of the injured eye.
- DO NOT rub or apply pressure, ice, or raw meat to the injured eye.
- If the injury is a black eye, you may apply ice to cheek and area around eye, but not directly on the eyeball itself.

How to flush the eyes: If chemical is in only one eye, flush by positioning the victim's head with the contaminated eye down. . . to prevent flushing the chemical from one eye to another. Flush with cool or room temperature water for 15 minutes or more. Remove contact lenses after flushing.

BURNS

First Degree Burn: Skin will appear red and may be swollen or painful. Generally does not require medical attention.

Second Degree Burn: Skin will appear red, blistered and swollen. May require medical attention.

Third Degree Burn: Skin will be visibly charred and may be white. Usually very painful. REQUIRES MEDICAL ATTENTION.

Basic first aid treatment for 1st degree & some 2nd degree burns:

Submerge burn area immediately in cool water until pain stops. If affected area is large, cover with cool wet cloths. Do not break blisters if they are present. If pain persists but no medical assistance is needed, apply medicated first aid cream or gel and cover with sterile dressing. If medical attention is needed, do not apply any cream. Just cover with a dry, sterile dressing and seek medical help immediately. basic first aid treatment for 3rd degree & some 2nd degree burns: CALL 911!! Third degree burns MUST RECEIVE MEDICAL ATTENTION IMMEDIATELY! DO NOT try to remove any clothing stuck to the burned area. Cover with sterile dressing or clean sheet. DO NOT apply any creams or gels.

CHEMICAL BURNS

- Flush the affected area with cool running water for at least 15 minutes.
- Remove all clothing and jewelry that has been contaminated.
- Monitor victim for shock and seek medical assistance.
- If chemical burn is in the eyes, flush continuously with water and seek medical attention immediately.

https://first-aid-product.com/free-first-aid-guide.html

First Aid (continued)

SUNBURN

- Avoid any further exposure to direct sunlight.
- Drink plenty of water to prevent dehydration.
- Do not apply cold water or ice to a severe burn.
- Use over-the-counter remedies to remove discomfort.
- If burn is severe and blisters develop, seek medical attention.

UNCONSCIOUSNESS

- Do not leave an unconscious victim alone except to call 911 for medical help.
- Assess victim's state of awareness by asking if they are OK.
- Check the victim's Airway, Breathing, and Circulation (ABC's).
- If the victim's ABC's are not present, perform CPR. IMPORTANT: only a trained & qualified person should administer CPR.
- If ABC's are present and spinal injury is not suspected, place victim on their side with their chin toward the ground to allow for secretion drainage.
- Cover the victim with blanket to keep warm and prevent shock. If victim communicates feeling warm, remove blanket.

CHOKING

- Ask the victim, "Are you OK?"
- do not interfere or give first aid if the victim can speak, breathe, or cough.
- If the victim cannot speak, breathe, or cough, ask for someone to call 911 and then perform the Heimlich maneuver (abdominal thrust).
- How to perform the Heimlich maneuver: Position yourself behind the victim with your arms around victim's stomach. Place the thumb-side of your fist above the victim's navel and below the lower end of the breastbone. Take hold of your fist with your free hand and pull fist upward and in, quickly and firmly. Continue with thrusts until the object is dislodged or airway is clear.

INFANT CHOKING

- Place infant face down on your forearm supporting the head and neck with your hand. Rest your hand on your knee with the infant's head lower than it's body.
- With the heel of your hand give four blows between the infant's shoulder blades.
- Turn infant over, place two fingers on the center of the infant's chest (just below the nipples) and perform up to five chest thrusts.
- Repeat until obstruction is clear.
- seek medical attention after any choking incident, since complications may arise.

POISON

- Call your local Poison Control Center or 911 for immediate medical attention.
- Antidotes on labels may be wrong!! do not follow them unless instructed by a physician.
- never give anything by mouth (milk, water, Ipecac, etc.) until you have consulted with a medical professional.
- Keep a one ounce bottle of Ipecac on hand at all times in case of an emergency, and give only when instructed by a physician.
- If the poison is on the skin, flush skin with water for 15 minutes, then wash and rinse with soap and water.
- If poison is in the eye, flush with lukewarm water for 15 minutes. Adults can stand under the shower with eyes open. always consult medical professionals after any eye injury has occurred.

https://first-aid-product.com/free-first-aid-guide.html

First Aid (continued)

ANIMAL BITES

- Control any bleeding by applying direct pressure or with elevation. To avoid risk of infection, do not close wound.
- Rinse the bite thoroughly, holding it under running water. Cleanse with soap and water and hold under water again for five minutes.
- do not put ointments or medicines on wound. Cover with dry sterile bandage or gauze.
- seek medical assistance immediately.
- note: report animal and human bites to local police and/or health authorities.

BEE STING

- If possible, remove stinger by scraping it off with a blunt edge (e.g. credit card).
- Clean wound and apply cold compress to reduce swelling.
- Remove tight clothing and jewelry from areas near the bite in case swelling occurs.
- Watch for signs of shock or allergic reaction. Signs include swelling or itching at the wound site, dizziness, nausea or difficulty breathing. Seek medical attention immediately if any of these signs occur.
- Continue monitoring victim for shock until medical help arrives.
- Check victim's Airway, Breathing, and Circulation (ABC's). If ABC's are impaired then call 911 and begin CPR. IMPORTANT: only a trained & qualified person should administer CPR.

https://first-aid-product.com/free-first-aid-guide.html

First Aid (continued)

HEAT-RELATED ILLNESSES

WHAT TO LOOK FOR	WHAT TO DO

HEAT STROKE

• High body temperature (103°F or higher) • Hot, red, dry, or damp skin • Fast, strong pulse • Headache • Dizziness • Nausea • Confusion • Losing consciousness (passing out)	• Call 911 right away-heat stroke is a medical emergency • Move the person to a cooler place • Help lower the person's temperature with cool cloths or a cool bath • Do not give the person anything to drink

HEAT EXHAUSTION

• Heavy sweating • Cold, pale, and clammy skin • Fast, weak pulse • Nausea or vomiting • Muscle cramps • Tiredness or weakness • Dizziness • Headache • Fainting (passing out)	• Move to a cool place • Loosen your clothes • Put cool, wet cloths on your body or take a cool bath • Sip water **Get medical help right away if:** • You are throwing up • Your symptoms get worse • Your symptoms last longer than 1 hour

HEAT CRAMPS

• Heavy sweating during intense exercise • Muscle pain or spasms	• Stop physical activity and move to a cool place • Drink water or a sports drink • Wait for cramps to go away before you do any more physical activity **Get medical help right away if:** • Cramps last longer than 1 hour • You're on a low-sodium diet • You have heart problems

SUNBURN

• Painful, red, and warm skin • Blisters on the skin	• Stay out of the sun until your sunburn heals • Put cool cloths on sunburned areas or take a cool bath • Put moisturizing lotion on sunburned areas • Do not break blisters

HEAT RASH

• Red clusters of small blisters that look like pimples on the skin (usually on the neck, chest, groin, or in elbow creases)	• Stay in a cool, dry place • Keep the rash dry • Use powder (like baby powder) to soothe the rash

https://media.defense.gov/2019/Jul/01/2002152655/-1/-1/0/
190627-F-RA446-001.JPG

Forms

These forms will speed up your day and make sure you don't miss a detail.

- Morning Checklist
- Wrap Checklist
- Comtek Directory Template
- Transportation Run Slip
- Day-Player Notes
- Loss and Damage Form
- Loss and Damage Report Example
- Daily Timesheet Example
- Daily Time Card Example

Morning Checklist

- ☐ Stage: bell and light system first!
- ☐ Test ground at location and connect power to the carts. Set cart brakes.
- ☐ Mixer cart (voltage regulator/turning on carts)
- ☐ Follow carts (power, cable to main cart)
- ☐ Walkie-talkie (obtain/install in comm system)
- ☐ Boom op and UST IFBs and boom pole assemblies
- ☐ Assemble radio mics
- ☐ Set up VOG
- ☐ Assemble antennae mast
- ☐ Set up Comteks
- ☐ Deliver to Camera (slates, Lock-it boxes, Comteks)
- ☐ Get sides
- ☐ Connect with video assist
- ☐ Video playback
- ☐ Music playback
- ☐ Comtek distribution: DIR, SCR, 1st AD, 2nd AD, 2nd 2nd AD, VID, PRODS, Extras coordinator, Cam operator, Guests

_____

_____

_____

_____

_____

_____

_____

_____

_____

_____

PM

Wrap Checklist

- ❑ De-rig actors
- ❑ De-rig plant mics
- ❑ Disconnect video, playback
- ❑ Retrieve gear from other departments (Props, SP FX, Grip, etc.)
- ❑ Return any borrowed gear
- ❑ Retrieve Comteks from Production people and then from the video village
- ❑ Retrieve gear from Camera (at truck saves time)
- ❑ Return location to original condition
- ❑ Charge batteries
- ❑ Wrap gear to truck/tarp for walk-away wraps
- ❑ Secure all equipment
- ❑ Turn in media, timesheets
- ❑ Pick up callsheet if not delivered
- ❑ Adjust any call times to day players

_____

_____

_____

_____

_____

_____

_____

_____

_____

_____

_____

_____

Comtek Directory Template

#	Position	Name	Accessory

Notes: _____

_____

_____

_____

_____

_____

_____

_____

_____

_____

PM

Transportation Run Slip

Date: _____

Time: _____

Phone: _____ PO#: _____

Location: _____

Address: _____

_____

_____

Specific contact: _____

☐ Sales   ☐ Repair

☐ Pickup   ☐ Dropoff   ☐ Wait for service

☐ Urgent   ☐ Today   ☐ Normal

Bill to

☐ Mixer   ☐ Production company

Mixer name: _____

UST name: _____

Phone: _____

Notes: _____

_____

_____

_____

_____

_____

_____

_____

PM

Day-Player Notes

Date: _____

When we wrapped:

☐ Finished a scene

_____

☐ Middle of a scene

_____

☐ **DO FIRST!** _____

_____

_____

Slates + Sync Boxes

_____ #slates _____ # sync boxes ☐ rechargeables ☐ standard

2nd AC name: _____

Slate/Jam notes: _____

_____

_____

Sound Dept

Mixer notes: _____

_____

Boom notes: _____

_____

Crew Notes

2nd 2nd AD name: _____

Unfinished business to check up on: _____

_____

_____

PM

Day-Player Notes (continued)

Wires

TX#	Character	Actor	Placement-Gain-Mic

On-set costumer's name: _____

Notes: _____

_____

Transportation Coordinator's name: _____

☐ Transportation Run Slip attached

_____

Wrap: _____

_____

_____

Overnight charging: _____

Misc: _____

_____

_____

Thanks for filling in! (my name) _____

(my number) _____

PM

Loss and Damage Form

Name of Show: _____

UST: _____

Report Prepared by (Employee Name): _____

Department: _____ Position: _____

Property Owner: _____

Address: _____

_____

Contact Name/Phone/Email: _____

_____

Description of Incident (Date, Time, Location, Circumstances, etc.):

_____

_____

_____

_____

Description of Property (Model Number, Brand, Value, etc.):

_____

Witnesses Name/Phone/Email: _____

_____

Police Report?   Yes ☐   No ☐   Report #: _____

Employee Box Rental?   Yes ☐   No ☐

Purchase?   Yes ☐   No ☐

Third-Party Rental?   Yes ☐   No ☐

Please attach a copy of the employee box rental agreement, purchase agreement, and/or third-party rental agreement, as applicable, along with detailed inventory.

Employee Signature: _____

Department Head Signature: _____

Line Producer/UPM Siguature: _____

PM

Loss and Damage Report Example

An Excel report makes tracking easier for everyone.

WORKING TITLE L&D REPORT						
DATE	**SCENE**	**SERIAL**	**ITEM**	**DESCRIPTION**	**STATUS**	**L&D FILED**
8/6/19	43	481	Lectrosonics HMa	Boom 1 Transmitter	Repaired & Returned	8/7/19
8/24/19		151	Lectrosonics SMWB	#2 Transmitter	Returned	no L&D - Mix
8/25/19	101	U5054032	WisyCom LNNA	Powered Antenna	In Service 8/31/2019	8/26/19
25-Aug	101	U0549309	WisyCom LNNA	Powered Antenna	Repaired & Returned	8/26/19
8/29/19	60	-	150FT RG58	50 Ohm Antenna Cable	Repaired & Returned	8/29/19
8/29/19	99	R30079B	DPA 4071	Beige TA5 Lavalier	Repaired & Returned	8/29/19
8/30/20	51	-	Remote Audio Single Ear	Comtek Monitor	Disgarded	11/13/19
9/8/19	49	R30519B	DPA 4071	White TA5 Lavalier	Repaired & Returned	9/8/19
9/22/19	130	R324287	DPA4071	Beige TA5 Lavalier	Repaired & Returned	9/22/19
10/5/19	2	151	Lectrosonics SMWB	#2 Transmitter	Repaired & Returned	10/5/19
10/5/19	2	TBA	Lectrosonics SMV	# 12 Transmitter	Repaired & Returned	10/5/19
10/3/19	2	-	DPA 6061 Capsule	Frequency Capsule/Screen	Lost Not replaced yet	10/3/19
10/23/19	73		50 Ohm RG58	Antenna Cable for Comtek	Repaired & Returned	10/24/19
10/28/19	67	-	50 Ohm RG58	100FT Antenna Cable	Repaired & Returned	10/31/19
10/28/19	73	-	100FT XLR	XLR Cable	Repaired & Returned	10/31/19
10/31/19	67		Comtek Belt Clip	Belt Clip	Discarded Not replaced yet	11/13/19
11/11/19		436656	Comtek Mini Mite	Comtek Antenna+Cable	In trailer case	11/11/19
11/13/19	various	-		Comteks Headsets	Apple/Hamilton/Williams/Remote A.	Discarded	11/13/19

PM

Daily Timesheet Example

2nd AD Micah Steele created this daily time sheet with a conversion chart on the back.

ACTUAL HOUR	CONVERSION
4:00 AM	4.0
5:00 AM	5.0
6:00 AM	6.0
7:00 AM	7.0
8:00 AM	8.0
9:00 AM	9.0
10:00 AM	10.0
11:00 AM	11.0
12:00 PM	12.0
1:00 PM	13.0
2:00 PM	14.0
3:00 PM	15.0
4:00 PM	16.0
5:00 PM	17.0
6:00 PM	18.0
7:00 PM	19.0
8:00 PM	20.0
9:00 PM	21.0
10:00 PM	22.0
11:00 PM	23.0
12:00 AM	24.0
1:00 AM	25.0
2:00 AM	26.0
3:00 AM	27.0
4:00 AM	28.0
5:00 AM	29.0
6:00 AM	30.0
7:00 AM	31.0
8:00 AM	32.0

ACTUAL MINUTE	CONVERSION
0:06	0.1
0:12	0.2
0:18	0.3
0:24	0.4
0:30	0.5
0:36	0.6
0:42	0.7
0:48	0.8
0:54	0.9

STEP 1: Go down list of hours to find your "Time In" and convert
STEP 2: Go down list of minutes to add appropriate decimal conversion to your "Time In"
STEP 3: Proceed down hour list from your time in to find "Lunch" and "Time Out"
STEP 4: Repeat Step 2 for "Lunch" and "Time Out"

Note: Always round to the nearest click (6 minutes), but round to your advantage

EXAMPLE:

	Time In	Time Out	Lunch
Actual	7:18 AM	8:24 PM	2:00 PM - 2:30 PM
Conversion	7.3	20.4	14.0 - 14.5

Daily Time Card Example

This sample shows how to fill out a time card from a popular payroll company.

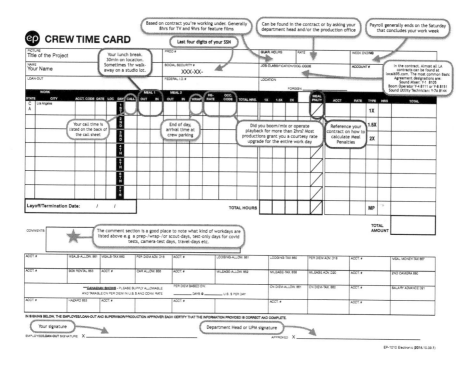

Glossary

1st team is in. The actors are on the set.

2nd team rehearsal. The stand-ins will be rehearsing the scene or shot.

10-100. A radio code used to denote a bathroom break.

86. A code word meaning remove or cancel something.

600 pound chicken. What can it do? Anything it wants!

A-B. This means to compare one thing to another.

Abby or Abby Singer. The penultimate, or next-to-the-last, shot. So named after the fabled Abner E. Singer, an American production manager and assistant director who famously would give the crew a heads-up by announcing one shot in advance of a move or wrap so that the crew could prepare, using time efficiently so the director had more time to shoot.

Aspect ratio. A proportional relationship between an image's width and height. Essentially, it describes an image's shape. **Aspect ratios** are written as a formula of width to height, like this: 3:2. For example, a square image has an **aspect ratio** of 1:1, since the height and width are the same.

The most common **aspect ratios** used today in the presentation of films in cinemas are 1.85:1 and 2.39:1. Two common videographic **aspect ratios** are 4:3 (1.3:1), the universal video format of the 20th century, and 16:9 (1.7:1), universal for high-definition television and European digital television.

Blacks. A black length of fabric used to cover or conceal. Also, a name for non-reflective clothing.

Boom. Sound: *v.* the act of operating the microphone. *n.* The rig that the microphone is mounted to. Camera: To move the camera dolly arm up or down.

Coverage. Shooting various views of the scene.

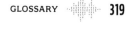

Crew has the set. This phrase signals that the blocking or rehearsal is over, and the crew may make its way onto the set to work.

Cutter. A flag that is used to cut the light.

Dante. A system that delivers uncompressed, multichannel digital audio over an Ethernet network.

Expendables. Items that become depleted during their use.

Fisher boom. A moving platform onto which a telescoping arm is mounted.

Flag. A square or rectangular duvetyne-covered frame, used to block (usually light).

Follow cart. A cart used to hold sound equipment not on the Mixer's primary cart.

Fraturday. A shooting day that begins with a Friday evening call time and ends with a Saturday morning wrap (also known as a blown weekend and sleep deprivation sickness).

Free driving. The hero vehicle is operated without being tethered to a production vehicle.

Going again. There will be another take.

Gold room. A temporary lock-up room built on stage for most departments for the duration of the show.

Grace. A 6-minute forgiveness of the meal penalty provided for in an IATSE contract when the crew works past lunchtime.

Green bed. Walkways above the set, hung from the perms (*see* Perms). They allow crew to adjust lighting and grip equipment without the need for ladders. Also called *greens*.

Green screen/Blue screen. www.premiumbeat.com/blog/chroma-key-green-screen-guide/

High-frequency roll-off. The filtering out of problematic high frequencies.

Honeywagon. The slang term for a compartmentalized truck that contains bathrooms and small dressing rooms for actors or a Production office.

Horsehair. A plastic lace material that deadens the sound of water hitting it.

IFB. Interruptible FoldBack—A monitoring system for one-way communication.

In Case of Emergency (ICE). Phone number: *Always* program a number so strangers can reach a significant person.

Industrials. Projects whose intended audience is employees or management of a company. Industrials are typically considered for in-house use only, not for commercial screening or broadcast.

ISO tracks. An isolated track—a track recorded on its own channel.

ITC. Intermittent Traffic Control, used to attenuate traffic when close to a shooting crew.

Izotope. A postproduction sound editing software program that can alter sound in specific ways, primarily to restore sound quality.

Jam/jamming. To time code sync a machine.

Joe's Sticky Stuff/Snot Tape/English Butyl. An aggressive, double-sided sticky tape.

Lectrosonics tool. A small two-sided screwdriver with a flat head on one side and a Phillips head on the other.

Local vs. local. A basic unit of a union organization vs. belonging to a particular area.

Low-end pickup. Sensitivity to the bass frequencies.

Magic hour. The time just before the sun sets.

Maglite. A small, powerful high-intensity flashlight made by Maglite.

Martini. The last shot of the workday.

Master. The widest shot of a scene that encompasses the most action.

Mickey Rooney. A slight dolly move-in during a shot (a little creep).

Mixer cart/Main cart. The trolley holding the recorder and primary equipment used by the Mixer.

Moving on. We've completed this work.

Off-axis rejection. The ability of the microphone to reject sounds outside of its pattern.

OTS. Over-The-Shoulder—a perspective used to create a shot.

Perms. The permanent walkways and railings near the ceiling of a stage that crewmembers use to move about safely while hanging lights and related equipment.

Personal protection equipment, or PPE. Personal equipment used to protect the individual from dangerous elements.

Pictures up. Shooting will begin imminently.

Plant mics. Microphones that are neither boomed nor worn.

PMP (poor man's process). An effect that simulates a vehicle's driving movement without actually moving.

POV. Point of view. From the perspective of.

Pre-call. A time to start work prior to the general crew call.

RX. A receiver.

Self-noise. The inherent sound of a piece of equipment.

Sider. A flag that is positioned on the side of a lamp to stop light.

Sides. The day's work copied and made available for crew, rather than managing a full script. They come in ¼ and full-size pages.

Solid overall. A cheeky way to ask that a lamp be turned off.

Split call. A work time that begins after the morning and continues into evening.

Steadicam. A brand of camera stabilizer mounts for motion picture cameras invented by Garrett Brown and introduced in 1975 by Cinema Products Corporation. It mechanically isolates the camera from the operator's movement, allowing for a smooth shot, even when the operator moves over an irregular surface.

Stingers. Electrical extension cords.

Strain relief. Providing an anchoring point so that a cable is not pulled.

This shot takes us to. Once this shot has concluded, the company will move to another location or part of the script.

Tie downs. Hardware that allows strapping to secure equipment during travel.

Topper. A flag that cuts light from the top of a lamp.

TX. Transmitter

Undercovers. A small circle of napped fabric made by Rycote, which provides wind protection for a lavalier.

Voice of God, or VOG. Slang for a public amplification system; a PA system.

Zero proximity effect. Proximity does not affect its frequency response.

Index

NOTES

NOTES

NOTES

NOTES

NOTES

About the Author

 **Patrushkha Mierzwa** is one of the first women boom operators in Hollywood, starting in 1980. She has worked on 80 movies and television shows for major directors including Robert Altman, Robert Rodriquez, Roger Corman, James Gray, and Quentin Tarantino. She has also been a judge for the Emmys and was a Director on the Board of the sound union, IATSE Local 695.

Ms. Mierzwa has spoken on multiple panels and given workshops at universities in China, Ireland, Oslo, London, Bath, Los Angeles, and New York City on the duties and responsibilities of a qualified boom operator and utility sound technician (UST). She has lectured on the performance work skills necessary to succeed under a fast production schedule with A-list talent. Her last two credits, *Ad Astra* and *Once Upon a Time...in Hollywood*, were both Oscar-nominated for Sound.

Made in the USA
Columbia, SC
20 May 2022